The
GUIDE TO BOOK
& Learning
PUBLISHERS
2000

*The complete guide to book
publishers in the UK & Ireland*

- 3rd Edition -

© Writers' Bookshop 1999
ISBN 1 902713 01 X

First published by Writers' Bookshop
Remus House, Coltsfoot Drive,
Woodston, Peterborough PE2 9JX

Edited by Kerrie Pateman

From the publisher

This is the third edition of this guide to book publishers in the UK and Ireland. The information it contains has been supplied by the publishers and editors themselves, and is current at time of going to press.

We hope to continually improve the book's usefulness to writers and other users, and welcome any comments or suggestions for future editions.

Introduction — by Gordon Wells

Every writer needs a publisher. To write and not get your work published is, at the very least, frustrating. Equally, of course, publishers need writers. Without writers, publishers would have nothing to publish and would…go out of business. Many publishers would welcome the offer of a relevant and publishable new book manuscript.

So, we both need each other. The big problem is to bring us together. And, as not all writers 'write to order', the best solution is for writers to seek out publishers.

Using The Guide

We've all heard of the major publishing houses — and the amazing sums they pay to a few favoured authors. Dream on! Often though, a book will stand a better chance of success — and sympathetic treatment — with one of the 'other-than-major', often specialist, publishers. Of which there are many.

This book, The Guide to Book Publishers, will help you to find the right publisher for your book — whether it's a complete novel or a non-fiction book at the synopsis/proposal stage.

But it's not enough merely to consult a reference book, pick a publisher at random and offer him your masterpiece. It will come back as though on elastic — rejected. No, you've got to identify THE RIGHT PUBLISHER. (There may be several equally suitable, likely publishers: in the end, the RIGHT one is the one that will accept your work.)

Novels

Let's say you've written a novel. You think it's finished — and good. Your first step should be to work through this Guide, identifying all the publishers who publish fiction. (The result of this exercise may surprise you — there are far more publishers of non-fiction than of fiction.)

Make a list of the fiction publishers — and within that, at least for now, identify those you would prefer to be published by. Some publishers will have given an idea of the type of fiction they are interested in. If your novel is a hard-nosed crime story, it's not a lot of sense offering it to a firm publishing only romances. (Believe it. Even worse has been known to happen. The leading romance publishers have been offered non-fiction books and more than one specialist non-fiction publisher has been offered romances. Amend your list as necessary.

Contact the publishers on your preferred list. Ask for a copy of their current catalogue.

Another option, in March/April, is to visit the annual London International Book Fair. Many publishers — mostly the big names — have stands there and you can collect their catalogues and see many of the books. Don't expect to talk about your book to anyone on the stands though: they are mainly sales staff, not editorial.

What sort of fiction?

Study the catalogues. Note the types of fiction published. One firm will publish almost exclusively 'literary' novels; another, mainly first novels. One firm will publish only crime, another only science fiction. Notice too, the number of pages in the books. As a very rough guide, most paper-back novels have 3-400 words per page. A 200-page book is therefore somewhere around 70,000 words long. How long is your novel? If it's only 40,000 words long...*you won't sell it*. You should have studied the market before you finished it.

Browse round your local bookshop. Look specifically for current books by authors in your preferred firms' catalogues. Is your novel of a similar type or nature to any of them? If so, make a note of the book and author and mention the similarity when you submit your work — the publisher might welcome your awareness of the sort of books he publishes.

If none of the books in one or more of the preferred publishers' lists bear any resemblance to yours, cross these firms off your list. You'll be wasting postage.

If many publishers have no books like yours you may have a problem. It may be your book that's wrong. Wrong or not, it's going to be difficult to find your RIGHT publisher.

Although many wannabes start by writing a 'straight' or 'literary' novel — often, to some extent, related to their own experiences — they would probably stand more chance of success if they attempted a genre novel.

Many publishers prefer genre novels to the more literary ones. Booksellers too — reflecting the reading tastes of the general public — like books that can be classified: crime, romance, science fiction, mystery, fantasy, sex 'n' shopping, etc. And it is — usually — preferable for a novel to fit clearly within a single genre. Otherwise, there is the danger of falling between two stools. Is that a romance or a thriller? Which bookshop section does it belong in?

Unsolicited manuscripts

Consult The Guide again. Are your preferred publishers willing to consider unsolicited manuscripts and if so, in what form? You will find that some say 'No unsolicited manuscripts'. Do not let this discouraging attitude completely deter you. It's nearly always worth sending them an enthusiastic enquiry letter — if your book sounds really good, they may be willing to look at the first two or three chapters plus a synopsis. And if you can't enthuse about your book, why should you expect them to? (With such a preliminary enquiry, remember to enclose a stamped addressed envelope. Even then, you still might not get a reply — publishers are not all as 'gentlemanly' as they once were.)

The Guide will also give you the name of the publishers' editor(s). It's often worth telephoning, though — just ask the operator whether Bill Bloggs is still in charge of the fiction list. Get the right name, and address your letter or other submission to them in person. You'll stand a (slightly) better chance of it being looked at.

Submissions

But some publishers DO welcome unsolicited fiction manuscripts. Usually, they ask for the first three chapters plus a synopsis. So...send them that. Add a brief covering letter and enclose a large stamped addressed envelope (big enough for the return of the manuscript). And then sit and wait — get on with something else. Don't deliver by hand; don't phone next day for their comments. If you're lucky, you'll hear from them within a month — but maybe two. (If I haven't had a response from a publisher after about a month I send a very polite letter, enquiring whether there is any news.)

The synopsis is always a worry for first-time authors. For most genre novels it should be about 1,500 words long (in my view, single-spaced typescript, but some use double-spaced) *and it must reveal the whole story*.

You mustn't be afraid to tell the publisher the 'punch line': he won't tell anyone else, your secret is safe with him. He hasn't got the time to write his own novels. But if he doesn't know the surprise ending, he can't judge whether the story is strong enough.

Agents

Another way that some publishers avoid the flood of unsolicited submissions is to specify (or respond to an enquiry) 'Submissions only from agents.' Getting an agent to take you on is often as hard as finding a publisher. (Once you HAVE interested a publisher — and therefore have that much less need of an agent — it's seldom hard to persuade one to take you on. An agent can still do a lot for you, negotiating contracts, etc., but they won't then have found you that first elusive publisher.)

There's no easy way around the chicken-and-egg agent/publisher problem. It may be worth approaching various agents at the same time as you trawl your sample chapters and synopsis around your preferred publishers. Once you get an agent, he/she can take on the search for the publisher.

Non-fiction books

Now let's consider the non-fiction author. In some ways their lot is better than the novelists' — although they probably won't make so much money. The non-fiction author's big bonus is that he/she doesn't have to write a whole book and then seek/hope to get it accepted for publication. The non-fiction author sells his/her book before much gets written.

So, we start at the book idea stage.

don't start writing anything yet — just get your ideas together.

Go back to the beginning and trawl through The Guide. Just as for fiction, make a list of publishers who publish non-fiction books — but only those who are interested in your subject. There are many potential non-fiction publishers — but not all of them are interested in rabbit-breeding or coin-collecting or…whatever is your 'thing'.

Look for series

As with fiction, obtain a copy of their current catalogue and study it. Look particularly for series of books into which your book idea could fit. Non-fiction books sell better in series than as one-off titles.

Get hold of — possibly in the library, more likely from a bookshop (book series quickly go out of date) — a copy of one of the books in what looks like an interesting and relevant series. Can you organise your book idea into a similar format — length, target readership, treatment, etc.? Try hard.

While looking around the libraries and bookshops, take particular note of all the other books on 'your' subject. Borrow them, or 'skim-read' them (in the shop). Get a 'feel' for the way they treat 'your' subject. Remember — your book has, in some way, to be better than the competition. (If not, why should anyone buy yours?)

You will need, when approaching potential publishers, to comment on these other books, and explain how yours will be better.

A query letter

If your book can be tailored to fit an existing series, it is worth writing a preliminary letter to the appropriate editor (by name, as for fiction) at the relevant publishers. Explain that you know a lot about Queen Felicity or flee-training or the 1923 Mudslinging World Cup or beer-mat collecting. Mention that you have already written extensively about the subject in various magazines — maybe enclose a photocopy of one of your articles. Say that you believe you could offer them a book that would fit well into their…series.

Ask if they would be interested in seeing a synopsis for such a book — to be followed by a couple of sample chapters.

You might get a reply back saying that the series is now closed, or that your subject doesn't interest them. OK, but it hasn't cost you much time or effort, has it? Try the same approach on another publisher.

Equally, your idea may have struck a chord with your first-choice publisher. You sound business-like; you've taken the trouble to investigate his list — and it does sound as though your idea would fit nicely into the series. He would like to see the synopsis, etc.

The book proposal

A non-fiction synopsis has to detail the content of each chapter in the proposed book; it has to demonstrate your coverage of the subject; it also has to show that you have enough material to make a book. (And a non-fiction book will seldom be shorter than about 30,000 words — for a simple How-to book — and often up to 70,000-plus words.)

Whether asked for or not, the synopsis should also be accompanied by a detailed proposal:

- a statement of why you are the right person to write the book;

- a review of the competition, and in which respects yours will be better; and

- an explanation of why, in your view, there is a need for the book and what the reader will get out of it.

If the publisher asks for the sample chapters to accompany this early-stage submission, so be it. Write them — they should not amount to more than about ten per cent of the book — and submit them exactly as you would a finished book. They should be immaculately presented, in double-spaced typescript, complete with any eventual illustrations, etc.

Be prepared for the publisher, if he is interested, to suggest changes in your synopsis. Consider such suggestions carefully and do your best to accommodate them. Their purpose will almost always be to enhance the sales potential of the book — and that's in both your interests.

A one-off proposal

But you will not always find a suitable series into which you can fit your proposed non-fiction book. Sometimes you will have to offer it on a one-off basis.

The procedure is much the same as for a series book. Identify a likely publisher and — depending on any further advice in The Guide — submit a proposal as above. Detailed synopsis plus proposal — plus sample chapters if specifically asked for at the initial stage. (If not, have them ready to send as soon as requested.)

If you have chosen your publisher well, your proposal will be accepted. This will be followed by a contract. Now you can write your book — in accordance with the synopsis — in the knowledge that it *will* be published.

But you have to kiss a lot of frogs to find a princely publisher: your proposal may not be accepted first time out. That's par for the course: send the package off, straight away, to another of your preferred publishers. If the idea is good, you will eventually find a publisher. (It took a dozen rejections before I got one of my books accepted; it's now in its third edition.)

Pre-submission polishing

With both novels and non-fiction book proposals it is essential that your work is as good as you can make it. Just as with apples on a market stall, it needs polishing.

Before submitting, re-read everything. Check for over-long, unwieldy sentences; check for mis-used or 'dictionary-only' words; check for ugly paragraph linkages, making the flow uneven; check for spelling errors (we all make 'em); check for repetitions and omissions. And read it aloud, to identify the inevitable pomposities. Polish out all of these faults before it leaves your desk.

And good luck. Remember…

the publishers need us as much as we need them.

AA Publishing

World travel guides, guides to Britain, walking and cycling guides, road maps of Britain and Europe, road atlases of Britain and Europe, accommodation and tourist guides to Britain and Europe, general travel-related illustrated books.

Editor(s): Michael Buttler, Connie Austen Smith
Address: Fanum House, Basingstoke, Hampshire RG21 4EA
Imprints: AA Publishing
Parent Company: The Automobile Association
Payment Details: Generally, fees are negotiated, rather than royalties
Unsolicited Manuscripts: No

AAVO

Specialises in books about television. On Camera and Directing On Camera are classic how-to handbooks about TV production and direction, both written by Harris Watts, a former Senior Instructor at the BBC's production training school. In April 1999 AAVO published 'Better than Working - Life Behind The Camera' by Richard Hakin, an entertaining behind-the-scenes account of life in a camera crew with an introduction by David Puttnam CBE, producer of 'Chariots of Fire', 'The Killing Fields' etc. Later this year AAVO will bring out the new edition of 'The PA Survival Guide' by Cathie Fraser, formerly published by BBC Training.

Editor(s): Harris Watts
Address: 8 Edis Street, London NW1 8LG
Telephone: 0171 722 9243
Fax: Same as phone
Email: tottatv@aol.com
Unsolicited Manuscripts: Yes, if about television

A
Abbotsford Publishing

Publishers of quality titles on poetry, children's books and local history. Member of the Independent Publishers' Guild.

Editor(s): K Simmons, H Clayton
Address: 2a Brownsfield Road, Lichfield, Staffs WS13 6BT
Telephone: 01543 255749 / 258903

ABC-Clio Ltd

ABC-Clio Ltd publishes general A-Z style encyclopedias and reference works on high interest topics in several areas of study including: world history; politics; international relations; society; biography; sport; folklore and mythology; and science and technology.

Editor(s): Robert G Neville
Address: 35A Great Clarendon Street, Oxford OX2 6AT
Telephone: 01865 311350
Fax: 01865 311358
Email: bneville@abc-clio.lid.uk
Parent Company: ABC-Clio Inc, Santa Barbara, California USA
Payment Details: By negotiation
Unsolicited Manuscripts: Yes

Abson Books London

Language glossaries, gardening.

Editor(s): Michael Ellison, Sharon Wright
Address: 5 Sidney Square, London E1 2EY
Telephone: 0171 790 4737
Fax: 0171 790 7346
Email: absonbooks@aol.com
Unsolicited Manuscripts: Yes

Council Of Academic And Professional Publishers

Trade association for academic and professional publishers.

Address: 1 Kingsway, London WC2B 6XF
Telephone: 0171 565 7474
Fax: 0171 836 4543
Email: @publishers.org.uk
Website: www.publishers.org.uk
Parent Company: The Publishers Association

Acair Ltd

Scottish Highlands and Islands, modern and historical, Gaelic and English, children's Gaelic, educational, music, poetry and song, learners of Gaelic.

Editor(s): Norma MacLeod
Address: 7 James Street, Stornoway, Isle of Lewis HS1 2QN
Telephone: 01851 703020
Fax: 01851 703294
Email: acair@sol.co.uk
Website: www.hebrides.com/acair
Imprints: Acair
Payment Details: Payment by arrangement if published
Unsolicited Manuscripts: Yes

A

Accountancy Books

Accountancy Books is the publishing arm of the Institute of Chartered Accountants in England and Wales. Providing support for the professionals in both practice and industry, we publish over 300 key titles covering the breadth of accounting, tax, auditing, company law, financial management and IT.

Address: 40 Bernard Street, London WC1N 1LD
Telephone: 0171 920 8991
Fax: 0171 920 8992
Email: abgbooks@icaew.co.uk
Website: www.icaew.co.uk
Imprints: Accountancy Books, Bottom Line Business Guides
Parent Company: ICAEW

Act 3 Publishing

A book publisher, established in 1985, with one book at present in print: Hypnosis in Psychotherapy - Understand Yourself, and Resolve Your Emotional Problems. Now considering potential best-selling fiction and non-fiction for publication.

Address: 67 Upper Berkeley Street, London W1H 7DH
Telephone: 0171 402 2231
Payment Details: No advances, payment negotiable
Unsolicited Manuscripts: In the first instance send only a one-page resumé with SAE

Adam Hart (Publishers) Ltd

Independent publishing company founded in 1992 to publish Elizabethan and Renaissance history books, especially the historical research of the historian A D Wraight on Christopher Marlowe and Shakespeare. To date four substantial historic works have been published, and due for publication in 2000 is 'The Legend of Hiram' by A D Wraight presenting documentary evidence of the First Folio's publication in 1623 by the Freemasons.

Editor(s): A D Walker-Wraight, Y M Hart
Address: Adam Hart (Publishers) Ltd, The Rose, 10 Idmiston Road, London SE27 9HG
Telephone: 0181 670 5182
Fax: Same as phone
Website: www. author.co.uk/marlowe.htm

African Books Collective Ltd

Founded in 1989, ABC is a major self-help initiative by a group of African publishers to promote their books in Europe, North America and Commonwealth countries outside Africa. It is collectively owned by its founder-member publishers. ABC is a donor organisation supported and non-profitmaking on its own behalf, and because of this, is in a position to offer its members more favourable terms than are normally available under conventional commercial distribution agreements. Titles in English and children's in Swahili are stocked. Membership has grown to 43 publishers in 12 African countries. Over 1700 titles are now stocked in ABC's UK warehouse.

Address: The Jam Factory, 27 Park End Street, Oxford OX1 1HU
Telephone: 01865 726686
Fax: 01865 793298
Email: abc@dial.pipex.com
Website: www.africanbookscollective.com
Unsolicited Manuscripts: No

A

Age Concern Books

Age Concern Books (the publishing wing of Age Concern England) produces a range of practical handbooks aimed at older people and their carers. The range includes personal finance and benefits guides, retirement titles, as well as series produced for both professional and family carers. We publish approximately 18 new titles each year, with annual sales exceeding 110,000 copies.

Editor(s): Publisher: Richard Holloway
Address: Age Concern Books, Age Concern England, Astral House, 1268 London Road, London SW16 4ER
Telephone: 0181 765 7454
Fax: 0181 679 6069
Email: hollowr@ace.org.uk
Website: http://www.ace.org.uk
Parent Company: Age Concern England (registered charity)
Payment Details: Normal royalty terms offered to authors
Unsolicited Manuscripts: Very rarely accepted

Agenda Ltd

Agenda publish books on popular music. The musicians covered in our books are considered intellectual or have academic influences within their music. Our books are ideal for basic ground work for thesis dissertations for colleges and universities. We hope to upgrade our Captain Beefheart book and publish investigations of the music of The Doors, Sun Ra and The Residents, adding to our existing catalogue which includes... Leonard Cohen, Arthur Lee, Joni Mitchell, Mike Bloofield, Al Cooper, Scott Walker, Van Morrison, Bob Dylan, Tom Watts, Tim Buckey, Mick Drake, Frank Zappa and The Incredible String Band.

Editor(s): Tony Coleman and Ken Brooks
Address: Units 1-2 Ludgershall Business Park, New Drove, Ludgershall SP11 9RN
Telephone: 01264 335388
Fax: 01264 335270
Email: PAUL@dmac.co.uk
Website: http://www.dmac.co.uk/AGENDAhtml
Payment Details: As negotiated

A

Air Research Publications

Publishers of specialist (non-fiction) aviation books. Especially World War 2 and military aviation history.

Editor(s): Simon Parry
Address: PO Box 223, Walton-on-Thames, Surrey KT12 3YQ
Telephone: 01932 243165
Fax: Same as phone
Email: simon_parry@hotmail.com
Website: www.btinternet.com/~air_research/webcat.htm
Payment Details: Royalty on sales
Unsolicited Manuscripts: Yes, and returned

Airlife Publishing Ltd

Three non-fiction imprints. Airlife: military aviation; civil aviation; military and naval history; military and naval biography; books for pilots. Waterline: practical books for cruising and racing yachtsmen; boatbuilding. Swan Hill Press: natural history; fishing; dog training; country sports; equestrian; walking and climbing; diving; art and decorative arts.

Editor(s): Peter Coles
Address: 101 Longden Road, Shrewsbury SY3 9EB
Telephone: 01743 235651
Fax: 01743 232944
Email: airlife@airlifebooks.com
Website: www.airlifebooks.com
Imprints: Airlife, Waterline, Swan Hill Press
Payment Details: Royalty
Unsolicited Manuscripts: Yes

Albrighton Publications

Two publications on education of minority groups in Britain: Language, Race And Education (1988); Equality And Education (1992).

Editor(s): Author for these publications: Gurbachan Singh
Address: 53 The Hollow, Littleover, Derby DE23 6GH
Telephone: 01332 764064

Ian Allen Publishing Ltd

Transport, aviation, military, sport and leisure. No fiction, poetry, children's titles, books of memories, biographies or autobiographies.

Editor(s): Peter Waller
Address: Riverdene Business Park, Molesey Road, Hersham, Surrey KT12 4RG
Telephone: 01932 266600
Fax: 01932 266601
Imprints: Ian Allan Ltd, Dial House, OPC
Parent Company: Ian Allan Group Ltd
Payment Details: Subject to contract terms agreed
Unsolicited Manuscripts: No

J A Allen & Co Ltd

An imprint of Robert Hale Limited. Equine and equestrian publishers - non-fiction titles on any area of horse-related subjects. Prefer authoritative works by established experts in their fields. Broad academic base, also publishing some commercial titles and have a junior list which does not include fiction.

Editor(s): Publisher: Caroline Burt
Address: Saddlewood, 51 Fourth Avenue, Frinton on Sea, Essex CO13 9DY
Telephone: Editorial: 01255 679388, Head Office: 0171 2512661
Fax: Editorial: 01255 670848, Head Office: 0171 4904958
Parent Company: Robert Hale Ltd
Payment Details: Royalties paid twice-yearly
Unsolicited Manuscripts: Yes, all submissions are read with interest

Allison & Busby

Publishes biography, history, crime and criminology, topical issues, and general non-fiction, literary fiction, crime fiction, translations and a series of writers' guides.

Editor(s): Roderick Dymott, David Shelley
Address: 114 New Cavendish Street, London W1M 7FD
Telephone: 0171 636 2942
Fax: 0171 323 2023
Email: davids@allisonbusby.co.uk
Website: www.allisonandbusby.co.uk
Parent Company: Editorial Prensa Iberica, SA, Barcelona
Unsolicited Manuscripts: Sample text and synopsis, plus SAE

Alun Books/Goldleaf Publishing

Small press, limited resources, specialising in books by Welsh authors/about Welsh subjects - mostly in English.

Editor(s): S Jones
Address: 3 Crown Street, Port Talbot, West Glamorgan SA13 1BG Wales
Telephone: 01639 886186
Imprints: Alun Books (literature: poetry and fiction), Goldleaf (local history), Barn Owl (children's)
Parent Company: Alun Books (founded 1977)
Payment Details: 10% royalty
Unsolicited Manuscripts: No

A

Amber Lane Press

Original modern play scripts - only plays that have been staged professionally will be considered; books on theatre and modern drama.

Editor(s): Judith Scott
Address: Church Street, Charlbury, Oxon OX7 3PR
Telephone: 01608 810024
Fax: Same as phone
Payment Details: Formal author's contract with advance and percentage royalty
Unsolicited Manuscripts: No

Amberwood Publishing Ltd

Introducing - Amberwood Publishing, founded in 1991 with the object of publishing affordable books on natural health care. All our titles are commissioned from authors who are chosen for their expertise. Each book is presented in a format suitable for the general public and students alike. All of us at Amberwood care about the information we publish. Our aim is to market factual scientifically-based literature for the benefit of the growing number of people wanting to use natural medicine, such as aromatherapy, herbal medicine and nutritional therapy.

Editor(s): Victor Perfitt
Address: Braboeuf House, 64 Portsmouth Road, Guildford, Surrey GU2 5DU
Telephone: 01483 570821
Fax: 01483 457101
Unsolicited Manuscripts: To Mrs June Crisp

AMCD (Publishers) Ltd

Key areas are China, the power sector, financial dictionaries, business books, local history (Croydon and Cheshire) and electronic books. We would like to develop our history titles: ideas for histories of the British Isles and European countries are of interest.

Editor(s): S J MacNally
Address: PO Box 182, Altrincham, Cheshire WA15 9UA
Telephone: 0161 434 5105
Fax: As phone
Email: j.s.adams@talk21.com
Imprints: AMCD, Jensen
Parent Company: AMCD
Payment Details: Royalties twice-yearly
Unsolicited Manuscripts: One short chapter only

Amnesty International Publications

Amnesty International is a worldwide voluntary human rights movement that campaigns for the release of prisoners of conscience, fair trials for political prisoners and an end to torture, 'disappearances', political killings and the death penalty. Amnesty International works impartially to promote all human rights enshrined in the Universal Declaration of Human Rights and other international standards. The organisation publishes books relating to this work, and produces short specialist reports on human rights abuse issues, which are available on the World Wide Web. It publishes an annual country-by-country report on human rights.

Address: 99-119 Rosebery Avenue, London EC1R 4RE
Email: info@amnesty.org.uk
Website: www.amnesty.org.uk
Parent Company: Amnesty International UK
Unsolicited Manuscripts: No

A

Amolibros

Amolibros manages a number of imprints which are usually distributed by Gazelle Book Services. It specialises in assisting small or private publishers to produce and market their books. Popular titles managed include Outrageous Fortune by Terence Frisby (author of There's A Girl In My Soup) and Thoth, published by Edlu Books. The Turquoise Conspiracy by Bilge Nevzat, the inside story on Asil Nadir.

Editor(s): Jane Tatam
Address: 5 Saxon Close, Watchet, Somerset TA23 0BN
Telephone: 01984 633713
Fax: Same as phone
Email: amolibros@aol.com
Website: www.author.co.uk/amolibros
Unsolicited Manuscripts: No

Anchor Books

A small poetry imprint, with the aim of getting lesser known poets into print.

Editor(s): Managing Editor: Steve Twelvetree; Editor: Kelly Deacon
Address: Remus House, Coltsfoot Drive, Woodston, Peterborough PE2 9JX
Telephone: 01733 898102
Fax: 01733 313524
Parent Company: Forward Press Limited
Payment Details: Top 100 Poets of the Year share a cash prize
Unsolicited Manuscripts: For anthologies: poems up to 30 lines any subject, any form

Andersen Press Ltd

Founded in 1976 by Klaus Flugge, Andersen Press publishes quality picture books and fiction for children. Main authors and artists on the list are David McKee, Tony Ross, Michael Foreman, Ruth and Ken Brown, Susan Varley, Colin McNaughton, Max Velthuijs, Emma Chichester Clark and Melvin Burgess. Specialises in selling foreign co-editions. Bestselling titles: Badger's Parting Gifts (Susan Varley), Elmer (David McKee), Junk (Melvin Burgess).

Editor(s): Editorial Director: Janice Thomson; Editor: Audrey Adams (Fiction)
Address: 20 Vauxhall Bridge Road, London SW1V 2SA
Telephone: 0171 840 8701
Fax: 0171 233 6263
Website: www.andersenpress.co.uk
Imprints: Tigers, Andersen Young Readers' Library, Andersen Press Paperback Picture Books, Andersen Giants
Payment Details: Royalties twice-yearly
Unsolicited Manuscripts: With SAE; 3 sample chapters and synopsis for novels

Anderson Rand

Publisher of 'The European Book World' the authoritative book trade directory, providing trade professionals with up-to-date business contact details from listings of over 25,000 publishing organisations, 63,000 libraries and 50,000 booksellers in East and West Europe and former Soviet Europe. Over 150 indexes include: 4000 subject specialities, named staff, library and bookseller types, telephone/fax, market types, non book stock and organisation size.

Editor(s): Dr Robin Anderson
Address: 10 Willow Walk, Cambridge CB1 1LA
Telephone: 01223 566640
Fax: 01223 566643
Email: ar.info@dial.pipex.com
Website: http://www.anderson-rand.com
Unsolicited Manuscripts: N/A

A

Anglia Publishing

Specialist in metal detecting and amateur archaeology. Most titles which Anglia has published relate to the identification of small metallic finds. The scope is large because metal detecting turns up a very wide variety of material: Bronze Age axes to Butlin's holiday camp enamel badges! The buyers of Anglia's titles also come from a wide spectrum, not just metal detectorists and amateur archaeologists but also museum staff, professional archaeologists and, of course, collectors. The possibilities to add to Anglia's growing lists are large indeed. New titles are eagerly sought: books and booklets, which can be as short as 10,000 words. Would someone like to write little books about pipe tampers through the ages, shotgun cartridges and bullets? Get the idea?

Editor(s): Derek Rowland
Address: Unit T, Godness, Priory Farm, Hazelshrub, Bentley, Ipswich IP9 2DF
Telephone: 01473 311138
Email: anglia@anglianet.co.uk
Website: www.anglia.anglianet.co.uk
Imprints: Anglia Publishing, Anglia Shoe-Box Library
Payment Details: Royalty negotiable, payable quarterly
Unsolicited Manuscripts: No - a synopsis first or a telephone call

Anglia Young Books

Cross-curricular stories for primary schools, specialising in historical fiction with support material for the literacy hour.

Editor(s): Rosemary Hayes
Address: Durhams Farmhouse, Butcher's Hill, Ickleton, Saffron Walden CB10 1SR
Telephone: 01799 531192
Fax: Same as phone
Email: r.hayes@btinternet.com
Imprints: Anglia Young Books
Unsolicited Manuscripts: No

Angling Publications Ltd

Angling Publications was founded in 1988, we publish two monthly magazines which are dedicated to carp fishing. The titled 'Carpworld' and 'Crafty Carper', and Tim Paisley is the editor of both publications. Carpworld is a full colour publication with a minimum of 176 pages, Crafty Carper is also full colour, 96 page publication. Both magazines run monthly competitions and contain articles on all aspects of carp fishing, tackle, tactics, waters, news, letters, bait, shops, stories etc.

Editor(s): Tim Paisley
Address: 272a London Road, Highfields, Sheffield, South Yorkshire S2 4NA
Telephone: 0114 2580812
Fax: 0114 2582728
Email: philippa.dean@virgin.net
Website: www.completeangler.co.uk/angpub.htm

Anness Publishing Ltd

Anness Publishing and Lorenz Books produce high quality photographic non-fiction titles for adults and children on a wide range of subjects including cookery, lifestyle, reference, health, new age, crafts, sports and hobbies, gardening and giftbooks.

Editor(s): Joanna Lorenz
Address: Anness Publishing Ltd, Hermes House, 88-89 Blackfriars Road, London SE1 8HA
Telephone: 0171 401 2077
Fax: 0171 633 9499
Email: info@anness.com
Imprints: Lorenz Books
Unsolicited Manuscripts: Summary, synopsis and proposals

$\mathcal{A}$

Antique Collectors' Club

Publishers of books on art, antiques, gardening and children's classics. We also publish a magazine - ten issues a year of articles on art, antiques and collectables.

Editor(s): Brian Cotton
Address: 5 Church Street, Woodbridge, Suffolk IP12 1DS
Telephone: 01394 385501
Fax: 01394 384434
Email: accbc@aol.com
Imprints: Garden Art Press, ACC Children's Classics
Payment Details: Negotiable
Unsolicited Manuscripts: No

Anvil Press Poetry Ltd

Poetry, poetry in translation.

Editor(s): Peter Jay
Address: Neptune House, 70 Royal Hill, London SE10 8RF
Payment Details: To be negotiated if work accepted
Unsolicited Manuscripts: Yes must include SAE

Apple Press

Apple Press publish a range of non-fiction, illustrated books and children's interactive books. The principal subject areas are food and drink, art and craft, antiques and collecting and children's non-fiction. Series include the Companion series, the Apple Identifier series and the best-selling Fridge Fun(TM) range.

Address: The Fitzpatrick Building, 188-194 York Way, London N7 9QR
Telephone: 0171 700 2929
Fax: 0171 609 6695
Imprints: Apple Kids
Parent Company: Quarto Plc
Payment Details: Negotiable upon acceptance
Unsolicited Manuscripts: Yes - send to sister company Quintet Publishing at same address

The Appletree Press Ltd

A wide range of internationally renowned giftbooks developed with the tourist market specifically in mind. Our range of over 400 titles cover the following areas: The Celtic Collection, English, Irish, Scots and Welsh Interest, Cookbook Collections featuring the cuisines of over 50 countries and regions, Yearbooks and Diaries, Travel Guides, Literature, Reference, Foreign Language editions (French, German, Spanish, Italian) of our most popular titles are available along with a full range of POS.

Editor(s): Robert Blackwell
Address: The Appletree Press Ltd, The Old Potato Station, 14 Howard Street South, Belfast BT7 1AP
Telephone: 028 90 243074
Fax: 028 90 246756
Email: reception@appletree.ie
Website: www.irelandseye.com
Imprints: Appletree Press
Payment Details: On selection and final approval
Unsolicited Manuscripts: The Manager, Creative Department

Applied Rural Alternatives (ARA)

ARA exists for the charitable purpose of advancing the education of the general public in rural development in an environmentally sensitive manner with particular reference to under-developed countries. ARA arranges visits/leatures, etc, in the UK on organic husbandry, environmental problems in farming and appropriate technologies. Details of the current programme are available on receipt of an SAE. Publications available are 'The Pace of Change in Farming - the organic option' (£2 remainder) and 'Cheap Food - can we afford it?' (£3). Cheques to 'ARA (SEBUNA)' with order.

Editor(s): D Cussens, D Stafford
Address: ARA, 10 Highfield Close, Wokingham, Berkshire RG40 1DG
Telephone: 0118 962 7797
Parent Company: ARA
Unsolicited Manuscripts: None, please

A
Arc Publications

Arc Publications is not only committed to publishing works by new British writers, but actively seeks to promote work by internationally significant poets higherto neglected in the UK, whether in their original English or in translation. Poets submitting work should be familiar with the type of work we publish.

Editor(s): Tony Ward
Address: Nanholme Mill, Shaw Wood Road, Todmorden, Lancashire OL14 6DA
Imprints: Arc Publications
Unsolicited Manuscripts: Send representative selection, no reply without SAE

Arcadia Books Ltd

Newly-established independent publishing house whose writers include Richard Zimler, author of the international bestseller The Last Kabbalist of Lisburn, Shere Hite, John Berger, Tariq Ali, Robert Dessaix, Clare Colvin, Michael Arditta, Dacia Maraini, Michael De-La-Noy, Kathy Acker, and A Sivanandan, author of the award-winning novel When Memory Dies. We publish in the areas of fiction (including translated fiction), biography/autobiography, travel, gay books and women's/gender studies.

Editor(s): Gary Pulsifer
Address: 15-16 Nassau Street, London W1N 7RE
Telephone: 0171 436 9898
Fax: Same as phone
Email: arcadia@atlas.co.uk
Unsolicited Manuscripts: Only with SAE and/or return postage for ms

Architectural Association Publications

Books on architecture and related disciplines, with special emphasis on unusual formats and reproduction techniques.

Editor(s): Pamela Johnston
Address: 36 Bedford Square, London WC1B 3ES
Telephone: 0171 887 4021
Fax: 0171 414 0782
Email: publications@arch-assoc.org.uk
Website: www.arch-assoc.org.uk
Imprints: AA Publications
Parent Company: Architectural Association
Unsolicited Manuscripts: No

Archive Editions

Publishers of historical documents, in facsimile, on the Middle East, Asia and conflict zones in Europe.

Address: 7 Ashley House, The Broadway, Farnham Common, Slough SL2 3PQ
Telephone: 01753 646633
Fax: 01753 646746
Email: ArchiveEdn@aol.com
Imprints: Archive Editions
Payment Details: Available on request

A
Aris & Phillips Ltd

Archaeology - Egyptology, classical (Greek and Latin) texts, Hispanic classics (Spanish and Portuguese).

Editor(s): A A Phillips, L M Phillips
Address: Teddington House, Church Street, Warminster, Wilts BA12 8PQ
Telephone: 01985 213409
Fax: 01985 212910
Email: aris.phillips@binternet.com
Website: www.arisandphillips.com
Imprints: Aris & Phillips
Unsolicited Manuscripts: Yes

Arnold Publishers (A Member Of The Hodder Headline Group)

Arnold is the academic and professional division within the progressive Hodder Headline Group, dedicated to the publication of high-quality books, journals and CD-ROMS for an international market. With key texts in a range of fields, including Engineering and Technology, Humanities and Social Sciences, and Medical and Health Sciences, the secret to Arnold's continuing success lies not only in our wealth of publishing experience, but also in our ability to respond rapidly to innovation, to pay individual attention to authors, to meet the best production standards and devise the most effective and influential marketing campaigns with outstanding results. Our books won three out of five British Medical Association 1998 publishing awards and our top-selling titles include, Topley and Wilson's Microbiology and Microbial Infections, 9th Edition, Clarke and Cooke's Basic Course in Statistics, 4th Edition and O'Sullivan's Studying the Media, 2nd Edition.

Editor(s): Engineering and Technology: Nicky Dennis; Humanities: Christopher Wheeler; Health Sciences: Georgina Bentliff
Address: 338 Euston Road, London NW1 3BH
Telephone: 0171 873 6000
Fax: 0171 873 6325
Email: arnold@hodder.co.uk
Website: www.arnoldpublishers.com
Parent Company: Hodder Headline Group

Art Sales Index Ltd

Founded in 1968, Art Sales Index Ltd produce publications, CD ROM and on-line database of the works of fine art sold at auction around the world. These are important references sources for anyone seriously interested in art.

Editor(s): Duncan Hislop
Address: 16 Luddington Avenue, Virginia Water, Surrey GU25 4DF
Telephone: 01344 841750
Fax: 01344 841760
Email: asi@art-sales-index.com
Website: www.art-sales-index.com
Unsolicited Manuscripts: No

Arthritis Research Campaign (ARC)

A national charity which exists to raise funds for research into arthritis and rheumatism. It produces a range of booklets and leaflets on arthritis, as well as publications for medical professionals and students.

Address: ARC Trading Ltd (Supplies), Brunel Drive, Northern Road Industrial Estate, Newark NG24 2DE
Telephone: 01636 673054
Fax: 01636 708714
Website: www.arc.org.uk
Parent Company: ARC, Copeman House, St Mary's Court, St Mary's Gate, Chesterfield S41 7TD

A

Articles Of Faith Ltd

Specialises in short print runs of religious books for the schools educational market.

Editor(s): C Howard
Address: Resource House, Kay Street, Bury BL9 6BU
Telephone: 0161 763 6232
Fax: 0161 763 5366
Email: edsltd@compuserve.com
Website: www.ed-dev.co.uk
Unsolicited Manuscripts: Yes

Aspire Publishing

Fiction (all genes), autobiography and biography. Founded 1997. Also non-fiction especially political or controversial issues. No unsolicited MSS. Send SAE for guidelines. Publications printed and produced in UK as a matter of policy. Trade clients include all major bookshop chains, wholesalers and library suppliers.

Editor(s): Senior Editor: Patricia Hawkes
Address: 8 Betony Rise, Exeter EX2 5RR or 9 Wimpole Street, London W1M 8LB
Telephone: 01392 252516
Fax: 01392 252517
Email: aspire@centrex.force9.net
Imprints: Aspire Publishing, Greenzone Publishing
Parent Company: XcentreX Ltd
Payment Details: None
Unsolicited Manuscripts: No

ASR Resources

Design, management, psychological and educational - with a cybernetic perspective.

Address: 465 Twickenham Road, Isleworth TW7 7DZ
Telephone: 020 8892 1933
Imprints: Resources Occasional Papers, SCOHNE Papers
Unsolicited Manuscripts: No

Association For Science Education

The professional body for anyone interested in science education - from birth to university level. Self-funded, the ASE publishes a range of periodical and book titles written by teachers and others for teachers and others. Safety advice, ideas for teaching, reference books, pupils' material, photocopiable worksheets and INSET publications.

Editor(s): Various
Address: ASE, College Lane, Hatfield, Herts AL10 9AA
Telephone: 01707 283000
Fax: 01707 266532
Email: janehanrott@ase.org.uk
Website: www.ase.org.uk
Unsolicited Manuscripts: Yes

Association For Scottish Literary Studies

The ASLS is an educational charity promoting the languages and literature of Scotland. We publish works of Scottish literature which have either been neglected or which merit a fresh presentation to a modern audience; essays, monographs and journals on the literature and languages of Scotland; and Scotnotes, a series of comprehensive study guides to major Scottish writers. We also produce New Writing Scotland, an annual anthology of contemporary poetry and prose in English, Gaelic and Scots from writers resident in Scotland or Scots by birth or upbringing.

Editor(s): Duncan Jones (Managing Editor, New Writing Scotland)
Address: ASLS, c/o Department of Scottish History, 9 University Gardens, University of Glasgow, Glasgow G12 8QH Scotland
Telephone: 0141 330 5309
Fax: Same as phone
Email: cmc@arts.gla.ac.uk
Website: http://www.st-andrews.ac.uk/~www_se/personal/cjmm/ASLShomepage.html
Payment Details: £10 per page
Unsolicited Manuscripts: For New Writing Scotland only

A
The Athlone Press

Academic publishers across the social sciences, humanities and the sciences. Anthropology, architecture, art history/theory, Asian studies, biology, business studies, chemistry, classics, climatology, cultural and media studies, education, English and world literature and literary studies, environmental sciences, film studies, history, history of science, law, museum studies, natural history, planning, performance studies, philosophy, physics, psychiatry, psychoanalysis, psychology, sociology, therapy, technology, urban studies.

Editor(s): Brian Southam, Tristan Palmer
Address: 1 Park Drive, London NW11 7SG
Telephone: 020 8458 0888
Fax: 020 8201 8115
Email: athlonepress@btinternet.com
Unsolicited Manuscripts: Yes

Aurelian Information Ltd

Internet books for beginners and office users in business and the charity sector. National charities database: the 7,500 leading national charities (and UK-based international charities) available for rental on electronic disks - floppy and CD-ROM.

Editor(s): Paul Petzold
Address: Aurelian Information Ltd Research Unit, 4a Alexandra Mansions, West End Lane, London NW6 1LU
Telephone: 0171 794 8609 (books) 0171 407 5987 (data)
Fax: Same as phone (books) 0171 407 6294 (data)
Website: www@dircon.co.uk/aurelian
Imprints: Internet-For-All Books (books), National Charities Database (database information)
Unsolicited Manuscripts: No - proposals only, by letter

Aureus Publishing

Primarily a leisure-driven company, Aureus Publishing specialises in sports books, music (all types) and other leisure titles. Aureus is a dynamic company with an international outlook.

Editor(s): Proprietor: Meuryn Hughes
Address: 24 Mafeking Road, Cardiff CF23 5DQ Wales
Telephone: 029 2045 5200
Fax: Same as phone
Email: meurynhughes@aureus.co.uk
Website: www.aureus.co.uk
Imprints: Aureus
Unsolicited Manuscripts: Synopsis only please, typed. SAE required for reply

Aurum Press

General illustrated non-fiction: film, music, art and design, craft, sport, military history, biography. Also, practical photography titles published under Argentum Press imprint.

Editor(s): Piers Burnett, Sheila Murphy, Graham Coster
Address: 25 Bedford Avenue, London WC1B 3AT
Telephone: 0171 637 3225
Fax: 0171 580 2469
Email: aurum@ibm.net
Unsolicited Manuscripts: Yes

Autumn Publishing Ltd

Children's publisher of quality mass-market activity books. These include 'Fun to Learn' sticker books and wall charts.

Address: Autumn Publishing Ltd, North Barn, Appledram Barns, Birdham Road, Chichester PO20 7EQ

$\mathcal{A}$
Avon Books

Works on the basis of shared responsibility between author and publisher. This involves a payment or subsidy by the author as a contribution towards the cost of publishing his or her work.

Editor(s): Robin Salkia
Address: 1 Dovedale Studios, 465 Battersea Park Road, London SW11 4LR
Telephone: 0171 978 4825
Fax: 0171 924 2979
Email: enquiries@avonbooks
Website: www.avonbooks.co.uk
Payment Details: Negotiable
Unsolicited Manuscripts: Yes

AvonAngliA

Innovative publisher covering not only books, pamphlets and leaflets but postcards, posters and 'talking books' as well. Specialising in guidebooks, local history, business and transport subjects, it also owns Kingsmead Press, which concentrates on art books, Bath history and historical reprints. Small-run reprints and special productions for special opportunities include anniversaries and company histories; the full range of facilities exist including a writing service for those with a subject but no material.

Editor(s): Ian Body, Margaret Leitch
Address: 74 Ryder Street, Pontcanna, Cardiff CF11 9BU Wales
Telephone: 01222 407336
Fax: 01222 407476
Website: www.ibody@aol.com.uk
Imprints: AvonAngliA, Kingsmead Press
Parent Company: AvonAngliA Publications and Services
Unsolicited Manuscripts: Accepted on most subjects - particularly transport, business and commerce, local history

Azure Books

Publishers of books in the broad subject area of human spirituality, such as you might find in the 'mind, body, spirit' section of a bookshop. These books explore what it means to be a spiritual person in the late 20th century, taking in how we relate to ourselves, others and the world around us. Some books on the list explore the subjects of mysticism and the nature of God, and how some world religions, like Christianity, are experienced today.

Editor(s): Alison Barr
Address: 1 Marylebone Road, London NW1 4DU
Telephone: 0171 387 5282
Fax: 0171 388 2352
Email: abarr@spck.org.uk
Imprints: Azure Books
Payment Details: By negotiation
Unsolicited Manuscripts: Please send synopsis and sample chapter

Bernard Babani (Publishing) Ltd

Bernard Babani (Publishing) Ltd has been established for over 50 years specialising only in radio, electronics and computer subjects. We are well known for tremendous value as well as accurate and up to date content. Our books are no more expensive than popular fiction paperbacks.

Editor(s): M H Babani
Address: The Grampians, Shepherds Bush Road, London W6 7NF
Telephone: 0171 603 2581
Fax: 0171 603 8203
Unsolicited Manuscripts: Yes only on the subjects of radio, electronics and computing

B
M & M Baldwin

Publishers of books on local history, second world war codebreaking, and inland waterways (including The Working Waterways series and the Historical Canal Maps series).

Editor(s): Mark Baldwin
Address: 24 High Street, Cleobury Mortimer, Kidderminster DY14 8BY
Telephone: 01299 270110
Fax: Same as phone
Email: mmb@mbaldwin.free-online.co.uk
Imprints: M & M Baldwin
Payment Details: Annual royalty on sales
Unsolicited Manuscripts: Yes

Ballinakella Press

Small publishing house (circa 28 books to date), we now limit our works to in-series books. Our County House books are comprehensive architectural and historical records of the houses and families associated with them, of each Irish county. Our People And Places series of Irish family names are small but fairly comprehensive records of major Irish families or clans. We also have biographical records of characterful or historic Irish citizens or people of Irish descent. We occasionally consider books with a family history bent.

Editor(s): Dr Hugh W L Weir (Senior), Hon Mrs Grania Weir, Ana Maria Hajba
Address: Whitegate, Co Clare, Ireland
Telephone: 353061 927030
Fax: 353061 9274418
Email: weir@iol.ie
Imprints: Weir's Guides
Payment Details: By arrangement
Unsolicited Manuscripts: Only for Irish topographical and historical books in series

The Banton Press

Makes reprints of esoteric and occult titles from the 4th to 20th century. Subject areas include alchemy, astrology, autobiography, biography, Celts, druids, Egypt, folklore, history, kabbala, tarot, witchcraft, religion, philosophy, symbolism and sex worship. The books are perfect bound facsimile reprints with card covers and the title page as front cover. Also some titles on the Isle of Arran. New titles are added on an irregular basis.

Editor(s): Mark Brown
Address: Dippin Cottage, Kildonan, Isle of Arran KA27 8SB
Telephone: 01770 820231
Fax: Same as phone
Website: www.gaelforce.ndirect.co.uk/bantonpress/index.htm
Imprints: Banton
Unsolicited Manuscripts: To Editor

Barefoot Books Ltd

Children's full-colour picture books: traditional myths, legends and fairytales, with a strong cross-cultural focus.

Editor(s): Publisher: Tessa Strickland
Address: PO Box 95, Kingswood, Bristol BS30 5BH
Imprints: Barefoot Beginners, Barefoot Books, Barefoot Collections, Barefoot Poetry Collections
Payment Details: Advance against royalty
Unsolicited Manuscripts: No

B
Barny Books

No restrictions. We mainly work with new writers and offer both a readership and advisory service and an editing one. There is a £20 fee for the readership scheme (£10 for less than 40 pages); editing by negotiation. We are a non-profitmaking group set up to help new talent.

Editor(s): Molly Burkett
Address: Hough-On-The-Hill, Grantham NG32 2BB
Payment Details: 50/50 on profits
Unsolicited Manuscripts: Accepted for the readership and advisory service only

Barry Rose Law Publishers Limited

This company is privately owned, yet has an astonishing wide range of authors on its books - in the purely legal field, Judges, Stipendiary Magistrates and Lay Magistrates; it traverses the field to include Academics and Authors who just write for the fun of it. But they are always legal - in the sense that they are barristers or solicitors that is: the legal side of the firm's publishing activities. It also publishes in Police and Local Government.

Editor(s): Barry Rose
Address: Little London, Chichester, West Sussex PO19 1PG
Telephone: 01243 775552
Fax: 01243 779278
Email: books@barry-rose-law.co.uk
Website: www.barry-rose-law.co.uk
Imprints: Countrywise Press and Rose Books
Payment Details: Royalties paid half-yearly
Unsolicited Manuscripts: No

Basic Skills Agency

Publish teaching and learning material to help children, young people and adults improve their basic skills, which we define as 'the ability to read, write and speak in English/Welsh and use mathematics at a level necessary to function and progress at work and in society in general.' We are a not-for-profit publisher. Our publications range from readers' packs, advice and material for teachers to some multimedia products. We also work with some commercial publishers. As well as publishing teaching and learning material, we also commission and publish research into the level of need, the cause of basic skills difficulties and the effectiveness of basic skills programmes.

Address: Commonwealth House, 1-19 New Oxford Street, London WC1A 1NU
Telephone: 0171 405 4017
Fax: 0171 440 6626
Email: enquiries@basic-skills.co.uk
Website: www.basic-skills.co.uk

Batsford Communications Plc

Batsford publish high quality non-fiction books in the following range of subject areas: aeronautical, art, bridge, business, chess, crafts, design, fashion and costume, film and entertainment, gardening, heritage, maritime, military, political directories and woodwork. Full details of all available titles can be found on Batsford's website at www.batsford.com, which includes secure online ordering facilities, company information and links to other key sites.

Editor(s): Caroline Bolton; Chris Fagg; Tim Harding; Mark Horton; John Lee; Isobel Smythe Wood
Address: 583 Fulham Road, London SW6 5BY
Telephone: 0171 471 1100
Fax: 0171 471 1101
Email: info@batsford.com
Website: www.batsford.com
Imprints: Batsford, Brassey's, Conway Maritime Press, Putnam Aeronautical and DPR
Parent Company: Batsford Communications Plc
Unsolicited Manuscripts: No

B

Beaconsfield Publishers Ltd

Beaconsfield Publishers specialise in carefully-developed market-specific books in nursing, medicine and patient health care. We are also major contributors to the professional market for books in homeopathic medicine. Full details of our list may be viewed on our website at : www.Beaconsfield-Publishers.co.uk

Editor(s): John Churchill
Address: 20 Chiltern Hills Road, Beaconsfield, Buckinghamshire HP9 1PL
Telephone: 01494 672118
Fax: Same as phone
Email: books@beaconsfield-publishers.co.uk
Website: www.beaconsfield-publishers.co.uk
Imprints: Beaconsfield
Payment Details: Royalty
Unsolicited Manuscripts: No

Ruth Bean Publishers

Needlecrafts: lace-making, embroidery (practical and historical). Costume and costume history and anthropology related to textiles.

Editor(s): N W and R Bean
Address: Victoria Farmhouse, Carlton, Bedford MK43 7LP
Telephone: 01234 720356
Fax: 01234 720590
Email: ruthbean@cwcom.net
Payment Details: Negotiable
Unsolicited Manuscripts: Yes

Belitha Press

Belitha Press publishes high quality illustrated non-fiction books for children in the 3-13 age range. Subject areas include: art; environment issues; geography; history; literacy; music; natural history; numeracy; personal and social education; reference; science; technology.

Editor(s): Chester Fisher, Publishing Director
Address: London House, Great Eastern Wharf, Parkgate Road, London SW11 4NQ
Telephone: 0171 978 6330
Fax: 0171 223 4936
Imprints: Belitha Press
Parent Company: C & B Publishing Plc

David Bennett Books Ltd

Books for babies, toddler play books, novelty books.

Editor(s): Helen Mortimer
Address: 15 High Street, St Albans, Herts AL3 4ED
Telephone: 01727 855878
Fax: 01727 864085
Parent Company: Collins & Brown
Payment Details: Advance plus royalty or flat fee
Unsolicited Manuscripts: No

The Berean Publishing Trust

Small Christian publishing trust promoting the truth of God's Word Rightly Divided. See 2 Tim 2:15. The publications are the writings of our own authors.

Editor(s): Principal: Alan Schofield
Address: The Chapel of the Opened Book, 52a Wilson Street, London EC2A 2ER
Telephone: 0181 446 2762
Email: bptsales@compuserve.com
Website: http://ourworld.compuserve.com/homepages/bptsales/homepage.htm
Parent Company: The Berean Forward Movement
Unsolicited Manuscripts: No

B
Berg Publishers

Berg Publishers is an academic publisher specialising in Anthropology, Material Culture, Dress and Fashion and European History and Politics. We also publish an academic journal Fashion Theory. Submission guidelines are available upon request. We do not return unsolicited manuscripts.

Editor(s): Kathryn Earle (Anthropology and Fashion/Material Culture), Maike Bohn (History and Politics)
Address: 150 Cowley Road, Oxford OX4 1JJ
Telephone: 01865 245104
Fax: 01865 791165
Email: enquiry@berg.demon.co.uk
Website: http://www.berg.demon.co.uk
Imprints: Oswald Wolff
Payment Details: Royalties paid annually
Unsolicited Manuscripts: No

Berghahn Books

Publishers of scholarly books in the humanities and social sciences with an emphasis on European studies and European, especially German-American, relations. Publish approximately 50 books and 10 journals a year, specifically in history, cultural studies, anthropology and sociology, politics and economics, Jewish studies, media and film studies, women's studies and military and war.

Editor(s): Marion Berghahn
Address: 3 Newtec Place, Magdalen Road, Oxford OX4 1RE
Telephone: 01865 250011
Fax: 01865 250056
Email: berghahnuk@aol.com
Website: www.berghahnbooks.com
Payment Details: Royalties paid once a year
Unsolicited Manuscripts: Yes

Berlitz Publishing Co Ltd

Publishers of self-teach language materials, pocket guides, phrase books and language travel products for children.

Address: Fourth Floor, 9-13 Grosvenor Street, London W1X 9FB
Telephone: 0171 518 8300
Fax: 0717 518 8310
Email: roger.kirkpatrick@berlitz.ie
Website: http://www.berlitz.com
Imprints: Berlitz
Parent Company: Berlitz International Inc
Unsolicited Manuscripts: No

Bible Reading Fellowship

The Bible Reading Fellowship (BRF) publishes resources for Bible reading and study, for Lent and Advent, for prayer and reflection, for individual and group use. BRF also publishes resources for children under the age of 11 (Barnabas imprint) and for 11-14-year-olds, encouraging them to a stronger commitment to build foundations to last a lifetime and beyond.

Editor(s): Sue Doggett, Naomi Starkey
Address: Peter's Way, Sandy Lane West, Oxford OX4 5HG
Telephone: 01865 748227
Fax: 01865 773150
Email: enquiries@brf.org.uk
Website: www.brf.org.uk
Imprints: Barnabas
Unsolicited Manuscripts: No

B

Bibliagora

Subject areas: contract bridge, philosophy and snooker. Publishers and international out-of-print book tracers.

Editor(s): David Rex-Taylor
Address: PO Box 77, Feltham, Middlesex TW14 8JF
Telephone: 020 8898 1234 / hotline: 07000 BIBLIO
Fax: 020 8844 1777
Email: biblio@bibliagora.com
Website: www.bibliagora.com
Payment Details: Negotiated
Unsolicited Manuscripts: No

BILD Publications (British Institute Of Learning Disabilities)

The British Institute of Learning Disabilities (BILD) publishes a range of materials for anyone with an interest in learning disabilities. BILD publications include: textbooks aimed at professionals and students in the field; workshop training materials and independent study materials designed and tested by leading experts and aimed at front-line staff and carers; accessible publications on a wide range of topics designed for independent use by people with learning disabilities or with support from carers or family members.

Address: Wolverhampton Road, Kidderminster DY10 3PP
Telephone: 01562 850251
Fax: 01562 851970
Email: bild@bild.demon.co.uk
Website: www.bild.org.uk
Payment Details: By negotiation
Unsolicited Manuscripts: No

BIOS Scientific Publishers Ltd

Life sciences and medicine; particularly molecular biology, biochemistry, genetics, cell biology, plant biology, microscopy, anaesthesia and obstetrics and gynaecology. We publish textbooks, practical handbooks, high-level review volumes and revision guides on all the above subjects.

Editor(s): J Ray, L Mansell
Address: 9 Newtec Place, Magdalen Road, Oxford OX4 1RE
Telephone: 01865 726286
Fax: 01865 200386
Email: mansell@bios.co.uk
Website: www.bios.co.uk
Payment Details: Royalties and advances (discussed on a book to book basis)
Unsolicited Manuscripts: Yes

Birlinn Limited And John Donald Publishers Limited

Birlinn Ltd specialises in Scottish non-fiction, particularly connected with the Highlands and Western Isles. At the same time, it is expanding into the field of military history and classic stories of adventure and exploration. John Donald publishes at an academic level mainly in the area of Scottish history and literary studies.

Editor(s): Hugh Andrew
Address: Unit 8, Canongate Venture, 5 New Street, Edinburgh EH8 8BH Scotland
Telephone: 0131 556 6660
Fax: 0131 557 6250
Email: info@birlinn.co.uk
Website: http://www.birlinn.co.uk
Imprints: John Donald
Unsolicited Manuscripts: Yes - send registered, hard copy only

ℬ
Black Ace Books

We are only interested in completed full-length books. Bright ideas, proposals in synopsis form, work in progress and so on are not of interest. As far as our own list is concerned, some of the categories we definitely do not require include children's, DIY, poetry, religion, short stories. Relatively few of our books are non-fiction. Occasionally, for a really exceptional book, and provided we can devise a suitable budget, we may offer to publish work in such categories as biography, history, philosophy and psychology. Most of our output is high-quality literary fiction. Works likely to excite us would include an oustanding first novel from a new author with a fresh perspective and distinctive voice.

Address: PO Box 6557, Forfar DD8 2YS
Unsolicited Manuscripts: Write for guidelines with SAE. We do not respond to cold-calls or faxes

Black Spring Press Ltd

A small, independent publisher specialising in modern literary fiction as well as non-fiction reflecting contemporary culture. Titles include: Nick Cave's King Ink and King Ink II, And The Ass Saw The Angel; Charles Jackson's The Lost Weekend; Kyril Bonfiglioli's The Mortdecai Trilogy, The Great Mortdecai Moustache Mystery.

Editor(s): Directors: Simon Pettifar, Maja Prausnitz
Address: 2nd Floor, 126 Cornwall Road, London SE1 8TQ
Telephone: 0171 401 2044
Fax: 1071 401 2055
Email: bsp@blackspring.demon.co.uk
Unsolicited Manuscripts: No

A & C Black

Children's and education books (including music) for 3-15 years, ceramics, calligraphy, drama, sport, theatre, travel guides, ornithology and books for writers.

Editor(s): Editorial Director: Jill Coleman
Address: 35 Bedford Row, London WC1R 4JH
Telephone: 0171 242 0946
Fax: 0171 831 8478
Email: publicity@acblack.co.uk
Imprints: Adlard Coles Nautical, Herbert Press, Christopher Helm Publishers
Parent Company: A & C Black (Publishers) Ltd
Unsolicited Manuscripts: Preliminary enquiry appreciated

blackhat

Independent small-press publisher, specialising in contemporary open-field poetry. Interested in poetry and prose that test the boundaries of language and structure, while still having something actual to say. Not interested in poetry found on a newspaper reader's page. Approach at manuscript stage made by publisher to author, not other way round. Suggest writers save cost of postage, unless invited by editor. Small one-off print-runs only.

Editor(s): Lloyd Robson
Address: 40 Ruby Street, Cardiff CF24 1LN
Imprints: Canarant (audio tapes)
Payment Details: Variable
Unsolicited Manuscripts: No. Any received not guaranteed a reply

B

Blackstaff Press Ltd

Blackstaff has published over 650 titles, mainly of Irish (especially Northern Irish) interest, but covering a range of categories including history, politics, poetry, fiction and humour.

Editor(s): Anne Tannahill
Address: Blackstaff House, Wildflower Way, Apollo Road, Belfast BT12 6TA
Telephone: 01232 668074
Fax: 01232 668207
Email: books@blkstafff.dnet.co.uk
Parent Company: W & G Baird
Unsolicited Manuscripts: Yes

Blake Publishing Ltd

Founded 1991 and rapidly expanding. Publishes mass-market non-fiction. No children's, specialist or non-commercial. 30 titles in 1998. No unsolicited mss; synopsis and ideas welcome. Please enclose SAE.

Address: 3 Bramber Court, 2 Bramber Road, London W14 9PB
Telephone: 0171 381 0666
Fax: 0171 381 6868
Email: words@blake.co.uk
Payment Details: Royalties paid twice yearly
Unsolicited Manuscripts: No

Bloodaxe Books

Contemporary poetry. Note to prospective authors and agents: when submitting work to Bloodaxe, please enclose SAE or International Reply Coupons. If your work is not accepted for publication, we will not be able to return it to you unless you have sent return postage. While we are pleased to consider unsolicited submissions, we cannot accept any responsibility for loss or damage to manuscripts or artwork. Please also note the following: * If you want a quick response, send a sample selection of up to a dozen poems rather than a full-length collection. If you want us to consider something other than poetry, please send a preliminary letter and synopsis rather than the book itself. * We are not publishing any more fiction. * If you do not read any contemporary poetry, we are unlikely to be interested in your work. * It is usually advisable to submit poems to magazines before thinking about putting a book together. * We regret that we aren't able to offer detailed criticism of poetry submitted for publication (we currently receive about 100 books to consider each week). There are specialist organisations offering critical services, writers' workshops and courses.

Editor(s): Neil Astley
Address: PO Box 1SN, Newcastle Upon Tyne NE99 1SN
Unsolicited Manuscripts: Yes

Bloomsbury Publishing

Literary fiction, biography, illustrated, reference, travel in hardcover; children's, trade paperback and mass market paperback.

Editor(s): Liz Calder, David Reynolds, Rosemary Davidson, Matthew Hamilton, Kathy Rooney, Sarah Oedina, Emma Matthewson, Bill Swainson, Alexandra Pringle
Address: 38 Soho Square, London W1V 5DF
Telephone: 0171 494 2111
Fax: 0171 434 1190
Website: www.bloomsbury.com

B
BMJ Books

BMJ Books publishes professional level medical titles for practitioners and trainees.

Address: BMA House, Tavistock Square, London WC1H 9JR
Telephone: 0171 383 6185
Fax: 0171 383 6662
Email: orders@bmjbooks.com
Website: www.bmjbooks.com
Parent Company: BMJ Publishing Group

Bodmin Books, The Cornish Capital Publishers

Founded in 1972 to promote Cornish history, tradition, and present attractions, Bodmin Books pioneered attention to Bodmin Moor ('72), the Bodmin Riding custom ('74), and the delights of Kynance on the Lizard in West Cornwall ('76); and still holds the only definitive study of a nationally-known murder mystery Charlotte Dymond 1844 ('78). The occasionals imprint Cotterill & Munn was launched in 1997 with the publication of the words/music pamphlet The Ballad Of '97 commemorating the 500th anniversary of the Cornish Rising, and the annual Bodmin Community Christmas Day Party tabloid. 1998 saw a re-launch of the Bodmin Map with historical notes and placename references; and, in 1999, came Whit's End, a verse play to mark the 450th Prayer Book Rising anniversary. Bodmin Books will continue with academic studies. Both imprints are voluntary co-operative hobbies, with authors contributing printing costs, and the company its storage space, production and promotional experience, and orders facilitation. If/when books sell, authors may be reimbursed some or all of their contribution.

Editor(s): Mrs P I Munn
Address: 4 Turf Street, Bodmin, Cornwall PL31 2DH
Imprints: Cotterill & Munn
Parent Company: Bodmin Books, The Cornish Capital Publishers
Payment Details: None
Unsolicited Manuscripts: No

Bogle-L' Ouverture Publications Ltd (Trading under the name of Bogle-L' Ouverture Press)

Founded in 1969 as Bogle-L'Ouverture Publications. This company went into voluntary liquidation in 1991 and Bogle-L'Ouverture Press was founded in its place. The press provides a window to the world of black experience, mainly in the UK. We publish work across the wide spectrum of poetry, fiction, non-fiction, children's etc.

Address: PO Box 2186, London W13 9QZ
Telephone: 0181 579 4920
Fax: As phone
Email: blp@huntleyfreeserve7.com.uk
Unsolicited Manuscripts: Yes

The Book Castle

Publishes non-fiction of local interest (Bedfordshire, Hertfordshire, Buckinghamshire, Northamptonshire, the Chilterns), 6 titles a year. About 50 titles in print, eg Chiltern Walks series, The Hill Of The Martyr, Journeys Into Buckinghamshire.

Editor(s): Paul Bowes, Sally Siddons
Address: 12 Church Street, Dunstable, Beds LU5 4RU
Telephone: 01582 605670
Fax: 01582 662431
Email: bc@book-castle.fpb.net
Website: http://www.book-castle.co.uk/
Payment Details: Royalty
Unsolicited Manuscripts: Yes

B
The Book Guild Ltd

Founded in 1982, we are a small, independent general publishing house. We carry a diverse list which includes sponsored books, fiction, autobiographies, biographies, military histories, human interest titles and children's titles. Also have an expanding mainstream list. Approximately 80 titles a year.

Editor(s): Carol Biss - Managing Director
Address: Temple House, 25 High Street, Lewes, East Sussex BN7 2LU
Telephone: 01273 472534
Fax: 01273 476472
Email: info@bookguild.co.uk
Website: www.bookguild.co.uk
Payment Details: Royalties paid twice-yearly
Unsolicited Manuscripts: No

Borthwick Institute Publications

The Institute publishes a series of studies concerned with the ecclesiastical history of the north of England and other aspects of the history or historiography of Yorkshire. Also concentrates on issuing editions and catalogues of its deposited archives and providing guides to the handwriting and contents of records.

Editor(s): Editorial board
Address: St Anthony's Hall, Peasholme Green, York YO1 7PW
Telephone: 01904 642315
Fax: 01904 633284
Website: www.york.ac.uk/inst/bihr
Imprints: Borthwick Papers, Borthwick Texts and Calendars, Borthwick Lists and Indexes, Borthwick Studies In History, Borthwick Wallets, Monastic Research Bulletin
Parent Company: University of York

Bowker-Saur

Library and information science, including series such as Guides To Information Sources, Information Services Management and British Library Research. Also business information.

Editor(s): Linda Hajdukiewicz, Steve Warriner
Address: Windsor Court, East Grinstead House, East Grinstead RH19 1XA
Telephone: 01342 326972
Fax: 01342 335612
Email: lis@bowker-saur.co.uk
Website: http://www.bowker-saur.co.uk
Imprints: Headland Business Information, Bowker-Saur
Parent Company: Reed Business Information
Unsolicited Manuscripts: Yes

Marion Boyars Publishers Ltd

An established literary imprint (since 1960) with specialisations in fiction, fiction in translation, cinema and avant-garde music. Famous authors include Ken Kesey, Hubert Selby Jnr, Gilbert Sorrentino, Michael Ondaatje, Yevgeny Yevtushenko, Kenzaburo Oe, Pauline Kael, Robert Creeley, Julio Cortazar, John Cage, Ingmar Bergman and Georges Bataille.

Editor(s): Ken Hollings
Address: 24 Lacy Road, London SW15 1NL
Telephone: 0181 7889522
Fax: 0181 7898122
Unsolicited Manuscripts: Accepted for literary standard works (as against mass-market) with return p&p

B

BPS Books (The British Psychological Society)

BPS Books is the publishing arm of the British Psychological Society, publishing books in psychology in relation to health, counselling, management, training, psychometrics and education titles. Books are both aimed at academics and practitioners. Catalogues and information on submitting proposals is available by contacting our office.

Editor(s): Joyce Collins, Jon Reed
Address: 48 Princess Road East, Leicester LE1 7DR
Telephone: 0116 254 9568
Fax: 0116 247 0787
Email: julmer@bps.org.uk
Website: www.bps.org.uk
Imprints: BPS Books
Payment Details: Royalties
Unsolicited Manuscripts: Yes

Barry Bracewell-Milnes

Economic policy, tax policy, tax avoidance and evasion.

Editor(s): Barry Bracewell-Milnes
Address: 26 Lancaster Court, Banstead, Surrey SM7 1RR
Telephone: 01737 350736
Imprints: Panopticum
Unsolicited Manuscripts: Write first

Bradford Libraries

Books of local interest.

Address: Central Library, Prince's Way, Bradford BD1 1NN
Telephone: 01274 753600
Fax: 01274 395108
Email: public.libraries@bradford.gov.uk
Parent Company: City of Bradford Metropolitan Council
Unsolicited Manuscripts: No

Bradt Publications

Country guides - a comprehensive selection of individual countries spanning all continents from Albania to Zanzibar. Hiking guides - to out-of-the-way places including South America and Eastern Europe. Rail and road guides - advice on travelling to and around destinations on a global scale; constantly updated. Wildlife guides - covering the natural history of areas rich in wildlife; highly illustrated.

Editor(s): Tricia Hayne
Address: 41 Nortoft Road, Chalfont St Peter, Bucks SL9 0LA
Telephone: 01494 873478
Fax: 01494 873478
Email: bradtpublications@compuserve.com
Payment Details: Royalties
Unsolicited Manuscripts: No

Nicholas Brealey Publishing

We are publishers of leading-edge books for business that inform, inspire, enable and entertain. We also focus on personal development, the international and intercultural fields and topical bestsellers that go beyond the traditional business book to look at the global picture.

Editor(s): Nicholas Brealey
Address: 36 John Street, London WC1N 2AT
Unsolicited Manuscripts: Yes

B

Breedon Books Publishing Co Ltd

Local history, sport, biography and autobiographies by sports personalities.

Editor(s): Anton Rippon
Address: 44 Friar Gate, Derby DE1 1DA
Telephone: 01332 384235
Fax: 01332 292755
Email: breedonbooks@netmatters.co.uk
Imprints: Breedon Sport, Breedon Heritage
Payment Details: By arrangement
Unsolicited Manuscripts: Yes if accompanied by return postage

Brewin Books

Midland regional history topics. Biographies. Transport history: railways, buses, aircraft and canals. Joint publications with trusts, local authorities etc (non-fiction topics).

Editor(s): Alan Brewin
Address: Doric House, 56 Alcester Road, Studley, Warwickshire B80 7LG
Telephone: 01527 854228
Fax: 01527 852746
Email: alan@brewinbooks.com
Website: www.brewinbooks.com
Imprints: Brewin Books
Parent Company: Brewin Books Ltd
Payment Details: Usual royalties payable six-monthly
Unsolicited Manuscripts: No. But preliminary letter with synopsis acceptable

B

The Bridgeman Art Library

Fine art photographic Library with over 120,000 images available for publication. Representing over 750 museums, galleries and private collections throughout the world, the collection covers every style, period and subject from cave painting to contemporary art and design. Our researchers can source the images on your behalf and will send transparencies or scans to suit your brief to perfection. Alternatively, search for images on our CD-ROM catalogue 'COMPLETE' or browse through our on-line database at www.bridgeman.co.uk. Clients can also contact us at Branch offices in New York and Paris.

Address: London: 17-19 Garway Road, London W2 4PH, New York: 65 East 93rd Street, New York NY 10128 USA, Paris: 31, rue Etienne Marcel, 75001 Paris, France
Telephone: London: 0171 727 4065
Fax: London: 0171 792 8509
Email: UK: info@bridgeman.co.uk, US: info@bridgemanart.com, Paris: paris@bridgeman.co.uk
Website: www.bridgeman.co.uk

Brilliant Publications

Brilliant Publications publishes books for teachers, parents and others interested in the education of children 0-13 years olds. The books are primarily resource books and activity sheets for use in classrooms, rather than stories for children. Potential authors are invited to phone or write for a catalogue so they can see the type of books we publish prior to sending in a proposal.

Editor(s): Priscilla Hannaford
Address: The Old School Yard, Leighton Road, Northall, Dunstable, Bedfordshire LU6 2HA
Telephone: 01525 222844
Fax: 01525 221250
Email: brilliantpublications@compuserve.com
Website: www.brilliantpublications.co.uk
Imprints: Brilliants Publications
Payment Details: Royalties, payable twice-yearly
Unsolicited Manuscripts: We are always happy to receive contributions from new authors but would prefer to receive a proposal and sample chapter initially, rather than a complete manuscript. Authors should supply an SAE

B

British Cement Association

Cement, concrete, civil and structural engineering, construction, materials science and standards.

Editor(s): Martin Clarke
Address: Century House, Telford Avenue, Crowthorne, Berks RG45 6YS
Email: library@bca.org.uk
Website: www.bca.org.uk
Payment Details: Negotiable
Unsolicited Manuscripts: Yes

British Library Publications

The British Library has a flourishing and expanding publishing programme of approximately 40 titles per year and over 600 titles in print. The majority of the titles are bibliographies and reference works; however there is also an expanding list of general and illustrated books, based primarily on the Library's extensive historic connections.

Editor(s): David Way
Address: 96 Euston Road, London NW1 2DB
Telephone: 0171 412 7704
Fax: 0171 412 7768
Email: blpublications@bl.uk
Website: www.portico.bl.uk
Imprints: British Library Publications
Parent Company: The British Library

British Museum Press

Subect areas: History and archaeology, Art History, Decorative Arts and Collecting, Numismatics, Ethnnography. Types of publications: Titles for the general reader, educational fiction and non-fiction books for children, Academic titles and Occasional Papers. Postcard sets and gift sets for adults and children.

Editor(s): Ms T Francis - Senior Editor (adults), Ms C Jones - Senior Editor (Childrens)
Address: 46 Bloomsbury Street, London WC1B 3QQ
Telephone: 0171 323 1234
Fax: 0171 436 7315
Email: sales.books@bmcompany.co.uk
Website: www.britishmuseumcompany.co.uk
Parent Company: British Museum Company Ltd
Payment Details: Variable
Unsolicited Manuscripts: Synopsis rather than manuscript

Brooklands Books Ltd

The Brooklands Books road test series provide an unparalleled source of motoring reference literature. The series includes the new Ultimate Portfolio series, as well as the popular Gold Portfolios, Performance/Muscle Portfolios and Limited Editions. New for 1999 is a series entitled 'Take on the Competition' which focuses on individual models. The Gold Portfolio and Performance Portfolio series now cover motor cycle marques. Our Motor Racing series, with collected contemporary race reports, summaries and results, cover some of the greatest motor races in the world. Brooklands Books also publish official technical literature fo MG, Land Rover, Jaguar, Triumph and Austin Healey, as well as their specially commissioned Owners Workshop Manuals.

Address: PO Box 146, Cobham, Surrey KT11 1LG
Telephone: 01932 865051
Fax: 01932 868803
Email: sales@brooklands-books.com
Website: www.brooklands-books.com

B

Brown, Son & Ferguson Ltd

Nautical and navigation both technical and non-technical (not biographical).

Editor(s): L Ingram-Brown
Address: 4/10 Darnley Street, Glasgow G41 2SD
Telephone: 0141 429 1234
Fax: 0141 420 1694
Email: info@skipper.co.uk
Website: www.skipper.co.uk
Payment Details: Standard royalty agreement
Unsolicited Manuscripts: Yes

Bryntirion Press

The literature arm of the Evangelical Movement of Wales, Bryntirion Press publishes books in English and Welsh for the Christian market. It publishes children's books in Welsh but not in English. Its books range from booklets to works of 300+ pages. Subjects covered include Christian doctrine, Church history, Christian living and biography.

Editor(s): Managing Editor: David Kingdon
Address: Bryntirion, Bridgend CF31 4DX
Telephone: 01656 655886
Fax: 01656 656095
Email: press@draco.co.uk
Parent Company: Evangelical Movement of Wales
Payment Details: 5% royalty paid annually
Unsolicited Manuscripts: No - but proposals welcomed

John Burgess Publications

Writer and publisher of history books, local and regional interest.

Address: 28 Holme Fauld, Scotby, Carlisle CA4 8BC
Telephone: 01228 513173

Edmund Burke Publisher

Specialises in fine historical publications and limited editions.

Editor(s): Eamonn de Burca
Address: Cloonagashel, 27 Priory Drive, Blackrock, Co Dublin, Ireland
Telephone: 003531 2882159
Fax: 003531 2834080
Email: deburca@indigo.ie
Website: http://indigo.ie/-deburca/deburca.htm
Imprints: Edmund Burke Publisher, Caislean Burc

Burral Floraprint Ltd

Publish good-value gardening titles, from eminent horticultural authors, featuring vibrant pictures and thoroughly helpful text, at at very reasonable prices. Examples include the 128-page Shrubs For Everyone by Peter Seabrook and Making The Most Of Clematis by Raymond Evison. Most of the photographs in the books come from Floraprint International's extensive plant picture library. The same company (Burall Floraprint Ltd) is the UK's leading supplier of pictorial plant labels, as used to label plants in the majority of UK garden centres and horticultural retailers.

Address: Oldfield Lane, Wisbech PE13 2TH
Telephone: 01945 461165
Fax: 01945 474396
Email: floraprint@burall.com
Website: www.burall.com
Imprints: Floraprint
Parent Company: Burall Ltd
Unsolicited Manuscripts: No

B

Butterworth Tolley

Publishers of law and accountancy titles for the legal profession. The entire product range comprises books, looseleaf works, encyclopaedias, reports and periodicals, as well as our rapidly-expanding portfolio of CD-ROM and online products. Butterworths has been at the forefront of innovative publishing for nearly 180 years, demonstrating the ability to respond to the changing needs of practitioners.

Address: Halsbury House, 35 Chancery Lane, London WC2A 1EL
Telephone: 0171 400 2500
Fax: 0171 400 2842
Website: http://www.butterworths.co.uk
Imprints: Tolley, Charles Knight, Barry Rose
Parent Company: Reed Elsevier
Unsolicited Manuscripts: Yes

Cairns Publications

Books and meditation cards which seek to unfold afresh the spiritual inheritance of the Christian church and to connect that inheritance to issues of contemporary concern.

Editor(s): Jim Cotter
Address: 47 Firth Park Avenue, Sheffield S5 6HF
Telephone: 0114 243 1182
Fax: As phone
Email: cottercairns@compuserve.com
Website: http://ourworld.compuserve.com/homepages/cottercairns
Parent Company: John Hunt Publishing

Cambridge University Press

Primary and secondary school books. English language teaching. Academic publishing embraces just about every subject seriously studied in the English speaking university world.

Editor(s): Many subject specialists
Address: The Edinburgh Building, Shaftesbury Road, Cambridge CB2 2RU
Imprints: Distribute worldwide: Stanford University Press, MacKeith Press
Parent Company: University of Cambridge
Payment Details: Varies according to the nature and level of the individual book
Unsolicited Manuscripts: Send outline proposal

Canongate Books Ltd

Fiction (not children's), poetry, mountaineering, travel, Scottish interest and classics, biography, art and history.

Editor(s): Colin McLear
Address: 14 High Street, Edinburgh EH1 1TE
Telephone: 0131 557 5111
Fax: 0131 557 5211
Email: crm@canongate.co.uk
Website: www.canongate.co.uk
Imprints: Rebel Inc, Payback Press
Unsolicited Manuscripts: Yes (not poetry)

Capall Bann Publishing

Mind body spirit, women's studies, personal development, nautical, environmental, occult, folklore, animals, mediumship, crystals, astrology, tarot, alternative health.

Editor(s): Julia Day, Jon Day
Address: Freshfields, Chieveley, Berks RG20 8TF
Telephone: 01635 248711(editorial) / 01635 247050 (sales)
Imprints: Capall Bann
Payment Details: 10% quarterly
Unsolicited Manuscripts: Yes - but send synopsis first

$\mathcal{C}$
Carcanet Press Ltd

'Everything an independent publisher should be' Willian Boyd. Since 1969, Carcanet has grown from an undergraduate hobby into one of the most prestigious 'small' publishers today. Strong Anglo-European, Anglo-Commonwealth and more local links ensure a quality and variety of publication from poetry, biography, translation and academic titles to its sturdy 'Fyfield' imprint, Carcanet is the market leader of its field. PN Review, its sister magazine showcases new writing and provides some of the best criticisms, reviews and articles around.

Editor(s): Michael Schmidt
Address: 4th Floor, Conavon Court, 12-16 Blackfriars Street, Manchester M3 5BQ
Telephone: 0161 834 8730
Fax: 0161 832 0084
Email: pnr@carcanet.u-net.com
Website: www.carcanet.co.uk
Imprints: Fyfield, Oxford Poets (1999)
Parent Company: Folio Holdings
Payment Details: Varies
Unsolicited Manuscripts: Brief synopsis (poetry preferred) to 'The Editor'

Cardiff Academic Press

Cardiff Academic Press is an independent academic publisher with particular interest in Religious Studies, Women's Studies and topics relating to Wales. Publishes under Cardiff Academic Press and Plantin imprints and distributes academic texts for overseas publishers Tuns Press, ILSI, ECW and Garamond.

Address: St Fagans Road, Fairwater, Cardiff CF5 3AE
Telephone: 01222 560333
Fax: 01222 554909
Email: E-bost:drakegroup@btinternet.com
Imprints: Plantins, ISLI, Tuns Press
Parent Company: The Drake Group Ltd
Payment Details: Pro-forma
Unsolicited Manuscripts: Yes but only biographical details and qualifications, brief synopsis, extent and target audience

Carlton Books

Books in all categories of popular culture, particularly sport, puzzles, quizzes and games, music, fashion, style and beauty, health and sex, television and popular science. We also publish TV tie-ins, particularly in association with Carlton Television.

Editor(s): Publishing Director: Piers Murray Hill
Address: 20 St Anne's Court, London W1V 3AW
Imprints: Carlton
Parent Company: Carlton Communications
Unsolicited Manuscripts: Yes, but no fiction

Jon Carpenter Publishing

Environment, sustainable economics and development, Green politics, social issues and health. Authors should send for our author information sheet before submitting any other material.

Editor(s): Jon Carpenter
Address: 2, The Spendlove Centre, Charlbury OX7 3PQ
Telephone: 01608 811969
Fax: Same as phone
Email: joncarpenterpublishing@compuserve.com
Payment Details: Royalties
Unsolicited Manuscripts: No

Casdec Print & Design Centre

Publishers and printers of educational non-fiction books, training materials for various bodies, and writers of open/distance learning materials. Specialise in publishing training and learning materials for universities, colleges, financial and other bodies. Publisher of the nationally-recognised Your Business Success bookkeeping and financial control system. Over 100,000 supplied to a national financial institution for use by clients.

Editor(s): T Moffat
Address: 21-22 Harraton Terrace, Birtley, Chester-le-Street, Co Durham DH3 2QG
Telephone: 0191 410 5556
Fax: 0191 410 0229

C

Frank Cass & Co Ltd

Publisher of academic books and journals including social science and Middle Eastern studies.

Editor(s): Andrew Humphries
Address: Newbury House, 900 Eastern Avenue, Newbury Park, Ilford IG9 7HH
Telephone: 0181 599 8866
Fax: 0181 599 0984
Email: info@frankcass.com
Website: www.frankcass.com
Imprints: Frank Cass, Woburn Press, Vallentine Mitchell

Cassell Publishers

Publishers of natural history, health, crafts, home decorating, interiors, spiritual, cookery, woodcrafts, gardening, personal development and science.

Editor(s): Mr Booth, Ms Washburn, Mrs Van Eesteren, Ms Churly
Address: Wellington House, 125 The Strand, London WC2R 0BB
Telephone: 0171 420 5555
Fax: 0171 420 7261
Website: www.cassell.co.uk
Imprints: Ward Lock, Blandford
Parent Company: Orion Publishing Group
Unsolicited Manuscripts: Yes

Catholic Institute For International Relations

Third world development, gender, peacebuilding, drugs and development, agriculture, transnational corporations, third world theology, Asia, Latin America, Europe and southern Africa.

Editor(s): Adam Bradbury
Address: Unit 3, Canonbury Yard, 190a New North Road, London N1 7BJ
Telephone: 0171 354 0883
Fax: 0171 359 0017
Email: ciir@ciir.org
Website: www.ciir.org
Unsolicited Manuscripts: No

Cavalier Paperbacks

Children's books. We publish pony books but would also like to expand and publish picture story books and adventure stories for boys.

Editor(s): Charlotte Fyfe
Address: Burnham House, Jarvis Street, Upavon, Wilts SN9 6DU
Telephone: 01980 630 379
Fax: Same as phone
Payment Details: Small advance and 7½% royalty
Unsolicited Manuscripts: Yes

Cavendish Publishing Limited

Publishers of Law and Medical books and journals for the student and professional markets.

Editor(s): Ms Jo Reddy
Address: The Glass House, Wharton Street, London WC1X 9PX
Telephone: 0171 278 8000
Fax: 0171 278 8080
Email: info@cavendishpublishing.com
Website: http://www.cavendishpublishing.com
Imprints: Cavendish Publishing
Parent Company: Cavendish Publishing (Jersey) Ltd
Payment Details: Royalties
Unsolicited Manuscripts: No

C

CCH Editions Ltd

Part of the Wolters Kluwer group, leading international publishers of business and professional information. CCH Editions Ltd produce a wide range of tax and business law publications in a variety of formats. Loose-leaf services, books, newsletters, seminars and electronic media deliver the knowledge businesses need across a broad spectrum of subjects including personnel management, commercial and company law, taxation, European law, insolvency and auditing.

Address: Telford Road, Bicester OX6 0XD
Telephone: 01869 253300
Fax: 01869 874700
Email: marketing@cch.co.uk
Website: www.cch.co.uk
Parent Company: Wolters Kluwer
Payment Details: Negotiable
Unsolicited Manuscripts: Brief explanatory letter invited as first step

Centaur Press

Subjects in the field of humane education, animal rights and classic literature.

Editor(s): Jeannie Cohen, Elisabeth Petersdorff
Address: 51 Achilles Road, London NW6 1DZ
Telephone: 020 7431 4391
Fax: 020 7431 5129
Email: books@opengatepress.co.uk
Website: www.opengatepress.co.uk
Imprints: Centaur Press, Linden Press
Parent Company: Open Gate Press
Unsolicited Manuscripts: Synopses and ideas for books only

The Central Bureau For Educational Visits & Exchanges

The Central Bureau, incorporating the UK Centre for European Education and Education Partners Overseas, forms part of the British Council. It is funded by the Education Departments of the United Kingdom and is the UK National Agency for many of the European Union Education and Training Programmes. The Bureau has over 50 years' experience publishing information guides on the theme of work, study and travel opportunities. Catalogue available.

Editor(s): Thom Sewell
Address: 10 Spring Gardens, London SW1A 2BN
Telephone: 0171 389 4886
Fax: 0171 389 4426
Email: books@centralbureau.org.uk
Website: www.britcoun.org/cbeve/
Parent Company: British Council

Centre For Economic Policy Research

A network of over 450 Research Fellows, based primarily in European universities. The Centre coordinates its Fellows' research activities and communicates their results to the public and private sectors. CEPR is an entrepreneur, developing research initiatives with the producers, consumers and sponsors of research. Established in 1983, CEPR is a European economics research organisation with uniquely wide-ranging scope and activities. CEPR is a registered educational charity, supported by various charitable trusts and banks, none of which gives prior review to the Centre's publications, nor necessarily endorses the views expressed.

Address: 90-98 Goswell Road, London EC1V 7RR
Telephone: 0171 878 2900
Fax: 0171 878 2999
Email: cepr@cepr.org
Website: www.cepr.org
Imprints: CEPR
Payment Details: Confidential
Unsolicited Manuscripts: No

C

Centre For Information On Language Teaching & Research (CILT)

The Centre for Information on Language Teaching & Research provides a complete range of services for language professionals in every stage and sector of education, including publications designed to support teachers.

Editor(s): Head of Publishing: Emma Rees
Address: 20 Bedfordbury, London WC2N 4LB
Telephone: 020 7379 5101
Fax: 020 7379 5082
Email: publications@cilt.org.uk
Website: http://www.cilt.org.uk

Chalcombe Publications

Technical publications for agriculture, specialising in animal nutrition, grass and forage crops and animal production systems. The books are for farmers, students, teachers, research workers and advisers.

Address: Painshall, Church Lane, Welton, Lincoln LN2 3LT
Telephone: 01673 863023
Fax: 01673 863108
Email: chalcombe@compuserve.com

Chambers Harrap Publishers Ltd

Dictionaries - English language and bilingual.

Address: 7 Hopetoun Crescent, Edinburgh EH7 4AY
Telephone: 0131 556 5929
Fax: 0131 556 5313
Email: Admin@chambersharrap.co.uk
Website: www.chambersharrap.com
Imprints: Chambers and Harrap
Parent Company: Havas, France
Unsolicited Manuscripts: No

Chapman Publishing

Chapman New Writing series aims to present up-and-coming writers, Scottish and international (short fiction, poetry and plays). We also publish a quarterly literary magazine that includes poetry, fiction and critical work from around the world, and reviews of new publications. Previously unpublished poetry, fiction (up to 3,000 words) and critical pieces accepted.

Editor(s): Joy Hendry
Address: 4 Broughton Place, Edinburgh EH1 3RX
Telephone: 0131 557 2207
Fax: 0131 556 9565
Email: chapman-pub@ndirect.co.uk
Website: www.airstrip-one.ndirect.co.uk/chapman
Imprints: Chapman New Writers Series, Chapman Magazine
Payment Details: Copies only
Unsolicited Manuscripts: Yes if accompanied by SAE/IRC

Zelda Cheatle Press

Specialist photography publishers.

Address: 99 Mount Street, London W1Y 5HF
Telephone: 0171 408 4448
Fax: 0171 408 1444
Email: photo@zcgall.demon.co.uk
Unsolicited Manuscripts: No

Checkmark Publications

Publishes 'The Step By Step Guide To Planning Your Wedding' by Lynda Wright (£5.95). Supplied through Gardners Books or Checkmark Publications.

Address: 2 Hazell Park, Amersham, Bucks HP7 9AB
Telephone: 01494 431289
Fax: As phone
Email: checkmark@avnet.co.uk
Unsolicited Manuscripts: No

C
Cherrytree Press

Cherrytree Press offers a superb range of books for PSE and full curriculum support. The highly aclaimed children's information book series, Cherrytree Books, offers a wide range of information books supporting the curriculum areas of PSE, Business Studies, ITC, English, History, Geography, Maths, Mythology and Science.

Address: Winsor Bridge Road, Bath, Avon BA2 3AX
Telephone: 01225 335336
Fax: 01225 310771
Email: sales@chivers.co.uk
Parent Company: Chivers Press

Child's Play (International) Ltd

Independent publisher of children's educational books, games and audio-visual materials - specialising in whole-child development, learning through play, life skills and values. Founded in 1972, Child's Play is non-sectarian, non-political, non-sexist, multi-cultural and eco-friendly. We encourage children to think about the world they want to live in, and provide challenging information books alongside beautifully illustrated fiction for the 2-10 age group.

Editor(s): Sue Baker
Address: Ashworth Road, Bridgemead, Swindon SN5 7YD
Telephone: 01793 616286
Fax: 01793 512795
Email: allday@childs-play.com
Imprints: Mission
Payment Details: Negotiable
Unsolicited Manuscripts: Yes - but no novels

The Children's Society

One of the UK's leading child care charities whose mission is to be a positive force for change in the lives of children and young people. Publishes books and reports for professionals on topics related to child welfare issues, and resources for children and young people in difficult circumstances. Does not publish general books for children.

Editor(s): Helen Marsden
Address: Edward Rudolf House, Margery Street, London WC1X 0JL
Telephone: 0171 841 4400
Fax: 0171 841 4500
Email: publishing@childsoc.org.uk
Website: www.the-childrens-society.org.uk
Imprints: The Children's Society
Payment Details: By negotiation
Unsolicited Manuscripts: On issues related to UK child welfare only

Chivers Press

Chivers Press offers a range of large print and audio books for both adults and children. Titles for both Large Print and Audios include the very best of contemporary fiction, best sellers and classics. For children our Galaxy Large Print offers modern children's fiction in clear, large type, for reluctant readers or those with poor eyesight. Read alongs produced especially for the National Year of Reading contain large print children's fiction book and cassettes in one attractive pack.

Address: Winsor Bridge Road, Bath, Avon BA2 3AX
Telephone: 01225 335336
Fax: 01225 310771
Email: sales@chivers.co.uk

C

The Christadelphian Magazine & Publishing Association Ltd

Publishes magazines, pamphlets and books on Bible topics, and to promote the Christadelphian faith.

Editor(s): M J Ashton
Address: 404 Shaftmoor Lane, Hall Green, Birmingham B28 8SZ
Telephone: 0121 777 6324
Fax: 0121 778 5024
Email: the_christadelphian@compuserve.com
Website: www.christadelphian.uk.com
Imprints: The Christadelphian, Faith Alive!

Christchurch Publishers Ltd

General book publishers. Publications include reference, fine art, architecture and fiction.

Editor(s): James Hughes, Leonard Holdsworth
Address: 10 Christchurch Terrace, London SW3 4AJ
Telephone: 0171 351 4995
Fax: Same as phone
Imprints: Albyn Press, Charles Skilton Ltd, Luxor Press, Tallis Press, Caversham Communications Ltd
Parent Company: Christchurch Publications Ltd
Payment Details: By negotiation
Unsolicited Manuscripts: Letter before sending anything

Christian Focus Publications

Christian books for all ages. We are an evangelical publisher that produces board books to children's bibles for younger people and biographies to theological books for adults. For an idea of our range write for our full catalogue.

Editor(s): Malcolm Maclean (Adult), Catherine Mackenzie (Children)
Address: Geanies House, Fearn, Tain, Ross-Shire Scotland IV20 1TW
Telephone: 01862 871 011
Fax: 01862 871 699
Email: info@christianfocus.com
Website: http://www.christianfocus.com
Imprints: Christian Focus, Christian Heritage, Mentor
Parent Company: Balintore Holdings
Payment Details: Negotiable royalty %, fixed fee
Unsolicited Manuscripts: Yes

Christian Music Ministries

CMM serves and resources churches, schools, bookshops and individuals through teaching, workshops, 'music in worship' seminars, musicals, training courses, day and weekend conferences and mail-order catalogue. Deals principally with the publishing, recording and marketing of music composed by Roger Jones, the Director. This includes his 16 musicals, the latest being Snakes And Ladders to be published in 1999. He has also released various collections of worship songs, Ways To Praise and Precious and Honoured being the two latest. CMM also run various Family Music Weeks during the summer which includes an annual visit to Lee Abbey in Devon.

Editor(s): Director: R W Jones
Address: 325 Bromford Road, Hodge Hill, Birmingham B36 8ET
Telephone: 0121 783 3291
Fax: 0121 785 0500
Email: roger@cmm.org.uk
Website: http://www.cmm.org.uk

C

Christian Research

Christian Research is a Christian charity serving all denominations. We are publishers of specialist reference books for leaders of churches and Christian organisations, including directories, handbooks, statistical works and an atlas. Also publish results of own research projects relating to Christian activity and behaviour, UK and worldwide.

Editor(s): Peter Brierley, Heather Wraight
Address: Vision Building, 4 Footscray Road, Eltham, London SE9 2TZ
Telephone: 020 8294 1989
Fax: 020 8294 0014
Email: admin@christian-research.org.uk
Website: christian-research.org.uk
Unsolicited Manuscripts: No

Church Pastoral Aid Society

The Church Pastoral Aid Society is a Christian charity associated with the Church of England. Dedicated to equipping church leaders, youth workers and small-group leaders, CPAS publish approximately 20 publications a year. Housing a direct marketing operation, CPAS combines both publishing and promotion to provide moral, biblical and religious resources.

Editor(s): Rory Keegan
Address: Athena Drive, Tachbrook Park, Warwick CV34 6NG
Telephone: 01926 458 458
Fax: 01926 458 459
Email: liselle@cpas.org.uk
Website: www.cpas.org.uk
Unsolicited Manuscripts: To the Editor

Church Society

As well as two regular quarterly publications, Churchman (a theological journal) and CrossWay (a magazine mainly for CS members), Church Society publishes pamphlets as the need arises, on vital issues facing the Church and nation, and theological works such as The Principles Of Theology by Griffith Thomas (an introduction to the 39 Articles) and An English Prayer Book (a prayer book in modern English).

Editor(s): David Phillips (CrossWay), Gerald Bray (Churchman)
Address: Dean Wace House, 16 Rosslyn Road, Watford, Hertfordshire WD1 7EY
Telephone: 01923 235111
Fax: 01923 800362
Website: http://www.churchsociety.org/

CIB Publishing

The publishing division of The Chartered Institute of Bankers. Titles include distance learning study texts for our qualifications and a growing number of practitioners text books and reference works. All academic levels covered from schools to degree. The CIB is a registered charity.

Editor(s): Philip Blake, Finola McLaughlin
Address: Emmanuel House, 4-9 Burgate Lane, Canterbury, Kent CT1 2XJ
Telephone: 01227 762600
Fax: 01227 497641
Email: pblake@cib.org.uk
Website: www.cib.org.uk
Imprints: CIB Publishing
Parent Company: Chartered Institute of Bankers
Payment Details: Advances or fees negotiable. Varies according to book
Unsolicited Manuscripts: Welcomed and reviewed within 2 weeks

C

Cicerone Press

Activity guides - walking, climbing, cycling etc. We are the leading publishers in this field with 300 titles.

Editor(s): Jonathan Williams
Address: 2 Police Square, Milnthorpe, Cumbria LA7 7PY
Telephone: 01539 562069
Fax: 01539 563417
Email: cicerone@demon.co.uk
Website: www.cicerone.demon.co.uk
Payment Details: Royalties every 6 months
Unsolicited Manuscripts: Jonathan Williams

Claridge Press

Books on politics, philisophy, history, culture and the arts (no fiction). Also publishes The Salisbury Review.

Editor(s): Roger Scruton
Address: 33 Canonbury Park South, London N1 2JW
Telephone: 0171 226 7791
Fax: 0171 354 0383
Email: salisbury-review@easynet.co.uk
Imprints: Claridge Press
Parent Company: Claridge Ltd
Payment Details: Royalties
Unsolicited Manuscripts: Yes

T&T Clark Ltd

Theology and religion - international, non-denominational, academic and professional - books and journals. Law - Scottish, national and international, academic and professional - books and journals.

Editor(s): Geoffrey Green
Address: 59 George Street, Edinburgh EH2 2LQ
Telephone: 0131 225 4703
Fax: 0131 220 4260
Email: mailbox@tandtclark.co.uk
Website: www.tandtclark.co.uk
Imprints: T&T Clark
Payment Details: Royalties or fees
Unsolicited Manuscripts: Yes

James Clarke & Co Ltd/The Lutterworth Press

James Clarke & Co publish scholarly and academic works of religion, history, biography and reference. The Lutterworth Press imprint includes general trade titles of religion, children's fiction and non-fiction, and adult non-fiction (including art history, biography, history, crafts and passtimes, popular science, natural history and environment, and other subjects. Patrick Hardy books are children's fiction and picture books. Acorn Editions include local interest (East Anglia) titles and sponsored books.

Editor(s): Adrian Brink
Address: PO Box 60, Cambridge CB1 2NT
Telephone: 01223 350865
Fax: 01223 366951
Email: sales@lutterworth.com
Website: http://www.lutterworth.com
Imprints: James Clarke & Co, The Lutterworth Press, Patrick Hardy, Acorn Editions
Parent Company: James Clarke & Co Ltd
Payment Details: Royalty
Unsolicited Manuscripts: Yes

C

Class Publishing

Popular health, medicine and law.

Address: Barb House, Barb Mews, London W6 7PA
Telephone: 0171 371 2119
Fax: 0171 371 2878
Email: class.co.uk
Unsolicited Manuscripts: Almost always rejected

Clwyd Family History Society

Publishers of parish register transcripts and indexes, and other indexes of value to the family and local historian.

Address: Pen y Cae, Ffordd Hendy, Gwernymynydd, Sir y Fflint CH7 5JP
Telephone: 01352 755138
Email: dafydd@wyddgrug.freeserve.co.uk
Website: http://sentinel.ac.uk/genuki/big/wal/fln/cllwydfhs/

Peter Collin Publishing Ltd

We publish a wide range of dictionaries for students and professionals, in English, and many other languages.

Editor(s): P H Collin and S Collin
Address: 1 Cambridge Road, Teddington, Middlesex TW11 8DT
Telephone: 020 8943 3386
Fax: 020 8943 1673
Email: general@pcp.co.uk
Website: hhtp://www.pcp.co.uk/
Payment Details: Fee for smaller glossaries, royalty for larger works
Unsolicited Manuscripts: No, but draft proposals acceptable

Collins & Brown

Collins & Brown are publishers of non-fiction titles in the following areas, photography, lifestyle, gardening, crafts, health, mind, body and spirit, practical needlecraft, history and art and design. Paper Tiger (an imprint of Collins & Brown) is the leading publisher of fantasy art titles.

Address: Collins & Brown, London House, Great Eastern Wharf, Parkgate Road, London SW11 4NQ
Telephone: 0171 924 2575
Fax: 0171 924 7725
Email: info@cb-publishing.co.uk
Website: www.cb-publishing.co.uk
Imprints: Collins & Brown, Paper Tiger
Parent Company: C & B Publishing Plc
Payment Details: To be agreed
Unsolicited Manuscripts: Yes

Colourpoint Books

Educational textbooks: special emphasis on Northern Ireland curriculum. Transport: railways, buses, shipping, air transport, trams, etc. Particular interest in all Irish subjects and the Isle of Man. Will also consider English, Scottish and Welsh subjects. History: books on Irish subjects and local history photographic albums.

Editor(s): Sheila Johnston, Norman Johnston
Address: Unit D5, Ards Business Centre, Jubilee Road, Newtownards, Co Down BT23 4YH
Telephone: 01247 820505
Fax: 01247 821900
Email: info@colourpoint.co.uk
Website: http://www.colourpoint.co.uk
Payment Details: Royalties on longer works; one-off fee on shorter books depending on the length
Unsolicited Manuscripts: Yes

C

Colt Books Ltd

Colt Books Ltd is a small privately owned publishing house run by the proprietors Robert and Linda Yeatman. We specialise in books about the countryside, and anthologies - fishing, shooting, racing, cricket, bridge. We supply books direct to customers and bookshops.

Editor(s): Linda Yeatman
Address: Colt Books Ltd, 9 Clarendon Road, Cambridge CB2 2BH
Telephone: 01223 357047
Fax: 01223 365866
Imprints: Colt Books, White Lion Books
Unsolicited Manuscripts: Not accepted for consideration without prior consultation

The Columba Press

Religious publisher specialising in books of a pastoral nature for the Roman Catholic and Anglican markets. We also publish a small list of counselling titles, and a number of books on Irish history.

Editor(s): Seán O Boyle
Address: 55a Spruce Avenue, Stillorgan Industrial Park, Blackrock, Co Dublin, Ireland
Telephone: 353 1 2942556
Fax: 353 1 2942564
Email: info@columba.ie
Website: www.columba.ie
Imprints: The Columba Press, Gartan
Parent Company: The Columba Press
Unsolicited Manuscripts: Send outline and sample chapter

Columbia University Press

Reference books: gay/lesbian/gender studies, social sciences/anthropology, international politics, Asian/Far Eastern studies, Middle-eastern studies, film, philosophy, psychology and natural sciences.

Address: 1 Oldlands Way, Bognor Regis, West Sussex PO22 9SA
Unsolicited Manuscripts: Yes

C

Community Of Poets Press

An independent press with an increasing focus on printing and publishing poetry with original artwork. Our magazine Community Of Poets is an international quarterly which seeks and publishes creative and innovative work in any genre. New voices from all communities are especially welcome and encouraged. Also publish hand-sewn collections under the Pamphlet Poets and Poems By Post imprints. Each ready-to-send poem has an original woodcut print. We hope to launch Community of Artists and Poets for the millennium, a series of fine books and magazine.

Editor(s): Philip Bennetta, Susan Bennetta
Address: Hatfield Cottage, Chilham, Kent CT4 8DP
Telephone: 01227 730787
Email: bennetta@cpoetspress.freeserve.co.uk
Imprints: Pamphlet Poets, Poems by Post
Parent Company: Community of Poets Press
Payment Details: % payment on all sales for Pamphlet Poets. Free magazine to non-subscriber contributors
Unsolicited Manuscripts: No. Prefer to see small selection of work and like to publish in magazine first. Should see a copy of magazine @ £2.50 (incl p&p)

Compendium Publishing

Compendium is a publishing and packaging business. Specialising in non-fiction illustrated books which normally, although not always, have a male subject interest. Compendium has a developing range of dictionaries and reference books.

Editor(s): Simon Forty, Claire Lister, Martin Windrow
Address: 1st Floor, 43 Frith Street, London W1V 5TE
Telephone: 0171 287 4570
Fax: 0171 494 0583
Email: compendium@compuserve.com
Imprints: Wag Books
Payment Details: By negotiation
Unsolicited Manuscripts: No - synopsis only first please

C

Computer Step

Established in 1991, the leading British publisher of computer books. All popular subject areas are covered in concise and easy-to-understand format. The main imprint is In Easy Steps and there are more of these titles in Booktrack's Top 50 best-selling list of computer books in UK than from most other publishers. Computer Step also exports, reprints and translates its work internationally. It is represented by Penguin for distribution to the book trade in UK and internationally.

Editor(s): Harshad Kotecha
Address: Southfield Road, Southam, Warwickshire CV33 0FB
Telephone: 01926 817999
Fax: 01926 817005
Email: publisher@computerstep.com
Website: http://www.computerstep.com
Imprints: In Easy Steps
Payment Details: Advance and royalties paid
Unsolicited Manuscripts: Yes

Constable & Co Ltd

History, biography, memoirs, travel, Celtic interest, guide books, mountaineering, popular science, psychology, and military history; plus crime fiction.

Editor(s): Editorial Director: Carol O'Brien
Address: 3 The Lanchesters, 162 Fulham Palace Road, London W6 9ER
Telephone: 0181 741 3663
Fax: 0181 748 7562
Website: www.constable-publishers.co.uk

Leo Cooper

Publishers of military, naval and aviation history covering most periods, especially WW1, WW2, the Falklands and Napoleonic wars.

Editor(s): Henry Wilson
Address: 47 Church Street, Barnsley, South Yorkshire S70 2AS
Telephone: 01226 734 222
Fax: 01226 734 438
Email: charles@pen-and-sword.demon.co.uk
Website: www.yorkshire-web/ps/
Imprints: Leo Cooper, Battleground Europe, Pals
Parent Company: Pen and Sword Books Ltd
Payment Details: Twice-yearly
Unsolicited Manuscripts: Yes, with synopsis

Cottage Publications

Publishers of Irish books and prints on specific towns and areas of Ireland. Each book is illustrated with paintings by a profssional artist from the area and the history, folklore, stories etc written by a local historian. Ideal gifts these full colour hardbacks are bestsellers in their areas and ideal for ex-pats.

Address: Cottage Publications, Laurel Cottage, 15 Ballyhay Road, Donaghadee, Co Down BT21 0NG
Telephone: 01247 888033
Fax: 01247 888063
Email: alison@cottage-publications.com
Website: www.cottage-publications.com

C
Council For British Archaeology

The Council For British Archaeology (CBA) is an educational charity which works to improve awareness and enjoyment of archaeology for the benefit of all. The CBA publishes two main series: research reports, which aim to disseminate information and stimulate further research, and practical handbooks which are aimed at a wider audience. Recent practical handbooks include 'Churches & Chapels: Investigating Places Of Worship' and 'Romano-British Glass Vessels'. In addition, the CBA publishes educational titles such as the 'Guide To Archaeology In Higher Education'.

Editor(s): Kate Sleight (Publications Officer), Jonathan Bateman (Assistant Publications Officer)
Address: Bowes Morrell House, 111 Walmgate, York YO1 9WA
Telephone: 01904 671417
Fax: 01904 671384
Email: cbabooks@dial.pipex.com
Website: www.britarch.ac.uk
Payment Details: No royalty fees paid
Unsolicited Manuscripts: Proposals for new publications accepted

Countryside Books

Established in 1976, we publish books of local interest, almost always relating to whole English counties. Non-fiction only. Main subjects local history and outdoor activities, especially walking.

Editor(s): Nicholas Battle
Address: Highfield House, 2 Highfield Avenue, Newbury RG14 5DS
Telephone: 01635 43816
Fax: 01635 551004
Unsolicited Manuscripts: Yes, but send outline and sample chapter first

R & E Coward

Publish Richard Coward's mystery thrillers only.

Address: 16 Sturgess Avenue, London NW4 3TS
Telephone: 0181 202 9592
Unsolicited Manuscripts: No

Crabtree Press

The Press was incorporated in 1946 but since delimited, and now under the sole proprietorship of Ernie Trory, who uses it to publish his own extensive writings, some of which are partly autobiographical. Apart from a biography of the poet Percy Bysshe Shelley, and another of Thomas Hughes, author of Tom Brown's School Days, Crabtree Press publishes only contemporary history (1913 to date) from a Marxist viewpoint.

Address: 4 Portland Avenue, Hove, E Sussex BN3 5NP
Unsolicited Manuscripts: No

Crafthouse

Publishers of interactive CD-ROMS on diet and health, cookbooks, art and craft, travel. Under Vigara: Interactive Contact magazine (worldwide). Also Crafthouse Advertiser, an internet directory for various small companies; contains 'new writers' section where authors can display samples of their work for publishers' attention. Launched in 1999; details on application.

Editor(s): W Nicholas
Address: 122a Cambridge Road, Southend on Sea, Essex SS1 1ER
Telephone: 01702 354621
Fax: 01702 347353
Email: crafthouse@clara.net
Website: www.crafthouse.uk.com
Imprints: Winslow, Vigara
Parent Company: Crafthouse
Unsolicited Manuscripts: Accepted with return postage

C

Creative Monochrome Ltd

Specialist books on the art and craft of monochrome photography.

Editor(s): Roger Maile
Address: Courtney House, 62 Jarvis Road, South Croydon, Surrey CR2 6HU
Telephone: 0208 686 3282
Fax: 0208 681 0662
Email: roger@cremono.demon.co.uk
Imprints: Creative Monochrome, Digital Photo Art, Photo Art International
Payment Details: Negotiable
Unsolicited Manuscripts: No - contact first

Crescent Moon

Crescent Moon aims to publish the best in contemporary writing in the fields of poetry, literature, painting, sculpture, media, cinema, feminism and philosophy. Also publishes a quarterly magazine, Passion, and a bi-annual anthology of new American poetry, Pagan America.

Editor(s): J Robinson
Address: PO Box 393, Maidstone, Kent ME14 5XU
Telephone: 01622 729593
Imprints: Crescent Moon, Joe's Press
Payment Details: To be negotiated
Unsolicited Manuscripts: Yes, with letter and SAE or IRCs

Cressrelles Publishing Company Ltd

Established in 1972 to publish general books, now concentrates on plays and theatre books.

Address: 10 Station Road Industrial Estate, Colwall WR13 6RN
Telephone: 01684 540154
Fax: Same as phone
Imprints: J Garnett Miller Ltd, Kenyon-Deane, Actinic Press
Parent Company: Cressrelles Publishing Co Ltd

C

Cresta Booksellers Direct

Publishers and booksellers of books and manuals concerning industrial and commercial cleaning chemicals, methods and techniques, also kitchen cleaning manuals and books on industrial housekeeping.

Editor(s): J K P Edwards, A M Edwards
Address: 14 Beechfield Road, Liverpool, L18 3EH
Telephone: 0151 722 7400
Imprints: Cresta Publishing Company

Critical Vision

Publishers of challenging, cutting-edge non-fiction. Previous books have included The X Factory: Inside The American Hardcore Film Industry; Psychotropedia: A Guide to Publications on the Periphery, Bizarrism: Strange Lives, Cults and Celebrated Lunacy. Pending are books on the history of horror comics, pop culture in the Sixties and Seventies, and See No Evil: Banned Films and Video Controversy. We are always on the look-out for thought-provoking and esoteric new work but will only consider non-fiction submissions and proposals. Critical Vision is an imprint of Headpress.

Editor(s): David Kerekes
Address: Headpress, 40 Rossall Avenue, Radcliffe, Manchester M26 1JD
Fax: 0161 796 1935
Email: david.headpress@zen.co.uk
Website: http://www.headpress.com/
Imprints: Critical Vision
Parent Company: Headpress
Payment Details: By arrangement with author
Unsolicited Manuscripts: Yes

ℰ
Crown House Publishing

Formed by The Anglo American Book Company in 1998 to publish a range of books by authors who are professionals of many years' experience, all highly respected in their own field. We specialise in the areas of psychotherapy, particularly NLP, hypnosis/hypnotherapy and personal growth, and choose our books with care for their content and character, and for the value of their contribution of both new and updated material to their particular field. The first of our books was published in 1995. From small beginnings the publishing business has grown so that up to December 1998 we have published 22 titles. All of these books fall within the category of psychology. In 1999 we plan to publish a further 15 titles.

Editor(s): David Bowman
Address: Crown Buildings, Bacyfelin, Carmarthen SA33 5ND
Telephone: 01267 211880
Fax: 01267 211882
Email: crownhouse@anglo-american.co.uk
Website: www.anglo-american.co.uk
Payment Details: 6-monthly
Unsolicited Manuscripts: Yes

G L Crowther

Author/publisher of a series of railway, tramway and waterway atlases of the UK (63 vols). They show navigable rivers; canals, locks, wharves, warehouses, towpaths; mineral tramroads; railways, locations of over 11000 railway stations including obscure and short-lived ones, tunnels, viaducts, rail-served factories, collieries and docks; horse, steam, cable and electric street tramways, termini and depots, as well as thousands of dates of use.

Address: 224 South Meadow Lane, Preston PR1 8JP
Telephone: 01772 257126

CRU Publishing Ltd

The world's leading information provider in the field of precious metals, minerals and chemicals.

Editor(s): Lisa Connock, Mark Cockle, Chris Cunningham, Lynda Davies, Anthony Doyle, Mark Evans, Richard Hands, Cristopher Hourmouzions, James Robertson
Address: 31 Mount Pleasant, London WC1X 0AD
Telephone: 0171 837 5600
Fax: 0171 837 0292
Email: smoore@cruint.tcom.co.uk
Website: cru.co.uk
Parent Company: CRU International Ltd

Crux Press

Crux Press publishes Christian books. Most of their books are written or produced in-house, but they also publish books by authors outside the organisation. They specialise in bible-based puzzle books which encourage the study of the bible.

Editor(s): Mr Alick Hartley BSc
Address: Gwelfryn, Llanidloes Road, Newtown, Powys SY16 4HX
Telephone: 01686 623484
Fax: 01686 623784
Email: crux@press.mid-wales.net
Website: www.press.mid-wales.net/index.html
Imprints: Crux Press
Parent Company: Impart Books
Unsolicited Manuscripts: After permission obtained

_C_
Crécy Publishing Ltd

Publisher of aviation and military books, with over 150 titles in the range. Majority of titles second world war biographies and autobiographies. Also distribute for a number of other publishers.

Editor(s): Nancy Rolph
Address: 1a Ringway Trading Estate, Shadowmoss Road, Manchester M22 5LH
Telephone: 0161 499 0024
Fax: 0161 499 0298
Email: books@airplan.u-net.com
Website: www.airplan.u-net.com
Imprints: Crécy, Goodall
Unsolicited Manuscripts: Yes with SAE

CTBI Publications

Absolutely all areas that Christianity impinges upon. For example: ecumenism, faith and order, interfaith relations, women in church and society, human sexuality, ethics, communication, racism, economics, healing, mission and evangelism and international affairs.

Editor(s): Colin Davey
Address: Inter-Church House, 35-41 Lower Marsh, London SE1 7RL
Telephone: 0171 620 4444
Fax: 0171 928 0010
Email: book_ccbi@cix.co.uk
Website: www.ccbi.org.uk
Imprints: CTBI, CEC, WCC
Parent Company: Churches Together in Britain and Ireland
Payment Details: By negotiation
Unsolicited Manuscripts: Very rarely

James Currey Publishers

Specialist publishers of academic paperbacks on Africa and the Caribbean in the fields of History, Socio-Anthropology, Geography, Politics, Literary Criticism, Development Economics; also on World Anthropology.

Editor(s): Douglas Johnson
Address: 73 Botley Road, Oxford OX2 0BS
Telephone: 01865 244111
Fax: 01865 246454
Website: www.jamescurrey.co.uk
Payment Details: Royalties paid
Unsolicited Manuscripts: Send proposal first

Curzon Press

Academic and reference books on all aspects of Asian and Middle Eastern studies, and on religious studies and linguistics worldwide.

Editor(s): Jonathan Price
Address: 15 The Quadrant, Richmond, Surrey TW9 1BP
Telephone: 0181 948 4660
Fax: 0181 332 6735
Email: publish@curzonpress.demon.co.uk
Website: http://mias.ku.dl/curzonpress.htp
Imprints: Curzon, Japan Library, Caucasus World
Unsolicited Manuscripts: Johnathan Price

D
Dalesman Publishing Company

3 regional magazines - Dalesman, Cumbria And Lake District Magazine, Peak District Magazine. Also regional books on each of these areas about history and culture. Humour books. Walking guides for all abilities, mountain safety, potholing and mountain biking.

Editor(s): Terry Fletcher
Address: Stable Courtyard, Broughton Hall, Skipton, North Yorkshire BD23 3AZ
Email: editorial@dalesman.co.uk
Payment Details: Negotiable
Unsolicited Manuscripts: Yes

The C W Daniel Company Ltd

Alternative healing and the metaphysical.

Editor(s): Sebastian Hobnut
Address: 1 Church Path, Saffron Walden, Essex CB10 1JP
Telephone: 01799 526216, 01799 521909
Fax: 01799 513462
Email: daniel_publishing@dial.pipex.com
Website: cwdaniel.com
Imprints: Health Science Press, Neville Spearman Publishers, LN Fowler & Co Ltd
Unsolicited Manuscripts: No

Darf Publishers

Darf Publishers specialises in good quality facsimile reprints of out-of-print and rare books written in the eighteenth and nineteenth centuries. Our list is predominantly taken up with books on the geography culture, history, literature and theology of the Middle East and North Africa. As well as this we also publish original titles which will appeal to a different readership entirely - notably on cricket and racing.

Editor(s): A Bentaleb, Richard King
Address: 277 West End Lane, West Hampstead, London NW6 1QS
Telephone: 0171 431 7009
Fax: 0171 431 7655
Website: www.darfpublishers.com
Unsolicited Manuscripts: No

David & Charles

Crafts, art techniques, decorative art and interiors, fine art, woodwork, photography, gardening, equestrian, country, walking, pets and natural history.

Editor(s): Publishing Director: Pippa Rubinstein
Address: Brunel House, Forde Close, Newton Abbot TQ12 4PU
Telephone: 01626 323200
Fax: 01626 364463
Imprints: Godsfield, David & Charles Children's Books, Pevensey Press
Parent Company: D&C Group Ltd
Payment Details: Royalties paid twice-yearly
Unsolicited Manuscripts: Yes, synopsis or sample chapters

D

Christopher Davies Publishers Ltd

Non-fiction: history, biography, natural history, and sport of Welsh interest only.

Editor(s): Christopher Davies
Address: PO Box 403, Swansea SA1 4YF
Telephone: 01792 648825
Fax: Same as phone
Imprints: Christopher Davies, Triskele Books
Payment Details: Royalty payments twice-yearly in April and October
Unsolicited Manuscripts: No

John Dawes Publications

Self-publisher of books about swimming pools: design, trade information etc. Catalogue available. Also consultant adviser to the Author-Publisher Network and the Institute of Swimming Pool Engineers, concerned with self-publishing information and technical issues.

Editor(s): John Dawes, Pam Davis
Address: 12 Mercers, Hawkhurst, Kent TN18 4LH
Telephone: 01580 753346
Fax: Same as phone
Imprints: John Dawes Publications
Payment Details: Self-payment by result
Unsolicited Manuscripts: Author-publisher primarily, but willing to discuss means of publishing mss concerned with swimming pool technology/design, and now also material concerning Hawkhurst Gang of Smugglers, 1750

Giles de la Mare Publishers Ltd

Art and architecture, biography, history, music, general non-fiction.

Editor(s): Editor and Director: Giles de la Mare
Address: 3 Queen Square, London WC1N 3AU
Telephone: 0171 465 7607
Fax: 0171 465 7535
Email: gilesdlm@faber.co.uk
Payment Details: Royalty
Unsolicited Manuscripts: No

Andre Deutsch Ltd

Biography, cookery, children's, humour, history, film and TV, music, natural history, photography, sport, politics and current affairs, lifestyle, fitness.

Editor(s): Louise Dixon, Nicky Paris, Ingrid Connell
Address: 76 Dean Street, London W1V 5HA
Fax: 0171 316 4499
Imprints: Andre Deutsch, Chameleon, Manchester United Books, Granada Media, Andre Deutsch Classics, Madcap
Parent Company: VCI
Unsolicited Manuscripts: No

D

Diehard Publishers

Small, specialist publisher of quality poetry and drama of Scottish and International interest. Run from an Antiquarian bookshop. We also publish the quarterly broadsheet Poetry Scotland which should be the first point of contact for poets. Poetry books by Ian Blake, Elizabeth Burns, Angus Calder, Bashabi Fraser, Alan Jackson, Richard Livermore, Richard Price, Martha Modena Vertreace, Colin Will and others, plays by John Cargill Thompson and others, books attractively produced at £4.90 post free. ISBN prefix 0946230.

Editor(s): Ian W King and Sally Evans
Address: 3 Spittal Street, Edinburgh EH3 9DY
Imprints: Diehard Poetry and Diehard Drama
Unsolicited Manuscripts: Rarely accepted

Dillons Publishers

Publish only commissioned books. Next publications, commissioned books: 1. 'The Universe And Philip Larkin' by William Larkin. ISBN 1-901851-0-79. 2. 'Millennium Poems From The Beyond' by William Larkin. ISBN 1-901851-11-7.

Editor(s): John Grant
Address: 641 Castle Lane West, Bournemouth BH8 9TS
Telephone: 01202 396230
Unsolicited Manuscripts: No

Discovery Walking Guides Ltd

Walking guides/maps to popular holiday destinations. Essential to study our style, subject matter, on our website before approaching us.

Editor(s): David A Brawn, Ros Brawn
Address: 10 Tennyson Close, Northampton NN5 7HJ
Telephone: Initial contact by letter
Website: www.walking.demon.co.uk
Imprints: Warm Island Walking Guides
Payment Details: Negotiable
Unsolicited Manuscripts: No

Dolphin Book Co Ltd

Publish books of Spanish, Catalan and Latin American interest.

Address: Tredwr, Llangrannog, Llandysul SA44 6BA
Telephone: 01239 654404
Fax: 01239 654002
Unsolicited Manuscripts: No

Donhead Publishing Ltd

Donhead publishes books on building and architectural conservation, heritage and museum studies; scientific and technical books concerning the use of traditional building materials, and the conservation of those materials, looking at both the research and theory, along with the practical aspects of conservation. Would prefer it if potential authors were to contact us before sending a manuscript, either by telephone or letter to outline their ideas in order for us to assess whether it would be suitable for our list.

Editor(s): Jill Pearce, D Newbury (Publishing Co-ordinator)
Address: Lower Coombe, Donhead St Mary, Shaftesbury SP7 9LY
Telephone: 01747 828422
Fax: 01747 828522
Email: jillpearce@donhead.u-net.com
Website: www.donhead.u-net.com
Imprints: Donhead
Unsolicited Manuscripts: Only if relevant to our list

Dorling Kindersley Ltd

Editor(s): Editorial Directors: Robin Wood (Adult); Ruth Sandys (Children's)
Address: 9 Henrietta Street, Covent Garden, London WC2E 8PS
Telephone: 0171 753 3594
Fax: 0171 753 7561
Website: www.dk.com
Parent Company: Dorling Kindersley
Unsolicited Manuscripts: No

D
The Dovecote Press Ltd

The Dovecote Press publishes books reflecting the history, culture and way of life of individual English counties. The range is wide, and includes natural history, architecture, guide books, walking books and photographed portraits of individual counties in full colour. We take a great deal of trouble over production in an attempt to make every book we publish as well designed and of as high a quality as possible.

Editor(s): David Burnett
Address: Stanbridge, Wimborne, Dorset BH21 4JD
Telephone: 01258 840549
Fax: 01258 840958
Email: dovecote@mcmail.com
Unsolicited Manuscripts: Please enclose SAE - No fiction

Downlander Publishing

Highly selective publishers of poetry of outstanding merit. This is a non-profit foundation interested only in poetry which contributes in real terms to literature and which has both philosophical and technical quality. Selection of submitted titles (letter and examples initially) is rigorous.

Editor(s): D F Bourne-Jones, MA (Oxon)
Address: 'Downlander' 88 Oxendean Gardens, Lower Willingdon, Eastbourne, East Sussex BN22 0RS
Telephone: 01323 500 437
Payment Details: Applicant must be prepared to meet basic production cost
Unsolicited Manuscripts: None, letter and up to 10 examples of work, plus SAE

Downside Abbey Publications

A department of the famous Somerset Benedictine monastery Downside Abbey, it specialises in English Roman Catholic history and produces about two books a year in addition to the quarterly periodical of theology, philosophy and history The Downside Review. This latter also reviews books in its subject area.

Address: Downside Abbey, Stratton on the Fosse, Bath BA3 4RH
Telephone: 01761 235 109
Fax: 01761 235 124
Email: domcharles@downside.co.uk
Imprints: Downside Abbey
Parent Company: Downside Enterprise Ltd
Payment Details: No royalties on 1st editions
Unsolicited Manuscripts: Only after consultation

Dragon's Head Press

Independent small-press publishing project, founded in 1993 and affiliated to the Association of Little Presses. Aims to publish affordable, specialist books, booklets and periodicals devoted entirely to dragons, associated lore and related themes. Provides a forum for writers, researchers, poets and artists, as well as being an invaluable resource in its chosen literary and academic field.

Editor(s): Project Co-ordinator/Editor: Ade Dimmick
Address: PO Box 3369, London SW6 6JN
Website: http.//www.medp.freeserve.co.uk/dc/
Imprints: Dragon's Head Press
Payment Details: Negotiable
Unsolicited Manuscripts: No

D
Drake Educational Associates

Drake Educational Associates publishes an extensive list of Teacher Reference books and videos alongside its list of classroom resources for Primary and Secondary schools. We also distribute Teacher Reference titles for three overseas publishers Pembroke, Eleanor Curtain and Highsmith.

Address: St Fagans Road, Fairwater, Cardiff CF5 3AE
Telephone: 01222 560333
Fax: 01222 554909
Email: E-bost:drakegroup@btinternet.com
Imprints: Pembroke, Eleanor Curtain, Highsmith
Parent Company: The Drake Group
Payment Details: Pro-forma

Dramatic Lines

Dramatic Lines is a small independent company dedicated to the publication of dramatic material for use in schools and acting examinations. Publications include monologues, duologues, an introduction to Shakespeare through one-act plays, a resource book of drama lessons for teachers, Shakespeare rewrites, plays linked to history national curriculum and performance pieces for three and four players.

Editor(s): John Nicholas
Address: PO Box 201, Twickenham, London
Telephone: 0181 296 9502
Fax: 0181 296 9503
Email: mail@dramaticlinespublishers.freeserve.co.uk
Imprints: Dramatic Lines
Payment Details: Negotiable
Unsolicited Manuscripts: Yes. All unsolicited manuscripts must be accompanied by SAE

Dublar Scripts

Publishers of pantomimes, one-act and full-length plays. Drama and comedy. Scripts aimed at the amateur theatre. Founded 1994.

Address: 204 Mercer Way, Romsey, Hants SO51 7QJ
Telephone: 01794 501377
Fax: 01794 502538
Email: bobheather@dublar.freeserve.co.uk
Imprints: Sleepy Hollow Pantomimes
Unsolicited Manuscripts: All unsolicited manuscripts must be accompanied by SAE for return

Martin Dunitz Ltd

High-quality medical publishers covering areas such as dermatology, cardiology, neurology and orthopaedics. New areas include oncology, psychiatry, endocrinology and bone metabolism.

Address: The Livery House, 7-9 Pratt Street, London NW1 0AE
Telephone: 0171 482 2202
Fax: 0171 267 0159
Website: http://www.dunitz.co.uk

Eagle Publishing

Specialises in Christian books, primarily on prayer and spirituality, but also including a number of gift books incorporating classic and modern art.

Editor(s): Sue Wavre
Address: 6-7 Leapale Road, Guildford, Surrey GU1 4JX
Telephone: 01483 306309
Fax: 01483 579196
Email: eagle_indeprint@compuserve.com
Imprints: Eagle
Parent Company: Inter Publishing Services (IPS) Ltd
Payment Details: On application
Unsolicited Manuscripts: Yes

_E_
Earlsgate Press

Publisher of business management books.

Address: The Plantation, Rowdyke Lane, Wyberton, Boston, Lincs PE21 7AQ
Telephone: 01205 350764
Fax: 01205 359459
Email: earlsgatepress@btinternet.com
Website: www.btinternet.com/~earlsgate.press
Parent Company: Roberston Cox Ltd
Unsolicited Manuscripts: Yes but only business management

Earthscan Publications Ltd

Non-fiction publishers of books on environmental and sustainable development issues for academics, professionals, business people, policy makers and general readers. Broad categories within the fields of environment and development include: business and industry; cities and the built environment; climate; ecology and conservation; economics; food and agriculture; forestry; health; international relations; law; politics and society; popular science; natural resource management; risk; tourism.

Editor(s): Managing Editor: Frances MacDermott
Address: 120 Pentonville Road, London N1 9JN
Telephone: 0171 2780433
Fax: 0171 27811442
Email: earthinfo@earthscan.co.uk
Website: www.earthscan.co.uk
Parent Company: Kogan Page Ltd
Unsolicited Manuscripts: Yes

Ebury Press

Division of Random House UK, specialising in adult non-fiction publishing over a broad range of subjects, from cookery, gardening and lifestyle to psychology, health and personal development, and including high-quality illustrated books, film and television tie-ins, sports and popular music. Sales force of 15 reps working across the UK, supported by 25 head office sales staff, a dedicated marketing and publicity team; sales offices in the USA, Canada, Australia, New Zealand and South Africa; and a rights department selling rights in all languages throughout the world.

Editor(s): Fiona MacIntyre, Julian Shuckburgh, Denise Bates, Jake Lingwood (Ebury Press); Joanna Carreras (Vermilion); Judith Kendra (Rider Books)
Address: Random House, 20 Vauxhall Bridge Road, London SW1V 2SA
Telephone: 0171 840 8400
Fax: 0171 840 8406
Website: www.randomhouse.co.uk
Imprints: Ebury Press, Vermilion, Rider Books, Barrie & Jenkins
Parent Company: Random House UK Ltd
Unsolicited Manuscripts: Yes with return postage

Eco-Logic Books

Promoting and publishing books that provide practical solutions to environmental problems eg Agenda 21 issues, Permaculture, Sustainability, Alternative Energy and Organic Gardening.

Address: 10-12 Picton Street, Bristol BS6 5QA
Telephone: 0117 942 0165
Fax: 0117 942 0164
Email: books@eco-logic.demon.co.uk
Imprints: Grover Books, Eco-Logic Books
Parent Company: Eco-Logic Books
Unsolicited Manuscripts: No

𝓔
Eddison Sadd Editions

A packaging company creating illustrated non-fiction titles as international co-editions for publisher clients. Experience in producing kits. Particularly interested in all self-help titles - new age, health, craft, gardening, sex. Authors often need to write to fit a layout and be closely involved in design stages.

Editor(s): Ian Jackson
Address: St Chad's House, 148 King's Cross Road, London WC1X 9DH
Telephone: 020 7837 1968
Fax: 020 7837 2025
Email: postmaster@edd-sadd.demon.co.uk
Payment Details: Fees when appropriate, or royalties based on net receipts
Unsolicited Manuscripts: No - synopsis first

Educational Publishers Council

Trade association for school Publishers.

Address: 1 Kingsway, London WC2B 6XF
Telephone: 0171 565 7474
Fax: 0171 836 4543
Email: @publishers.org.uk
Website: www.publishers.org.uk
Parent Company: The Publishers Association

Egmont Children's Books

Egmont Children's Books publish the leading list for children. We have two imprints: Mammouth: Mammouth publish the leading list in quality picture books, fiction and non-fiction for children of all ages. Written and designed to the highest standards, this list is the natural home for the greatest talents in children's publishing. Prize-winning and best-selling authors like Anee Fine, Michael Morpurgo and Michelle Magorian feature. Characters: We have the premier list of classic children's characters, including well-loved classic names like Thomas the Tank Engine and Friends, Winnie the Pooh to popular contemporary figures like Barbie.

Address: 239 Kensington High Street, London W8 6SA
Telephone: 0171 761 3500
Fax: 0171 761 3510
Imprints: Mammouth, Methuen
Parent Company: Egmont
Unsolicited Manuscripts: Care of the Editorial Department

Egmont World Ltd

Specialises in children's books for home and international markets: activity, sticker, baby, early learning, novelty, character books and annuals. Series - Mr Men; I Can Learn; Learning Rewards.

Editor(s): Nina Filipek, Stephanie Sloan, Shirley Jackson
Address: Deanway Technology Centre, Wilmslow Road, Handforth, Cheshire SK9 3FB
Parent Company: Egmont Group, Denmark
Unsolicited Manuscripts: No - rarely used. No responsibility taken for the return of unsolicited submissions

E

Edward Elgar Publishing

A leading publisher in economics and related social sciences, Edward Elgar continues to commission actively, publishing 200 titles a year - monographs, reference works and advanced textbooks. In additon to economic science, we publish extensively on the politics and sociology of the national economies of Eastern Europe as well as the theory and practice of public policy.

Editor(s): Edward Elgar, Dymphna Evans
Address: Glensanda House, Montpellier Parade, Cheltenham GL50 1UA
Telephone: 01242 226934
Fax: 01242 262111
Website: http://www.e-elgar.co.uk
Imprints: EE

Elliot Right Way Books

We specialise in practical self-help instructional books covering a wide range of subjects, including: cookery, wine and beer making, weddings, speeches, letters, family finance, job search, business, health, quizzes, games and pastimes, pets, equestrian, motoring, fishing, sport and hobbies. Non-fiction only. Low prices - big sales.

Editor(s): Clive Elliot, Malcolm Elliot
Address: Kingswood Buildings, Brighton Road, Lower Kingswood, Tadworth, Surrey KT20 6TD
Telephone: 01737 832202
Fax: 01737 830311
Email: info@right-way.co.uk
Website: www.right-way.co.uk
Imprints: Right Way, Clarion (bargain books)
Payment Details: Choice of royalty and advance or outright copyright payment
Unsolicited Manuscripts: Yes

Aidan Ellis Publishing

History, biography/autobiography, gardening, cookery, maritime; some novels.

Editor(s): Aidan Ellis, Lucinda Ellis
Address: Whinfield, Herbert Road, Salcombe, Devon TQ8 8HN
Telephone: 01548 842755
Fax: 01548 844356
Email: aidan@aepub.demon.co.uk
Website: www.demon.co.uk/aepub
Imprints: Aidan Ellis
Payment Details: Royalties
Unsolicited Manuscripts: Yes if non-fiction - synopsis and sample chapters and return postage. No fiction please

ELM Publications/Training

Independent publisher of business and law textbooks and teaching resources. Also of training materials for business management skills for first level supervisory up to middle management level in negotiating, group and team work and dynamics, motivation, personal and interpersonal skills.

Editor(s): Sheila Ritchie
Address: Seaton House, Kings Ripon, Huntingdon PE17 2NJ
Telephone: 01487 773254
Fax: 01487 773359 (do not use for proposals please)
Email: elm@ndirect.co.uk
Website: Under preparation
Payment Details: Annual in arrears, usually 10-25% depending on medium/format, eg printed materials usually 10%
Unsolicited Manuscripts: Do not send - outline preferred in first instance

E
Elmwood Press

Elmwood Press publish material for use in schools from KS2 to KS3 and KS4. So far mainly Mathematics, Science and English.

Editor(s): Various
Address: 80 Attimore Road, Welwyn Garden City, Herts AL8 6LP
Telephone: 01707 333232
Fax: 01707 333885
Email: elmwood@press.demon.co.uk
Payment Details: By arrangement
Unsolicited Manuscripts: Welcome from teachers

The Eothen Press

An academic press devoted to publishing scholarly, but generally accessible, books on Turkey and Cyprus, particularly in the fields of modern history and politics, foreign policy, economics and economic history, social anthropology and sociology.

Address: 10 Manor Road, Hemingford Grey, Huntingdon PE18 9BX
Telephone: 01480 466106
Fax: Same as phone
Email: theeothenpress@btinternet.com
Imprints: The Eothen Press
Unsolicited Manuscripts: No

EPA Press

Publishers of guides to electrical and electronic regulations.

Address: Bulse Grange, Wendens Ambo, Saffron Walden CB11 4JT
Telephone: 01799 541207
Fax: 01799 541166

Epworth Press

Academic and theological works.

Editor(s): Gerald M Burt
Address: 20 Ivatt Way, Peterborough, Cambs PE3 7PG
Imprints: Epworth Press
Parent Company: Methodist Publishing House
Payment Details: Subject to negotiation
Unsolicited Manuscripts: Yes

The Erskine Press

Founded in 1986, the Erskine Press publishes, twice a year, books on the 'Golden Age' of Antarctic exploration, covering facsimiles of diaries long out of print, new diaries and previously unpublished works, as well as first English translations of European expeditions of the late 19th and early 20th centuries. In recent years it has expanded its titles to cover general interest autobiographies and medical-related 'Patient's Guides' (Hip and Knee Replacement, Chronic Fatigue Syndrome). Its founding company Archival Facsimiles Limited produces scholarly reprints and high quality limited edition publications for academic/business organisations, ranging from leather-bound folios of period print reproductions to small illustrated books. It undertakes private publications as well for individuals and organisations.

Editor(s): Stephen Easton
Address: The Old Bakery, Banham, Norwich, Norfolk NR16 2HW
Telephone: 01953 887277
Fax: 01953 888361
Email: erskpres@aol.com
Imprints: Archival Facsimiles Ltd
Payment Details: Royalties paid 6 monthly
Unsolicited Manuscripts: No

E

estamp

estamp was set up to meet the largely unfulfilled information needs of professionals and students specifically in the fields of printmaking, papermaking and book making. Our aim initially was to produce books which document what is going on in Britain today, reflecting contemporary ideas and attitudes as well as being a resource for working artists, printers and makers of all disciplines. Dedicated to expanding both the practical and aesthetic horizons, all books bearing an estamp imprint are carefully chosen, researched and prepared. estamp books have a unique blend of common sense and informed opinion and often represent some of our most authoritative and inspirational guidance available. We have recently begun a new series of books about particular artists and their working methods and a number of documentaries about specific practices on an international scale. estamp continues to look for new titles.

Editor(s): Freelancers
Address: 204 St Albans Avenue, London W4 5JU
Telephone: 0181 994 2379
Fax: Same as phone
Email: st@estamp.demon.co.uk
Unsolicited Manuscripts: Yes

Euromoney Plc

A division of Euromoney Plc, Euromoney Books is a leading publisher of specialist financial books. Publishing over 100 titles, including textbooks, yearbooks, directories and country guides, the company provides authoritative and up-to-date information on financial products, practices and markets worldwide. Visit the website bookshop for details of new and best-selling titles, or for more information about the full range of books that Euromoney publishes contact by email.

Editor(s): Managing Editor: Christopher Garnett
Address: Nestor House, Playhouse Yard, London EC4V 5EX
Telephone: 0171 779 8860
Fax: 0171 779 8841
Email: books@euromoneyplc
Website: www.euromoneybooks.com
Imprints: Euromoney Books
Parent Company: Associated Newspapers
Unsolicited Manuscripts: To Jacqueline Grosch Lobo, Commissioning Editor

New European Publications Limited

New European Publications Limited was founded in 1987 to publish the Journal New European which is now published in associated with MCB University Press in Bradford. NEP publishes world reviews (Ed by Sir Richard Body MP). It consists of articles by authors writing on the themes of their own books. NEP also publishes books, mainly on european subjects, both independently and with other publishers, but also likes to branch out into fields which happen to interest its directors.

Editor(s): Sir Richard Body, John Coleman
Address: 14-16 Carroun Road, London SW8 1JT
Telephone: 0171 582 3996
Imprints: NEP
Parent Company: New European Publications Limited
Unsolicited Manuscripts: Authors should consult us before sending mss

Evangelical Press

Publishers of evangelical Christian literature and Bible study material.

Address: Grange Close, Faverdale North Industrial Estate, Darlington DL3 0PH
Telephone: 01325 380232
Fax: 01325 466153
Email: sales@evangelical-press.org
Website: www.evangelical-press.org
Imprints: Grace Publications Trust, Carey Press
Payment Details: Royalty paid on publication
Unsolicited Manuscripts: Prefer outlines and contents list on first contact

E
Evans Brothers Ltd

Children's publishers specialising in educational non-fiction texts for school age children. We also publish in overseas markets, especially in Africa.

Editor(s): Su Swallow
Address: 2a Portman Mansions, Chiltern Street, London, W1M 1LE
Telephone: 0171 935 7160
Fax: 0171 487 5034
Email: sales@evansbrothers.co.uk
Website: To be launched shortly
Imprints: Evans Educational
Unsolicited Manuscripts: Please send to Su Swallow

Ex Libris Press

Illustrated paperbacks on West Country, mainly Wiltshire and Somerset; also books on various country topics and books on the Channel Islands. Also book production service.

Editor(s): Roger Jones
Address: 1 The Shambles, Bradford-on-Avon BA15 1JS
Telephone: 01225 863595
Fax: Same as phone
Imprints: Ex Libris Press, Seaflower Books
Payment Details: 10% royalty twice-yearly
Unsolicited Manuscripts: Prefer initial letter with outline

Executive Grapevine International Ltd

A specialist information provider, we publish a series of directories on executive recruitment consultants, training and development consultants and providers of interim managers and non-executive directors. Each directory contains the leading suppliers in their respective fields and highlights the specialist areas in which they work. Comprehensive indexes assist the reader in their navigation of each directory. To complement this, we also produce a range of titles, focusing on the leading executives in the UK top companies. Organised by function, we have a dedicated edition for the following areas: chairmen chief executives and managing directors, finance executives, human resource executives, sales and marketing executives and information technology executives. All of these titles are updated on a regular basis.

Address: 2nd Floor, New Barnes Mill, Cottonmill Lane, St Albans AL1 2HA
Telephone: 01727 844335
Fax: 01727 844779
Email: executive.grapevine@dial.pipex.com
Website: www.executive-grapevine.co.uk
Unsolicited Manuscripts: No

Eyelevel Books

Publishers of biographical and historical titles, plus some children's material. Specialises in niche and unusual titles.

Editor(s): Jon Moore
Address: The Flat, Oldbury Grange, Lower Broadheath, Worcester WR2 6RQ
Telephone: 01905 427825
Email: books@eyelevel.enterprise-plc.com
Imprints: Eyelevel Books
Payment Details: By negotiation
Unsolicited Manuscripts: To Editor, non-returnable

F
Fabian Society

Britain's senior think-tank. Affiliated to Labour Party, but editorially independent. Publishes pamphlets and quarterly magazine. Aims to help shape the agenda for the medium and long term of the Labour Government. Also holds seminars and conferences. The Fabian Society has 6000 members and to local societies, as well as corporate, trade union and non-governmental organisation subscribers.

Editor(s): Research Director
Address: 11 Dartmouth Street, London SW1H 9BN
Telephone: 0171 222 8877
Fax: 0171 976 7153
Email: fabian-society@geo2.poptel.org.uk
Website: www.fabian-society.org.uk
Imprints: Fabian Society
Unsolicited Manuscripts: Please send synopsis

CJ Fallon

Educational Publishers (Primary and Post-Primary schools market).

Editor(s): Niall White (Director)
Address: PO Box 1054, Lucan Road, Palmerstown, Dublin 20
Telephone: 01 6166400
Fax: 01 6166499
Email: cjfallon@iol.ie
Parent Company: Adare Printing Group Plc

Famedram Publishers Ltd

Publishers of Scotland's liveliest leisure guides.

Address: PO Box 3, Ellon, Aberdeenshire AB41 9EA
Telephone: 01651 842429
Fax: 01651 842180
Email: famedram@artwork.co.uk
Website: www.artwork.co.uk
Imprints: Northern Books

Farming Press

Countryside; farming and veterinary; tractor and transport history and technology.

Editor(s): Liz Ferretti, Hal Norman
Address: Miller Freeman UK Ltd, 2 Wharfedale Road, Ipswich IP1 4LG
Telephone: 01473 241122
Fax: 01473 242222
Email: farmingpress@unmf.com
Website: http://www.dotfarming.com
Parent Company: United News and Media
Unsolicited Manuscripts: No

Feather Books

Publishes secular and religious books and music. Children's fiction includes the Quill Hedgehog novels. Also humorous verse and CDs/cassettes. Religious publications include Feather Books Poetry Series and works in association with Arthur James Ltd. Has a small religious drama list. Publishes a leading Anglo-American Christian poetry/prayers quarterly, The Poetry Church, 40 pages in length, £7 pa.

Editor(s): John Waddington-Feather, Tony Reavill, David Grundy, Paul Evans
Address: Fair View, Old Coppice, Lyth Bank, Shrewsbury SY3 0BW
Telephone: 01743 872177
Fax: Same as phone
Email: john@feather-books.com
Website: www.feather-books.com
Parent Company: Feather Books
Payment Details: Nil for poetry, but free copies
Unsolicited Manuscripts: With SAE, otherwise non-returnable

F
Fernhurst Books

Watersports publisher specialising in 'how-to' books written by the leading expert in each field and where relevant endorsed by the National Authority. Books enable readers to get the very most out of their chosen sport. Covering all aspects of dinghies, catamarans, yachts and motorboats, whether racing or cruising; also seamanship, navigation, craft maintenance and equipment, plus surfing, waterskiing, kayaking.

Editor(s): Tim Davison
Address: Duke's Path, High Street, Arundel, West Sussex BN18 9AJ
Telephone: 01903 882277
Fax: 01903 882715
Email: sales@fernhurstbooks.co.uk
Website: www.fernhurstbooks.co.uk
Unsolicited Manuscripts: No, please phone and enquire

FHG Publications Ltd

Publisher of UK holiday accommodation guides, published annually. Titles include Pets Welcome, Golf Guide, Farm Holiday Guide. Paid entries accepted from owners of hotels, B&B, self-catering properties, etc.

Editor(s): Anne Cuthbertson
Address: Abbey Mill Business Centre, Seedhill, Paisley PA1 1TJ
Telephone: 0141 887 0428
Fax: 0141 889 7204
Email: fhg@lhm.co.uk
Parent Company: IPC Magazines

𝓕

Fiddle Faddle Press

Publishes the work of writing/editing/bookmaking project involving hundreds of school pupils in Hereford and Worcester. Provides a unique resource for teachers - an Imaginative Writing Teaching Package. Titles include A Donkity Crisis, Shapeshifter/Sands, Shapeshifters/Sea (£3.99 each) and Spellbound and Spellbound 2 (£2.99 each). Librarians' comments include 'Worthy of top marks!' 'Original and pleasingly readable book.' 'Amazing and captivating storyline…'

Editor(s): Publisher: Ann Palmer
Address: 6 Kensington House, 53 Graham Road, Malvern WR14 2HU
Telephone: 01684 574525
Unsolicited Manuscripts: No

First And Best In Education Ltd

Publishes educational books of all types for Primary and Secondary schooling, focussing on National Curriculum. All books are published as being suitable for photocopying. Materials are suitable for teachers, pupils, parents and school managers. Keenly looking for new authors all the time.

Editor(s): Senior Editor: Katy Charge, Assistant Editors: Julia Perkins and Linda Robinson
Address: Earlstrees Court, Earlstrees Road, Corby, Northants NN17 4HH
Telephone: 01536 399004
Fax: 01536 399012
Email: firstbest9@aol.com
Imprints: Multi-Sensory Learning
Payment Details: Royalties paid 7.5% twice yearly
Unsolicited Manuscripts: Send SAE for details of requirements and curret projects. Please do not telephone

ℱ
First Class Books

Specialises in study guides to help people working to obtain NVQ in Care awards at level 2 and level 3.

Address: PO Box 1, Portishead, Bristol BS20 9BR
Telephone: 01823 323126
Fax: 01823 321876
Email: ebw@dircon.co.uk
Unsolicited Manuscripts: No

Fitzroy Dearborn Publishers

Our reference books are designed to meet the needs of university, professional, secondary school, and public libraries. Our editorial staff, contributors, and boards of advisers are all committed to providing detailed and comprehensive analysis of subjects in the arts, humanities, business, and the sciences. Fitzroy Dearborn reference books are international in scope and appropriate for the general reader as well as the serious researcher.

Editor(s): Daniel Kirkpatrick, Lesley Henderson, Roda Morrison, Anne-Lucie Norton, Mark Hawkins-Dady
Address: 310 Regent Street, London W1R 5AJ
Telephone: 020 7636 6627
Fax: 020 7636 6982
Email: postroom@fitzroydearborn.demon.co.uk
Website: www.fitzroydearborn.com
Unsolicited Manuscripts: No thank you

Flambard Press

Flambard, founded in 1991, is particularly sympathetic to new or neglected writers and is keen to nourish developing talent. Based in the North and supported by Northern Arts, Flambard sees itself as having a role to play in the literary life of the region, but is open to all-comers and is not a regional publishing house. Flambard began as a poetry press and still concentrates on poetry, but now includes fiction in its list, both novels and collections of short stories. It is developing a crime fiction series.

Editor(s): Margaret Lewis, Peter Lewis
Address: Stable Cottage, East Fourstones, Hexham NE47 5DX
Telephone: 01434 674360
Fax: 01434 674178
Website: signatur@dircom.co.uk
Imprints: Flambard
Payment Details: Royalty for fiction. Usually fixed fee for poetry.
Unsolicited Manuscripts: We accept these, but prefer a preliminary letter. Informative letter about writer needed with manuscript

Flicks Books

Specialist publishers of books and journals on film and cinema, and related media such as television. Our list covers fiction and non-fiction film, archival collections, histories of filmmaking in individual countries, monographs on important directors and films, reference works and directories, interviews with filmmakers, film scripts, and the reissue of out-of-print documents.

Editor(s): Matthew Stevens
Address: 29 Bradford Road, Trowbridge, Wiltshire BA14 9AN
Telephone: 01225 767728
Fax: 01225 760418
Email: flicks.books@dial.pipex.com
Payment Details: Royalty or fee system
Unsolicited Manuscripts: Yes

𝓕
Folens Publishers

Folens is Britain's largest publisher of teacher ideas materials and a significant publisher of curricular resources. The Dunstable site provides product creation, sales and marketing, financial and distribution services and employs over 100 staff. Growth has been rapid and sustained. We publish in excess of 1000 of our own titles and produce over 150 new titles per year for ages 4-16. Folens publish over 80 Big Books, 50 Belair books, 350 reading books, poetry, major resources for every curriculum area plus a wide range of teacher idea books.

Editor(s): Publishing Director - Steve Harrison
Address: Albert House, Apex Business Centre, Boscombe Road, Dunstable, Beds LU5 4RL
Telephone: 01582 472788
Fax: 01582 475524
Email: folens@folens.com
Website: http://www.folens.com
Imprints: Framework Press, Daniels Publishing, Belair Publications
Parent Company: Folens Publishers, Ireland
Unsolicited Manuscripts: To Steve Harrison, Publishing Director

Folly Publications

Paperback books about castles and fortified houses up to the 17th century and parish churches up to c1800. The 34 volumes published since 1988 cover all the relevant buildings in Scotland, Wales and the Isle of Man, plus a selection of castles in Ireland. For England there are castles and churches books for Shropshire, Staffordshire, Warwickshire, Herefordshire, Worcestershire, Cumbria and Northumberland, and there are churches books only for Cheshire, Derbyshire and the Forest of Dean. Each book has an introduction and a gazetteer illustrated with many plans and photos by author-publisher Mike Salter plus old postcards and prints. New titles released in 1999 are Old Parish Churches Of Cornwall and Castles Of Devon And Cornwall. A Churches Book For Sussex and a Castles Book For Kent, Sussex and Surrey are out Autumn 1999.

Address: Folly Cottage, 151 West Malvern Road, Malvern, Worcs WR14 4AY
Telephone: 01684 565211
Unsolicited Manuscripts: No

F

Food Trade Press Ltd

Books on food technology, science and processing, general food industry books, food hygiene, food engineering and historical books on food, plus directories.

Editor(s): Howard Binsted
Address: Station House, Hortons Way, Westerham, Kent TN16 1BZ
Email: ftreview@aol.com
Imprints: Food Trade Press, Food Trade Review
Payment Details: 10% royalty on retail price of books
Unsolicited Manuscripts: Yes

Footprint Handbooks

Footprint Handbooks are the ultimate guidebooks for all independently-minded travellers, providing expert knowledge, and explaining culture, places and people in a balanced, lively, and clear way. The handbooks cover Latin America, the Caribbean, Africa, India, Southeast Asia, coverage of European destinations commences shortly.

Address: 6 Riverside Court, Lower Bristol Road, Bath BA2 3DZ
Telephone: 01225 469141
Fax: 01225 469461
Email: info@footprintbooks.com
Website: www.footprintbooks.com
Imprints: Footprint Handbooks

Forbes Publications

Publishers of a wide range of books for teachers - at both primary and secondary level. Catalogues available on request.

Address: Abbott House, 1-2 Hanover Street, London W1R 9WB
Telephone: 0171 495 7945
Fax: 0171 495 7916
Parent Company: The Rapport Group

ℱ
The Forth Naturalist And Historian (FNH)

An informal enterprise of the University of Stirling. Set up 1975 to provide focus for activities and publications of environmental, heritage, historical interest for the area of mid Scotland. The annual FNH journal publishes papers, reviews - many authoritative and significant including annual bird and weather reports. A major work is the survey book Central Scotland - land, wildlife, people - others are on Loch Lomond, Mines of the Ochils, The Ochils Hills, Woollen Mills of the Hillfoots. An annual symposium Man and the Landscape has its jubilee (25 years) in November 1999.

Editor(s): Editor/Sec L Corbett
Address: University of Stirling, Stirling FK9 4LA
Telephone: 01259 215091
Fax: 01786 494994
Email: Lindsay.Corbett@stir.ac.uk
Website: http://www.stir.ac.uk/theuni/forthnat
Imprints: FNH is a member of the Scottish Publishers Association
Payment Details: No payments have been made to contributors
Unsolicited Manuscripts: Welcomed, but all referred

W Foulsham & Co Ltd

All non-fiction subject areas, especially new age, cookery and lifestyle.

Editor(s): Wendy Hobson, Jane Hotson
Address: The Publishing House, Bennetts Close, Cippenham, Slough, Berkshire SL1 5AP
Telephone: 01753 526769
Fax: 01753 535003
Imprints: Foulsham, Foulsham Educational, Quantum
Unsolicited Manuscripts: Yes

Four Courts Press

Founded in 1970, since 1992 the Press has expanded steadily through Celtic and Medieval Studies into Modern History, Philosophy, Art, Literature and Law. It is now a significant publisher of academic books, particularly, but not exclusively, in the area of Irish studies.

Editor(s): Martin Fanning
Address: Four Courts Press, Fumbally Lane, Dublin 8, Ireland
Telephone: 353 1 453 4668
Fax: 353 1 453 4672
Email: info@four-courts-press.ie
Website: www.four-courts-press.ie
Imprints: Open Air Publications
Parent Company: FCP
Unsolicited Manuscripts: Yes

Four Seasons Publishing Limited

Publishers of illustrated record books (eg Grandparents Books, Baby Books, Address Books) and, increasingly, illustrated anthology books for the International gift trade and book trade. Emphasis is on titles which enlarge people's enjoyment of life and their relationships.

Editor(s): C. Shepheard-Walwyn (Managing Director)
Address: Four Seasons Publishing Limited, 16 Orchard Rise, Kingston Upon Thames, Surrey KT2 7EY
Telephone: 0181 942 4445
Fax: 0181 942 4446
Payment Details: By negotiation
Unsolicited Manuscripts: Outlines of concepts only please

F
Fourth Estate Ltd

General trade publisher, independent. Publisher of the Year 1997. Literary fiction. Commercial fiction. General non-fiction: biography, autobiography, history, travel, popular science, popular culture. Humour. Illustrated non-fiction: cookery.

Editor(s): Virginia Bonham Carter, Louise Haines, Andy Miller, Nicholas Pearson, Christopher Potter, Clive Priddle, Caroline Upcher
Address: 6 Salem Road, London W2 4BU
Telephone: 0171 727 8993
Fax: 0171 792 3176
Email: general@4thestate.co.uk
Imprints: 4th Estate, Guardian Books
Unsolicited Manuscripts: No

Framework Press

In June 1996 Folens Publishers acquired the Framework Press list. Folens Framework INSET materials, handbooks and packs are aimed at secondary teachers and managers. Framework resources address key issues in teaching, management and other related issues; they are excellent value for money in comparison to the cost of using outside trainers. The packs and INSET materials are photocopiable.

Editor(s): Colin Forbes
Address: Framework Press, Folens Publishers, Albert House, Apex Business Centre, Boscombe Road, Dunstable, Beds LU5 4RL
Telephone: 01582 478110
Fax: 01582 475524
Email: folens@folens.com
Website: www.folens.com
Parent Company: Folens Publishers
Unsolicited Manuscripts: To the Editor

$\mathcal{F}$

Free Association Books

Psychotherapy, psychiatry, psychoanalysis, counselling, social welfare, addiction studies, organisational studies, child and adolescent studies, women's studies, cultural and social studies, philosophy, health and complementary medicine.

Editor(s): Publisher: Trevor Brown; Editors: David Stonestreet, Christian Braun, Kieran Corless
Address: 57 Warren Street, London W1P 5PA
Telephone: 0171 388 3182
Fax: 0171 388 3187
Email: fab@fitzrovia.demon.co.uk
Website: Yes
Imprints: Fab, Free Association Books, Fitzrovia
Payment Details: Standard academic terms
Unsolicited Manuscripts: Yes

Samuel French Ltd

Scripts of stage plays only, intended for performance by amateur and professional theatre companies and therefore accompanied by stage directions, lighting, sound effects, plots etc. Seldom text books and no screenplays or scripts for other media.

Address: 52 Fitzroy Street, Fitzrovia, London W1P 6JR
Telephone: 0207 387 9373
Fax: 0207 387 2161
Email: theatre@samuelfrench-london.co.uk
Website: www.samuelfrench-london.co.uk
Imprints: French's Acting Editions
Parent Company: Samuel French Inc, New York
Unsolicited Manuscripts: Yes

F
The Frogmore Press

Publishes the bi-annual literary magazine The Frogmore Papers (founded 1983) as well as occasional anthologies and collections by individual poets, most recently A Dozen Villanelles by Matthew Mead. The Frogmore Poetry Prize will be awarded for the 14th consecutive year in 2000. Previous winners include Tobias Hill, John Latham, Caroline Price and Mario Petrucci.

Editor(s): Jeremy Page
Address: 42 Morehall Avenue, Folkestone, Kent CT19 4EF
Imprints: Crabflower Pamphlets (1989-1997)
Unsolicited Manuscripts: No

David Fulton Publishers Ltd

David Fulton Publishers, established in 1987, has over 350 titles in print, covering the full range of education and teaching from 3 to 19 years. The Fulton list has a distinctive focus on textbooks for student teachers and practical, professional books for teachers, coordinators and managers in mainstream and special schools. We are always interested in ideas for new books. Prospective authors should contact John Owens at our London address.

Editor(s): John Owens, Alison Foyle (Special Education)
Address: 26-27 Boswell Street, London WC1N 3JD
Telephone: 0171 405 5606
Fax: 0171 831 4840
Email: mail@fultonbooks.co.uk
Website: www.fultonbooks.co.uk
Payment Details: Royalty (no advances) paid twice a year
Unsolicited Manuscripts: No

Funfax Ltd

Children's books - from pre-school to early teens, non fiction activity and novelty.

Editor(s): Lisa Telford
Address: Tide Mill Way, Woodbridge, Suffolk IP12 1AN
Imprints: Funfax, Microfax, Quiz Quest, The Lettermen, Mad Jack, Funpax, DK Stickers.
Parent Company: Dorling Kindersley Ltd
Payment Details: Flat fee no royalties
Unsolicited Manuscripts: No

Gallery Of Photography

Photography books, especially work by contemporary Irish photographic artists.

Editor(s): Tanya Kiang
Address: Meeting House Square, Temple Bar, Dublin 2, Ireland
Telephone: 353 1 6714654
Fax: 353 1 6709293
Email: gallery@irish-photography.com
Website: www.irish-photography.com
Payment Details: Negotiable
Unsolicited Manuscripts: No

Garnet Publishing Ltd

Subject areas art, architecture, photography, travel guides, cookery, fiction: all based on regions and different countries, especially the Middle East. 160 titles in all.

Editor(s): Emma Hawker (Editorial Manager)
Address: 8 Southern Court, South Street, Reading, Berkshire RG1 4QS
Telephone: 0118 959 7847
Fax: 0118 959 7356
Email: enquiries@garnet-ithaca.demon.co.uk
Imprints: Ithaca Press, South Street Press
Unsolicited Manuscripts: Please send synopsis and CV to Editorial Dept

g Gateway Books
(Now An Imprint Of Gill & Macmillan)

Alternative health, alternative science, cosmic questions, healing, self-help and psychology. Gateway publishes books which try to represent different ways of understanding the unfolding new spiritual and social changes of the coming millennium.

Editor(s): Submissions Editor: Alick Bartholomew
Address: The Hollies, Wellow, Bath BA2 8QJ
Parent Company: Gill & Macmillan Publishers
Unsolicited Manuscripts: No - synopsis only

Geddes & Grosset

Publishers of popular reference and children's books. Packagers of children's and general books. Publishers of books used as incentives.

Editor(s): Mike Miller, Ron Grosset
Address: David Dale House, New Lanark, Scotland ML11 9DJ
Telephone: 01555 665000
Fax: 01555 665694
Email: info@gandg.sol.co.uk
Imprints: Geddes & Grosset, Tarantula Books, Beano Books
Parent Company: DC Thomson & Co Ltd, Dundee
Payment Details: Royalty or fee
Unsolicited Manuscripts: Yes

The Geographical Association

The Geographical Association is the national subject teaching association for all geographers. It has around 11,000 members and 60 branches in England, Wales and Northern Ireland. The GA offers curriculum support for teachers at all levels, publishing three journals: Geography (quarterly: Honorary Editor Dr Hazel Barrett), Teaching Geography (quarterly: Honorary Editor Dr Margaret Mackintosh). The GA also publishes resources to support the teaching and learning of geography, from reception to post-16, and a growing range of titles on geographical subjects for the general public. The Geographical Association is a registered charity.

Editor(s): Publications Officer: Dr David Lambert; Production Editor: Fran Royle
Address: The Geographical Association, 160 Solly Street, Sheffield S1 4BF
Telephone: 0114 296 0088
Fax: 0114 296 7176
Email: ga@geography.org.uk
Website: http://www.geography.org.uk
Imprints: The Geographical Association
Parent Company: The Geographical Association
Payment Details: Royalty on resources for sale; no payment for journal articles
Unsolicited Manuscripts: Yes, but prefer synopsis first

The Geological Society Publishing House

The Geological Society Publishing House is part of the Geological Society of London. The Publishing House is responsible for the production of 7 journals and approximately 25 books per year. Publications include the highly acclaimed 'Geological Society Special Publications Series', 'Engineering Geology Special Publications', 'Memoirs' and Special Reports.

Editor(s): Mike Collins - Publications Manager
Address: Unit 7, Brassmill Enterprise Centre, Brassmill Lane, Bath BA1 3JN
Telephone: 01225 445046
Fax: 01225 442836
Email: collinsm@geolsoc.org.uk
Website: bookshop.geolsoc.org.uk
Imprints: The Geological Society Publishing House
Parent Company: The Geological Society

G
Robert Gibson & Sons Ltd

Educational publishers of primary and secondary school books.

Address: 17 Fitzroy Place, Glasgow G3 7SF
Telephone: 0141 248 5674
Fax: 0141 221 8219
Email: robert.gibsonsons@btinternet

Ginn & Co

Publishes materials for the teaching of a variety of subjects in primary schools. Provides a comprehensive range of resources offering solutions for teachers and schools throughout the UK and beyond. Aims to provide high quality materials and service to primary schools through a wide variety of resources to meet teachers' changing needs.

Editor(s): Publishers: Catherine Baker (literacy), Ruth Burdett (mathematics and foundation)
Address: Linacre House, Jordan Hill, Oxford OX2 8DP
Telephone: 01865 888000
Fax: 01865 314222
Email: services@ginn.co.uk
Website: www.ginn.co.uk
Parent Company: Reed Elsevier

Glas Publishers UK

Has been publishing the work of mainly present-day Russian writers in English translation since 1992. Authors range from Aleshkovsky to Zinik by way of Makanin and Pelevin. 'The texts and voices out of Russia come through with formidable insistence.' George Steiner.

Editor(s): Natasha Perova, Arch Tait
Address: Dept of Russian, University of Birmingham, Birmingham B15 2TT
Telephone: 0121 414 6047
Fax: Same as phone
Email: a.l.tait@bham.ac.uk
Website: www.bham.ac.uk/glas
Imprints: Glas New Russian Writing
Parent Company: Glas Publishers, Moscow
Payment Details: By agreement
Unsolicited Manuscripts: By contemporary Russian prose writers, in Russian or translation

Global Books Ltd

Publishers of Simple Guides, increasingly popular 'briefing' books currently including series on language, religions and customs and etiquette of countries worldwide. Imprints also include Global Oriental, with titles relating principally to Japan in the subject areas of memoirs and biographies, history, popular literature and poetry, travel, and Renaissance Books which features titles on contemporary social issues.

Editor(s): Paul Norbury
Address: PO Box 219, Folkestone, Kent CT20 3LZ
Telephone: 01303 226799
Fax: 01303 243087
Email: globook@aol.com
Imprints: Global Oriental, Renaissance Books
Unsolicited Manuscripts: No, introductory letter first please

G Gomer Press

Literature and non-fiction with a welsh background or relevance in english and welsh. Children's books founded in 1892

Editor(s): Mairwen Prys Jones, Gordon Jones, Bethan Matthews
Address: Gomer Press, Llandysul, Ceredigion SA44 4QL
Telephone: 01559 362371
Fax: 01559 363758
Email: gwasg@gomer.co.uk
Website: www.gomer.co.uk
Imprints: Pont
Payment Details: Royalties paid twice yearly
Unsolicited Manuscripts: No unsolicited mss, preliminary letter essential

Adam Gordon

Small publishing firm specialising in transport titles, especially relating to tramways.

Editor(s): Adam Gordon
Address: Priory Cottage, Chetwode, Nr Buckingham MK18 4LB
Telephone: 01280 848650
Unsolicited Manuscripts: Yes

Gospel Standard Trust Publications

The Trust publishes books that commend the free and sovereign grace of God. Writers are usually invited to write on given subjects. Titles cover the interest of the very young child through to the serious theologian.

Editor(s): B A Ramsbottom
Address: 12b Roundwood Lane, Harpenden, Herts AL5 3DD
Telephone: 01582 765448
Fax: 01582 469148
Email: gospelstandardpublications@btinternet.co
Imprints: Gospel Standard Trust Publications
Payment Details: By agreement
Unsolicited Manuscripts: No

Gower Publishing Co Ltd

Gower is widely recognised as one of the world's leading publishers on management and business practice. Its programmes range from 1000-page handbooks through practical manuals to popular paperbacks. These cover all the main functions of management: human resource development, sales and marketing, project management, finance, etc. Gower also produces training videos and activities manuals on a wide range of management skills, and publishes a well-regarded list of titles on library and information management.

Editor(s): Julia Scott, Josephine Goodenham, Jonathan Norman
Address: Gower House, Croft Road, Aldershot, Hants GU11 3HR
Telephone: 01252 331551
Fax: 01252 344405
Email: proposals@gowerpub.com
Website: www.gowerpub.com

Graham & Whiteside Ltd

Publishes high-quality printed and electronic data on major companies throughout the world. The Major Companies Series Of Directories are long established, the oldest having been published annually for the past 22 years. Our databases of 80,000 companies are updated rigorously by teams of editors and researchers, who contact every company directly to obtain information. This accurate and comprehensive series has become established as an essential business reference tool for many of the leading national and international coroporations and institutional and business libraries.

Editor(s): Refer to individual titles
Address: Tuition House, 5-6 Francis Grove, London SW19 4DT
Telephone: 0181 947 1011
Fax: 0181 947 1163
Email: sales@major-co-data.com
Website: www.major-co-data.com
Parent Company: The Thomson Corporation
Unsolicited Manuscripts: No

G
W F Graham (Northampton) Ltd

Publishers of the most extensive range of quality low priced mass market children's activity books representing excellent value for money within this competitive sector. The substantial and varied list includes colouring, puzzle, dot, magic painting, wordsearch, cut out, sticker, story books, activity and play packs. Several series of outstanding nature, animal and countryside to colour books popular with children and adults. New titles and finishes continually introduced. WF Graham have an established reputation as publishers of specialist and customer branded books. Experienced in foreign language overlays. Importers of fibre tip pens.

Address: 2 Pondwood Close, Moulton Park, Northampton NN3 6RT
Telephone: 01604 645537
Fax: 01604 648414
Imprints: Various. General title range - children's activity and colouring books

Graham-Cameron Publishing & Illustration

We act as packagers for other publishers usually acting on their initiatives. We also provide full editorial and production services for self-publishers. For this reason, please don't send us mss or proposals. We are also agents for 37 illustrators of educational and children's books.

Editor(s): Helen Graham-Cameron, Mike Graham-Cameron
Address: The Studio, 23 Holt Road, Sheringham, Norfolk NR26 8NB
Telephone: 01263 821 333
Fax: 01263 821 334
Imprints: Graham-Cameron Illustration, Graham-Cameron Publishing
Unsolicited Manuscripts: No

G

Grandreams Ltd

Children's book publishers. Novelty books, story books, pop-ups, annuals, colouring and activity, poster books and calendars. Minimum order £500 net in UK.

Address: 435-437 Edgware Road, London W2 1TH
Telephone: 0171 724 5333
Fax: 0171 724 5777
Imprints: Goodnight Sleeptight
Unsolicited Manuscripts: No

Grant Books

Specialists in golf books; publishers of limited edition golf books and golf club histories.

Address: The Coach House, New Road, Cutnall Green, Droitwich WR5 0PQ
Telephone: 01299 851 588
Fax: 01299 851 446
Email: golf@grantbooks.co.uk
Website: golf@grantbooks.co.uk
Unsolicited Manuscripts: On golf subjects (but not fiction or instructional) especially golf course architecture, biography, history and reference

Granta Books

Small independent publisher of fiction and non-fiction, including biography, travel writing and current affairs.

Editor(s): Frances Coady, Neil Belton
Address: 2/3 Hanover Yard, Noel Road, London N1 8BE
Telephone: 0171 704 9776
Fax: 0171 354 3469
Email: info@granta.com
Website: www.granta.com
Unsolicited Manuscripts: Yes - looked at

𝒢 Green Books

Environment, eco-spirituality, politics and cultural issues. No fiction or children's books. Publish around eight new books per year.

Editor(s): John Elford
Address: Foxhole, Dartington, Totnes, Devon TQ9 6EB
Email: greenbooks@gn.apc.org
Website: www.greenbooks.co.uk
Imprints: Green Books, Resurgence Books, Green Earth Books
Payment Details: Twice-yearly royalties
Unsolicited Manuscripts: No, brief synopsis intitially please

W Green - The Scottish Law Publisher

W Green, the Scottish law publishing company of Sweet and Maxwell, publishes an unrivalled collection of books, periodicals and encyclopaedias on Scots law, as well as digital products.

Address: 21 Alva Street, Edinburgh EH2 4PS
Telephone: 0131 225 4879
Fax: 0131 225 2104
Website: www.wgreen.co.uk
Parent Company: Thomson Corporation

Greenhill Books

Specialist publishers of books on military history, from ancient times to current.

Editor(s): Lionel Leventhal, Kate Ryle, Jonathan North
Address: Park House, 1 Russell Gardens, London NW11 9NN
Telephone: 0181 458 6314
Fax: 0181 905 5245
Email: LionelLeventhal@compuserve.com
Website: www.greenhillbooks.com
Imprints: Greenhill Books
Parent Company: Lionel Leventhal Ltd
Payment Details: Royalties
Unsolicited Manuscripts: Preliminary letter with information about project in advance of submission

Gresham Books Ltd

Specialised publisher offering hymn books, prayer books and service books in limited editions for schools and churches; schools histories have recently been added to the range of publications. Gresham Books continue to offer a reprint service and books on or about wood engraving; music books continue in their list.

Editor(s): Mary Green
Address: The Gresham Press, PO Box 61, Henley On Thames, Oxon RG9 3LQ
Telephone: 0118 940 3789
Fax: Same as phone
Email: greshambks@aol.com
Website: www.gresham-books.co.uk
Imprints: Gresham Books
Payment Details: Negotiable
Unsolicited Manuscripts: No

G
Grevatt & Grevatt

Small print runs in the following areas: descriptive linguistics; poetry; religious studies, especially Hinduism. Privately funded, so generally no royalties unless more than 500 copies are sold. Authors receive 2-10 complimentary copies.

Editor(s): S Y Killingley
Address: 9 Rectory Drive, Newcastle Upon Tyne NE3 1XT
Imprints: Grevatt & Grevatt, S Y Killingley
Unsolicited Manuscripts: No. All enquiries must include SAE

Grower Books

A specialist list providing books on commercial horticulture for professional growers and nurserymen. Subjects include growing fruit, ornamentals, cut flowers and nursery stock. Call Grower Books on 01322 616300 for further details.

Editor(s): Peter Rogers
Address: Nexus Media Ltd, Nexus House, Azalea Drive, Swanley, Kent BR8 8HU
Telephone: 01322 660070
Fax: 01322 616309
Website: www.nexusonline.com
Parent Company: Nexus Media Ltd
Payment Details: One off payment on completion
Unsolicited Manuscripts: Typewritten synopsis considered

Grub Street

Cookery, wine, health, aviation, military history.

Editor(s): John Davies, Anne Dolamore
Address: The Basement, 10 Chivalry Road, London SW11 1HT
Telephone: 0171 924 3966/0171 738 1008
Fax: 0171 738 1009
Email: post@grubstreet.co.uk
Payment Details: Standard contracts
Unsolicited Manuscripts: Yes, but must include return postage

Guild Of Pastoral Psychology

We publish booklets of lectures given to the Guild of Pastoral Psychology. The content is concerned with the depth psychology of C G Jung and spirituality. The pamphlets reflect the views and ideas of scholars and analysts since the Guilds inception in 1937. £2-£3 plus postage. Only lectures given to the Guild are considered.

Editor(s): Guild Committee
Address: 164 Ilbert Street, London W10 4QD
Telephone: 0181 964 1559
Fax: Same as phone

Gwasg Gwenffrwd

Academic; reference; bibliographies; Africa; Latin America; Pacific Islands; Czechoslovakia; poetry; labour history; Wales and Welsh; linguistics; anthropology; history and mission history.

Editor(s): H G A Hughes
Address: Fron Gelyn, Llandyrnog, Denbigh LL16 4LY
Imprints: Astic, Bronant, Translations Wales, Hanes Gweithwyr Cymru, Hyddgen, South Seas Studies
Payment Details: By agreement
Unsolicited Manuscripts: No, all work commissioned

Gwasg Y Dref Wen

Welsh language, children's books and books for adult Welsh learners.

Address: 28 Church Road, Whitchurch, Cardiff CF14 2EA
Telephone: 01222 617860
Fax: 01222 610507
Imprints: Dref Wen
Unsolicited Manuscripts: Yes

ℋ
Peter Halban Publishers

Publishers of general non-fiction, including biography, politics, history, with concentration on Jewish subjects and Middle East. While fiction is considered, very few titles are published annually. NB all trade orders to Littlehampton Book Services, Centre Warehouse, Columbia Building, Faraday Close, Durrington, Worthing BN13 3HD.

Editor(s): Martine Halban, Peter Halban
Address: 22 Golden Square, London W1R 3PA
Telephone: 0171 437 9300
Fax: 0171 437 9512
Email: peterhalbanpublishers@compuserve.com
Unsolicited Manuscripts: Synopsis and letter essential

Robert Hale Ltd

Independent General Publishers since 1936. Backlist covers wide range of fiction and non-fiction areas. Backlist 800 titles. New books 160 pa.

Editor(s): John Hale
Address: Clerkenwell House, 45/47 Clerkenwell Green, London EC1R 0HT
Telephone: 0171 251 2661
Fax: 0171 490 4958
Imprints: Robert Hale, NAG Press, JA Allen
Payment Details: Royalties paid 6 monthly
Unsolicited Manuscripts: Yes, synopsis and specimen copies first

Halsgrove Publishing

Non-fiction publishers and distributors, specialising in southern England, local studies, art, national history.

Editor(s): Steven Pugsley, Simon Butler
Address: Halsgrove House, Lower Moor Way, Tiverton, Devon EX16 6SS
Telephone: 01884 243242
Fax: 01884 243325
Email: steven@halsgrove.com
Imprints: Devon Books, Dorset Books, Somerset Books, Exmoor Books, Country Magazines, Redcliffe, Halsgrove
Parent Company: DA Atkin (Exmoor) Ltd

Hamlyn Octopus

Music, film, style, fashion, cookery, art and craft, interiors, gardening, beauty, sex, health, New Age, sport, pet care, natural history, history, reference and graphic novels.

Address: 2-4 Heron Quays, London E14 4JP
Telephone: 0171 531 8400
Fax: 0171 531 8650
Website: http://www.hamlyn.co.uk
Imprints: Hamlyn Octopus
Parent Company: Division of Octopus Publishing Group Ltd

Hanbury Plays

Publishers of plays, sketches, monologues and plays for all-women casts.

Editor(s): Brian J Burton
Address: Keeper's Lodge, Broughton Green, Droitwich WR9 7EE
Telephone: 01905 23132
Fax: Same as phone
Imprints: Hanbury Plays
Payment Details: Negotiable, but no charge to authors for publications accepted
Unsolicited Manuscripts: No - synopsis first

H
Hansib Publications Ltd

Publishers of books that are of interest to African, Asian and Caribbean people. History, politics, culture, sports, tourism and investments, biographical.

Editor(s): Arif Ali
Address: Tower House, 141-149 Fonthill Road, London N4 3HF
Telephone: 0181 523 0888
Fax: 0181 523 1155
Email: hansib@resolutions.netkonect.co.uk
Payment Details: For discussion
Unsolicited Manuscripts: Yes

Happy Cat Books

Children's books for under 5's: board books, sticker books, picture books with simple texts.

Editor(s): Martin C West
Address: Fieldfares, Mill Lane, Bradfield, Essex CO11 2UT
Telephone: 01255 870902
Fax: Same as phone
Email: mcwest@happycat.co.uk
Payment Details: Fee basis
Unsolicited Manuscripts: No

Happy Walking International Ltd

'We hike the paths and trails of the world for others to enjoy'. Authors, printer and publishers of local and national guides (walk guides). Publishers of : Nottingham Heritage Series, Derbyshire Heritage Series.

Address: Unit 1, Molyneux Business Park, Whitworth Road, Darley Dale, Matlock, Derbyshire DE4 2HJ
Telephone: 01629 735911
Fax: Same as phone
Email: john.merrill@virgin.net
Website: www.happywalkinginternational.co.uk
Parent Company: Happy Walking Ltd
Payment Details: Agreement is royalty, 5% up to and after 500 copies sold, 10% after 1,000 copies sold
Unsolicited Manuscripts: Yes

Harden's Guides

Producers of quality consumer guides to London and the UK, with a particular emphasis on restaurant guides. Leading publishers of quality corporate gifts.

Editor(s): Richard Harden, Peter Harden
Address: 14 Buckingham Street, London WC2N 6DF
Telephone: 0171 839 4763
Fax: 0171 839 7561
Email: mail@hardens.com

H
Harlequin Mills & Boon Ltd

Romance novels in varying lengths. Tipsheets available with SAE, or on website.

Editor(s): Editorial Director: K Stoeker
Address: Eton House, 18-24 Paradise Road, Richmond, Surrey TW9 1SR
Telephone: 0181 288 2800
Website: www.romance.com
Imprints: Mills & Boon, Silhouette, Mira
Parent Company: Harlequin Enterprises Ltd
Payment Details: Advance against royalties
Unsolicited Manuscripts: Prefer query first

Harvey Map Services Ltd

Publishers of specialist maps for walking and climbing. Popular areas throughout Great Britain covered, in easy to read waterproof maps which show extra detail necessary for sure navigation. Harveys also publish an assortment of books relating to orienteering. Teacher's and coach's manuals covering the basics to more specialised skills. Full catalogue of publications and equipment available.

Address: 12-22 Main Street, Doune, Perthshire FK16 6BJ
Telephone: 01786 841202
Fax: 01786 841098
Email: sales@harveymaps.co.uk
Website: www.harveymaps.co.uk

The Harvill Press

Independent publisher, chiefly of literature in translation. Also publishes illustrated books in the fields of ethography, travel, natural history, gardening and sailing.

Editor(s): Guido Waldman, Ian Pindar, Sophie Henley-Price, Margaret Stead, Victoria Millar, Editorial Consultants: Euan Cameron, Barbara Schwepcke
Address: 2 Aztec Row, Berners Road, London N1 0PW
Telephone: 0171 704 8766
Fax: 0171 704 8805
Email: k.bielenberg@harvill-press.com
Website: www.harvill-press.com
Imprints: Panther, Harvill Press Editions
Payment Details: Royalties paid twice yearly
Unsolicited Manuscripts: Yes, but outline and specimen chapter first

Hawke To Hutton Publishing Services

Provide publishing/typesetting service for potential authors/projects connected with cricket - history, biography, statistical. Works thus far published: 'Tragic White Roses' Biography of Yorkshire cricketers Alonzo Drake and Mayor Booth. 'A Century of Headingley Tests 1899-1999' by Paul E Dyson.

Address: 32 Louden Road, Scholes, Rotherham, South Yorkshire S61 2SU
Telephone: 0114 2540251
Fax: Same as phone
Email: pope@netmatters.co.uk
Payment Details: Work on 50/50 costing to cover printing etc where work would not normally be produced
Unsolicited Manuscripts: Only on request after initial enquiry

H

Hawthorns Publications Ltd

Children's illustrated story books; children's fiction and non-fiction; school aid books; biography; history.

Address: Pond View House, 6A High Street, Otford, Sevenoaks, Kent TN14 5PQ
Telephone: 01959 522325
Fax: 01959 522368
Imprints: Pond View Books
Payment Details: Royalties paid twice-yearly
Unsolicited Manuscripts: Yes must be supplied with SAE

Hayes Press

Christian publisher of hymn books, doctrinal books, gospel traits and calendars.

Address: Essex Road, Leicester LE4 9EE
Telephone: 01162 740 204
Fax: 01162 740 200
Email: hayespress@btinternet.com

Haynes Publishing

Haynes Publishing - car and motorcycle service and repair manuals, car handbooks/ servicing guides; do-it-yourself books; car, motorcycle, motorsport. Haynes Special Interest Publishing (Division): Cars, motorcycles motorsport, related biographies, practical maintenance and renovation. Haynes Home & Leisure Division: Home DIY and leisure activities (eg cycling). Haynes Motor Trade Division: Car and motorcycle service and repair manuals and technical data books. Also GT Foulis & Co, Oxford Illustrated Press and Patrick Stephens Ltd.

Editor(s): Editorial Directors: Darryl Beach, Alan Sperring, Matthew Minter
Address: Sparkford, Yeovil, Somerset BA22 7JJ
Telephone: 01963 440635
Fax: 01963 440023
Email: sales@haynes-manuals.co.uk
Website: www.haynes.com
Imprints: Haynes Special Interest Publishing Division, Haynes Home & Leisure Division, Haynes Motor Trade Division, G T Foulis & Co, Oxford Illustrated Press, Patrick Stephens Ltd
Payment Details: Normal royalty terms, twice yearly
Unsolicited Manuscripts: No (but proposals of synopsis - OK)

Hazleton Publishing

Widely recognised as the world's leading motorsport publisher. Our range of motorsport annuals dates back to 1951 with the birth of Autocourse, now in its 49th year of publication, dedicated to reviewing the Formula 1 season. Motocourse, 28th year, reviews the two-wheeled world championships, with Rallycourse, now in its 18th year, covering the World Rally Championships. Our range also includes a technical series and a history series, both on motorsports.

Editor(s): Peter Lovering
Address: 3 Richmond Hill, Richmond, Surrey TW10 6RE
Telephone: 0208 948 5151
Fax: 0208 948 4111
Email: hazleton@hazleton.uk.com
Imprints: Autocourse, Motocourse, Rallycourse
Unsolicited Manuscripts: No

ℋ
Headline Book Publishing Ltd

Fiction: general, saga, historical, romance, literary, thriller, crime, horror. Non-fiction: sport, humour, cookery, reference, biography, autobiography, popular culture, gardening, history, popular science.

Editor(s): Publishing Directors: Jane Morpeth (Fiction); Heather Holden-Brown (Non-fiction)
Address: 338 Euston Road, London NW1 3BH
Telephone: 020 7873 6000
Fax: 020 7873 6124
Email: headline.books@headline.co.uk
Website: www.headline.co.uk
Imprints: Headline, Headline Feature, Review
Parent Company: Hodder Headline Plc
Payment Details: Negotiable
Unsolicited Manuscripts: Synopsis and 5 chapters only; return postage

Health Education Authority

The Health Education Authority is England's leading provider of health promotion. It is the national centre of excellence for health education research and expertise and, through its campaigns, publications and work with health professionals, encourages the public to adopt a healthier lifestyle. Resources are produced in the following health categories: alcohol; cancer; coronary heart disease; drugs; folic acid; food and nutrition; HIV, AIDS and sexual health; immunisation; oral health; popular health books; physical activity and smoking. Resources produced for specific groups: minority ethnic groups, older people, pregnancy, parenting and child health and women's health.

Editor(s): Chris Owen, Delphine Verroest, Liz Niman, Flair Milne, Michele Appleton, Susannah Blake, Andrea Horth (New media).
Address: Trevelyan House, 30 Great Peter Street, London, SW1P 2HW
Imprints: HEA
Unsolicited Manuscripts: No

Heart Of Albion Press

Books, booklets and computer-readable publications on local history (especially Leicestershire), folklore, mythology and archaeology.

Editor(s): R N Trubshaw
Address: 2 Cross Hill Close, Wymeswold, Loughborough LE12 6UJ
Telephone: 01509 880725
Email: albion@indigogroup.co.uk
Website: www.indigogroup.co.uk/albion/
Imprints: Heart of Albion Press
Payment Details: Contact Editor
Unsolicited Manuscripts: Future publications will be CD-ROM only so conventional mss not of interest

Helicon Publishing

Publishers of the Hutchinson brand of encyclopedias, dictionaries and Almanacs, Helicon was formed in 1992 through a management buyout of the Hutchinson. Reference division of Random House. The first British company to publish a multimedia encyclopedia, and the first to put that encyclopedia online, Helicon continues to publish in book, CD-ROM and online form.

Editor(s): Hilary McGlynn - Editorial Director
Address: Helicon Publishing, 442 Hythe Bridge Street, Oxford OX1 2EP
Telephone: 01865 204204
Fax: 01865 204205
Email: admin@helicon.co.uk
Website: www.helicon.co.uk
Parent Company: WHS

ℋ
Christopher Helm (Publishers) Ltd

Ornithology.

Editor(s): Robert Kirk
Address: 35 Bedford Row, London WC1R 4JH
Telephone: 0171 404 5630
Fax: 0171 404 7706
Email: ornithology@acblack.co.uk
Parent Company: A & C Black
Payment Details: Advances against royalties and flat fees
Unsolicited Manuscripts: Yes

Hendon Publishing Co

Publisher of local history books. A4 landscape 44 pages, mainly photographs, with some text.

Address: Hendon Mill, Nelson, Lancashire BB9 8AD
Telephone: 01282 613129
Fax: 01282 870215
Parent Company: Hendon Trading Co Ltd
Payment Details: Negotiable
Unsolicited Manuscripts: Send sample of work with SAE

The Herb Society

Exists for amateurs and professionals alike with a keen interest in any aspect of herbs. We produce a quarterly magazine Herbs, which covers topics such as culinary, medicinal, aromatic, history, future and cultivation of herbs.

Editor(s): Barbara Segall
Address: Deddington Hill Farm, Warmington, Banbury OX17 1XB
Telephone: 01295 692000
Fax: 01295 692004
Email: herbsociety.co.uk
Website: www.herbsociety.co.uk
Parent Company: The Herb Society
Unsolicited Manuscripts: Yes

Highfield Publications

Publishers of food hygiene training aids to all sections of the food industry throughout the world. Publications, training videos and educational material, including interactive hygiene training software and CD-ROMs.

Address: Vue Pointe, Spinney Hill, Sprotbrough, Doncaster DN5 7LY
Telephone: 01302 850007
Fax: 01302 311112
Email: jayne@highfieldpublications.com
Website: www.highfieldpub.u-net.com

ℋ
Highgate Publications (Beverley) Ltd

A company established in 1985 which has issued over 100 publications, the majority relating to East Yorkshire, some to Yorkshire as a whole, and a small number of wider than local interest. Highgate is interested in publishing good quality, readable books.

Editor(s): John Markham
Address: 4 Newbegin, Beverley, East Yorkshire HU17 8EG
Telephone: 01482 886017
Fax: Same as phone
Imprints: Highgate Publications
Payment Details: Quarterly 10% of net price
Unsolicited Manuscripts: Preliminary letter required. Not interested in autobiographies except in rare circumstances

Hilmarton Manor Press

Publishers, distributors and mail order booksellers of art and antique reference books.

Editor(s): Charles Baile De Laperierre
Address: Calne, Wiltshire, SN11 8SB
Telephone: 01249 760208
Fax: 01249 760379
Email: hilmartonpress@lineone.net
Imprints: Hilmarton Manor Press
Unsolicited Manuscripts: No

Hippopotamus Press

Founded in 1974 and specialises in first collections of new verse by those that have had the usual magazine appearances and are ready for book publication. We also publish occasional larger books of selected poems by those that we feel are unfairly neglected. Recently we have added a few titles of criticism and literary essays. Our current list consists of 70% first collections, 15% of second and third books from these authors, 10% selected poems, the remaining 5% is prose. We only publish a narrow range of contemporary verse, so it is important to read some of our authors before submitting a collection.

Editor(s): Roland John, Anna Martin
Address: 22 Whitewell Road, Frome, Somerset BA11 4EL
Fax: 01373 466653
Imprints: Outposts Poetry Quarterly Magazine
Parent Company: Hippopotamus Press
Payment Details: 7½% royalty
Unsolicited Manuscripts: Yes

Hodder & Stoughton

Commercial and literary fiction, biography, autobiography, history, self-help, humour, travel and general interest non-fiction, audio.

Editor(s): Sue Fletcher, Roland Philipps, Carole Welch, Carolyn Mays, Carolyn Caughey, Rupert Lancaster
Address: 338 Euston Road, London NW1 3BH
Telephone: 0171 873 6000
Fax: 0171 873 6198
Website: www.hodder.co.uk
Imprints: Hodder & Stoughton, Sceptre, Coronet, Nel, Flame, LIR
Parent Company: WH Smith Ltd
Unsolicited Manuscripts: No

H

Hodder & Stoughton Educational

We publish books for schools, colleges of further education, universities and general interest. Subject areas include: science, mathematics, information technology, tests and assessment, psychology, business studies, child care, teacher education, geography, beauty therapy, history, religious education, PSE and English.

Editor(s): Various
Address: 338 Euston Road, London NW1 3BH
Telephone: 0207 873 6000
Fax: 0207 873 6299
Website: www.educational.hodder.co.uk
Imprints: Teach Yourself
Parent Company: Hodder Headline
Unsolicited Manuscripts: No

Hodder Children's Book

$\mathcal{H}$

All Hodder's books are designed to hook children into the reading habit and hold them there. Several formats: Picture Books - Picture story books illustrated in full colour, approx 1,000 words, aimed at 2-5 year olds. My First Read Alone - 48-64 pages,1,000-1,500 words, for very young, early readers; illustrated, simple and fun stories. Read Alone - B format (197 x 130mm approx.) 64 pages, 2-4,000 words; for children who are beginning to read on their own. Story Books - B format, 96-128 pages, 8-12,000 words; for young, confident readers aged 7-9, who want a satisfying read. Novels - 20-50,000 words, for children of 8 and upwards, on any theme; a strong original story and good characters, as well as particular relevance to children, are most important. Information Books - For ages 6-8, 7-11, teen - must work in standard paperback format, 64, 96 or 128 pages, with black and white line artwork; looking for original, accessible, child-centred approaches. We also offer an extensive list of classics by authors like Enid Blyton, Joan Aiken, Helen Cresswell as well as 'modern' classics such as David Almond's 'Shellia'.

Editor(s): Publishing Director: Margaret Conroy
Address: 338 Euston Road, London NW1 3BH
Telephone: 0207 873 6000
Fax: 0207 873 6024
Imprints: My First Read Alone, Read Alone, Story Book, Signature, Hodder Home Learning
Parent Company: Hodder Headline
Payment Details: Subject to contract
Unsolicited Manuscripts: Yes, but no poetry, rhyming texts, counting books or ABC's

Hollis Directories Ltd

Offer a range of publications providing information for marketing communications specialists. Publishers of Willings Press Guide (previous year's edition available at half-price), Hollis UK Press & Public Relations Annual, Hollis Europe, Marketing Handbook and other similar titles. Catalogue available.

Editor(s): Publishing Director: Rosemary Sarginson
Address: Harlequin House, Teddington, Middx TW11 8EL
Telephone: 0181 977 7711
Fax: 0181 977 1133
Email: gary@hollis-pr.co.uk
Website: www.hollis-pr.uc.uk

ℋ
Honeyglen Publishing Ltd

Small publisher specialising in history, biographies, belles-lettres and selected fiction.

Editor(s): Nadia Poderegin, Jelena Poderegin-Harley
Address: 56 Durrels House, Warwick Gardens, London W14 8QB
Telephone: 0171 602 2876
Fax: Same as phone
Unsolicited Manuscripts: Please send synopsis and sample chapter first. Must fit within our subject range.

Honno

Small publishing press dedicated to giving women from Wales the opportunity to see their work in print. Although we do publish longer pieces of fiction and children's books, our emphasis is on anthologies and collections by various writers. The press is registered as a community co-operative, and any profit goes towards the cost of future publications.

Editor(s): Gwenllian Dafydd
Address: Honno Editorial Office, The Theological College, King Street, Aberystywyth SY23 2LT
Telephone: 01970 623 150
Fax: Same as phone
Email: gol.honno@virgin.net
Imprints: Honno Modern Fiction, Honno Children's Books, Honno Autobiography, Honno Classics
Unsolicited Manuscripts: Yes, with a Welsh connection

Hope UK

Drug education leaflets, booklets and prevention manuals published. For children and young people and those working/caring for them. Hope UK is a drug education charity which concentrates on prevention issues and includes alcohol and tobacco in its brief.

Editor(s): Martin Perry, George Ruston
Address: 25F Copperfield Street, London SE1 0EN
Telephone: 0171 928 0848
Fax: 0171 401 3477
Email: enquries@hopeuk.org

Horizon Scientific Press

Publisher of a wide range of books and journals for the scientific community, mainly in the subjects molecular biology and microbiology. Publisher of The Journal Of Molecular Microbiology And Biotechnology.

Address: PO Box 1, Wymondham, Norfolk NR18 0EH
Telephone: 01953 601106
Fax: 01953 603068
Email: mail@horizonpress.com
Website: www.horizonpress.com
Imprints: Horizon Scientific Press, Wensum Academic Press, Caister Academic Press

ℋ
How To Books Ltd

The series reference book publisher with three imprints: Pathways, How To, and Essentials. Practical, accessible books in the following subject areas: Business and Management, Computer Basics, Jobs and Careers, Living and Working Abroad, Personal Finance, Self-development, Small Business, Student Handbooks, Successful Writing and Family Reference.

Editor(s): Nikki Read
Address: 3 Newtec Place, Magdalen Road, Oxford OX4 1RE
Telephone: 01865 793 806
Fax: 01865 248 780
Email: info@howtobooks.co.uk
Website: www.howtobooks.co.uk
Imprints: Pathways, Essentials
Parent Company: How To Books Ltd
Payment Details: Royalties paid annually
Unsolicited Manuscripts: Well-structured proposals from qualified and experienced writers welcome

John Hunt Publishing

Books across the spectrum of Christian publishing, with an extensive children's illustrated list. Publishes 50 new titles a year.

Editor(s): J Hunt
Address: 46a West Street, New Alresford, Hants SO24 9AU
Telephone: 01962 736880
Fax: 01962 736881
Email: john@johnhuntpub.demon.co.uk
Imprints: Arthur James Ltd, Hunt & Thorpe
Payment Details: Various
Unsolicited Manuscripts: Yes

H

Hymns Ancient And Modern Ltd

Publishes hymn books for churches, schools and other institutions. All types of religious books, general and educational. Divisions of SCM Canterbury Press Ltd cover SCM Press - religious and thelogy from an open perspective, ethics and philosophy. The Canterbury Press Norwich - General religious books, theological, liturgical, prayer and guides. Religious And Moral Education Press (RMEP) - Religious, personal and social education books for primary, middle and secondary schools (including assembly material) and teachers'/administrative books. G J Palmer & Sons Ltd - publisher of Church Times weekly newspaper (ideas welcome, no mss). The Sign; Home Words - monthly nationwide parish magazine inserts. Also, Hart Advertising - advertising agency offering specialist service to religious and charitable organisations.

Editor(s): John Bowden, Christine Smith, Mary Mears
Address: St Mary's Works, St Mary's Plain, Norwich, Norfolk NR3 3BH
Telephone: 01603 612914
Fax: 01603 624483
Website: (Church Times) www.churchtimes.co.uk
Imprints: Divisions: SCM Press, The Canterbury Press Norwich, RMEP, G J Palmer & Sons Ltd
Payment Details: Standard advances and royalties paid annually
Unsolicited Manuscripts: Yes (Canterbury, SCM and RMEP)

IC Publications Ltd

A major publishing force in the Middle East and in Africa. From its offices in London and Paris, IC publishes three magazines and a yearbook in English and thirteen newsletters in French.

Editor(s): Baffour Ankomah, Pat Lancaster, Anver Versi
Address: 7 Coldbath Square, London EC1R 4LQ
Telephone: 0171 713 7711
Fax: 0171 713 7970
Email: icpubs@dial.pipex.com
Website: www.africasia.com/icpubs
Imprints: IC Publications Ltd
Payment Details: By negotiation
Unsolicited Manuscripts: By negotiation

I
ICSA Publishing Ltd

The official publishing company of the Institute of Chartered Secretaries and Administrators (ICSA). Publishes a range of looseleaf and book products for managers in the private, public and voluntary sectors, including Company Secretarial Practice, The Charities Manual and the One Stop series.

Editor(s): Clare Grist Taylor
Address: 16 Park Crescent, London W1N 4AH
Telephone: 0171 612 7020
Fax: 0171 323 1132
Email: icsapub@icsa.co.uk
Payment Details: On application
Unsolicited Manuscripts: No

IFLA Offices For UAP And International Lending

Universal availability of publications. International lending. Document delivery. Conference proceedings.

Editor(s): Various
Address: c/o The British Library, Boston Spa, Wetherby, West Yorkshire, LS23 7BQ
Telephone: 01937 546124
Fax: 01937 546478
Email: ifla@bl.uk
Unsolicited Manuscripts: No

Impart Books

Impart Books operate in the fields of education and accounting. They mostly publish books which are written or produced in-house; exceptionally, they do publish books by authors outside the organisation. They specialise in producing educational books in co-operation with publishers outside the United Kingdom for printing and publication in those countries. Most of such books are produced to assist the countries concerned rather than to obtain a profit.

Address: Gwelfryn, Llanidloes Road, Newtown, Powys SY16 4HX
Telephone: 01686 623484
Fax: 01686 623784
Email: impart@books.mid-wales.net
Website: www.books.mid-wales.net/index.html
Unsolicited Manuscripts: After permission obtained

Imperial College Press

Imperial College Press was established in 1995 to produce high-quality books and journals in both printed and electronic formats. It is a joint venture between Imperial College of Science, Technology and Medicine and World Scientific Publishing, bringing together into one company the experience of an internationally-recognised institution of higher education and that of an established science publisher. ICP publishes scholarly books and journals in the physical, earth and life sciences, business and management and medicine for university students, academic researchers and practitioners. The Press gives special emphasis to research areas and educational subjects in which the College has particular strengths. Authors are sought from the College and elsewhere.

Editor(s): Dr J Navas, Ms A Parlane, Ms G Nair
Address: 57 Sheldon Street, Covent Garden, London WC2H 9HE
Telephone: 0171 8363954
Fax: 0171 8362002
Email: edit@icpress.demon.co.uk
Website: http://www.icpress.demon.co.uk
Parent Company: World Scientific Publishing Co (PTE) Ltd, Singapore

I

Incorporated Council Of Law Reporting For England & Wales

Not-for-profit publishers of The Law Reports, which are always cited in precedence. Also publishers of The Weekly Law Reports, The Industrial Cases Reports, The Consolidated Index Of Law Reports and The Statues And Public General Acts. All law reports are written by barristers who attend the cases reported, and the texts of judgements are judicially reviewed prior to publication. Circulation is worldwide. A registered charity established in 1865.

Editor(s): Robert Williams
Address: Mogarry House, 119 Chancury Lane, London WC2A 1PP
Telephone: 0171 242 6471
Fax: 0171 831 5247
Email: postmaster@iclr.co.uk
Website: www.lawreports.co.uk
Imprints: The Law Reports, The Weekly Law Reports, The Industrial Cases Reports
Unsolicited Manuscripts: N/A

The Industrial Society

The Industrial Society is a non-profit organisation which publishes books and special reports independently. We publish approximately 30 new titles a year in areas such as self-development, business skills, and general management.

Editor(s): Commissioning Editor: Susannah Lear
Address: The Industrial Society, 48 Bryanston Square, London W1H 7LN
Telephone: 0171 479 2000
Fax: 0171 723 7375
Email: infoserv@indusoc.demon.co.uk
Website: www.indsoc.co.uk
Parent Company: The Industrial Society
Payment Details: Royalties
Unsolicited Manuscripts: Accepted

Insights

Insights is published by the English Tourist Board. It is a bi-monthly subscription service providing the latest information on the tourism market, in an easy-to-use format. It combines the analysis and interpretation of trends and opportunities in the tourism industry with the experience of tourism experts who comment on market developments and give practical advice on marketing and management.

Editor(s): Anna Ryland
Address: Thames Tower, Blacks Road, London W6 9EL
Telephone: 0181 563 3362
Fax: 0181 563 5058
Email: aryland@bta.org.uk
Website: www.visitbritain.com
Parent Company: ETB/BTA
Payment Details: Depends on type of report: £350-600, in-depth market profiles, max £1,000
Unsolicited Manuscripts: Yes

Institute For Fiscal Studies

The Institute For Fiscal Studies is an independent research institute that carries out in-depth research into fiscal policy. Through our publications, we aim to create a forum for debate on all aspects of taxation and government microeconomic policy. The IFS publishes a series of reports and working papers, and a quarterly journal Fiscal Studies.

Editor(s): (Of Fiscal Studies) Ian Preston, Gareth Myles, David Miles
Address: 7 Ridgmont Street, London WC1E 7AE
Telephone: 0171 291 4800
Fax: 0171 323 4780
Email: mailbox@ifs.org.uk
Website: www.ifs.org.uk
Unsolicited Manuscripts: Articles can be submitted to the editors of Fiscal Studies

I

Institute Of Economic Affairs

Books on economic, social, environmental and educational policy issues.

Editor(s): Professor Colin Robinson
Address: 2 Lord North Street, London SW1P 3LB
Telephone: 0171 799 3745
Fax: 0171 799 2137
Email: editor@iea.org.uk
Website: http://www.ica.org.uk
Unsolicited Manuscripts: Yes, but mainly commissioned

Institute Of Food Science & Technology (IFST)

The UK independent professional qualifying body for food science and technology, and a registered educational charity. IFST publishes two journals, the International Journal Of Food Science & Technology (bi-monthly) and Food Science & Technology Today (quarterly). Also publishes books and pamphlets: Development and Use of Microbiological Criteria for Foods ('99); Addition Of Micronutrients To Food ('97); Guide To Food Biotechnology ('96); Listing of Codes Of Practice Applicable To Foods ('93); Shelf Life Of Foods ('93); Guidelines To Good Catering Practice ('92); Food Hygiene Training ('92); Food & Drink - Good Manufacturing Practice ('98); Guidelines For The Handling Of Chilled Foods ('90).

Editor(s): P Goodenough (IJFST); E A Nash (FSTT)
Address: 5 Cambridge Court, 210 Shepherds Bush Road, London W6 7NJ
Telephone: 0171 603 6316
Fax: 0171 602 9936
Email: ifst@easynet.co.uk
Website: www.easynet.co.uk/ifst/
Payment Details: N/A
Unsolicited Manuscripts: Yes

The Institute Of Irish Studies, The Queen's University Of Belfast

The aim of the Institute is to encourage interest and to promote and co-ordinate research in those fields of study which have a particular Irish interest, and it is an important multidisciplinary centre. The publications department reflects the growth and diversity of Irish studies today. The list includes a range of academic or semi-academic books, focused on aspects of Irish studies including archaeology, anthropology, biography, botany, cultural studies, history, history of science, local studies, politics, language, literature, proverbs, religion, transport, women's studies. There are two major series, The Ordnance Survey Memoirs Of Ireland (40 vols) and Northern Ireland Place-names (7vols).

Editor(s): Margaret McNulty
Address: Queen's University Belfast, 8 Fitzwilliam Street, Belfast BT9 6AW
Telephone: 01232 273235
Fax: 01232 439238
Email: iispubs@qub.ac.uk
Website: http://www.qub.ac.uk/iis/publications.html
Parent Company: The Queen's University of Belfast
Unsolicited Manuscripts: Yes - academic work only. Please write in the first instance

The Institute Of Personnel And Development

Business and management texts for students and practitioners of training, development and personnel, and line managers.

Editor(s): Commissioning Editors: Richard Goff, Anne Cordwent
Address: IPD House, Camp Road, London SW19 4UX
Email: publishing@ipd.co.uk
Website: www.ipd.co.uk
Imprints: IPD
Payment Details: Royalty agreement by negotiation
Unsolicited Manuscripts: Outline with SAE please for initial consideration

I

Institute Of Physics Publishing

One of the world's leading science publishers. The company publishes books, journals and magazines in physics and related subject areas. Within the books programme, produces reference works for industry and academia, research monographs, graduate textbooks, high level undergraduate textbooks, and popular science books. The author base is international. Subjects: astronomy and astrophysics; condensed matter physics; high energy physics; history of physics; materials science; mathematical physics; measurement and instrumentation; medical physics; nuclear physics; optics; plasma physics; sensors and smart materials.

Editor(s): Penelope Barber, Kathryn Cantley, Gillian Lindsey, Robin Rees, Jim Revill, Michael Taylor
Address: Dirac House, Temple Back, Bristol BS1 6BE
Telephone: 0117 930 1147
Fax: 0117 930 1186
Email: nicki.dennis@ioppublishing.co.uk
Website: www.bookmark.iop.org
Parent Company: Institute of Physics
Payment Details: Royalty as agreed
Unsolicited Manuscripts: Yes: to Nicki Dennis

The Institution Of Chemical Engineers

The IChemE sets out to publish books and journals which allow engineers and scientists to improve their professional skills and performance. Subjects: environment; safety and loss prevention; contract and project management; process design and operation; dust handling; process control; biotechnology; oil, gas and energy. IChemE is the agent in the UK, Europe and Asia for the American Institute Of Chemical Engineers (AIChE).

Editor(s): Various
Address: 165-189 Railway Terrace, Rugby CV21 3HQ
Telephone: 01788 578214
Fax: 01788 560833
Email: jcressey@icheme.org.uk
Website: www.icheme.org
Imprints: IChemE
Payment Details: Royalties on discussion
Unsolicited Manuscripts: No

The Institution Of Electrical Engineers

The Institution of Electrical Engineers (IEE) is the professional association representing 135,000 electrical, electronics, communications and information engineers worldwide. Its activities include organising conferences, maintaining standards (such as the IEE wiring regulations), regulating professional engineers and providing technical and information services. As such it is a large technical publisher, producing books, magazines and journals - as well as electronic publications - for a global, professional and postgraduate audience.

Editor(s): Director of Publishing: R Mellors-Bourne
Address: Publishing Dept, Michael Faraday House, Six Hills Way, Stevenage SG1 2AY
Telephone: 01438 313311
Fax: 01438 360079
Email: books@iee.org.uk
Website: www.iee.org.uk/publish
Imprints: Peter Peregrinus Ltd
Unsolicited Manuscripts: Yes but only in restricted subject area

Intellect Books

Digital creativity, writing and language, computers and humanity and learning and education - all edited by Masoud Yazdani. Arts and media (including film and television), culture and heritage - all edited by Robin Beecroft. Our European Studies series crosses all our subject areas and is edited by Keith Cameron.

Editor(s): Masoud Yazdani, Robin Beecroft, Keith Cameron
Address: EFAE, Earl Richards Road North, Exeter EX2 6AS
Telephone: 01392 475110
Fax: Same as phone
Email: books@intellect-net.com
Website: www.intellect-net.com
Payment Details: Standard contract
Unsolicited Manuscripts: Yes

I

Inter Varsity Press

Inter Varsity Press operates as IVP and also under the imprints of apollos and crossway. It publishes christian books which are true to the Bible and which will communicate the Gospel, develop disciplineship and strengthen the church for its mission in the world.

Address: 38 De Monfort Street, Leicester LE2 4AF (editorial and design), Norton Street, Nottingham NG7 3HR (production and marketing)
Telephone: 0116 255 1754 (Leics), 0115 978 1054 (Nottm)
Fax: 0116 254 2044 (Leics), 0115 942 2694 (Nottm)
Email: ivp@uccf.org.uk (Leics), ivp@ivpnottm.compulink.co.uk (Nottm)
Imprints: IVP, Apollos, Crossway
Parent Company: Universities and Colleges Christian Fellowship
Payment Details: Royalties (variable)
Unsolicited Manuscripts: Please submit outline and sample

Intercept Limited

Intercept has 15 years' publishing expertise in science and technology. We have distribution partnerships with the Natural History Museum (London), National Research Council Research Press (Canada), The Ray Society and the United Nations Environment Programme. We have a world-wide marketing database for promoting titles and we are part of an international publishing group, giving access to even wider audiences. Our subject areas include Biotechnology, Water, the Environment, Natural History, Ecology, Pest Management, Agricultural Science, Zoology, Botany, Geology and Food Science and Technology.

Editor(s): Andrew Cook (Managing Editor)
Address: PO Box 716, Andover, Hampshire SP10 1YG
Telephone: 01264 334748
Fax: 01264 334058
Email: intercept@andover.co.uk
Website: http://www.intercept.co.uk
Parent Company: Technique & Documentation - Lavoisier (Paris, France)
Payment Details: Variable, as agreed between publisher and author
Unsolicited Manuscripts: Accepted

Intermediate Technology Publications

Publisher and distributor of books and periodicals at practical and policy levels on appropriate technology, Third World development, water and sanitation, agriculture, enterprise development, small-scale construction and manufacture, energy and workshop equipment.

Editor(s): Neal Burton (Senior Editor), Angela Royal (Managing Director)
Address: 103-105 Southampton Row, London WC1B 4HH
Telephone: 0171 436 9761
Fax: 0171 436 2013
Email: itpubs@itpubs.org.uk
Website: www.oneworld.org/itdg/publications.html
Imprints: Intermediate Technology Publications
Parent Company: Intermediate Technology Development Group
Unsolicited Manuscripts: Yes

International Maritime Organisation (IMO)

IMO is a specialised agency of the United Nations dealing with maritime safety and the prevention and control of marine pollution. IMO's publishing activities include the production and sales of numerous texts (conventions, codes, regulations, recommendations, etc) both in print and in electronic form. IMO has some 250 titles in English; they are translated into French and Spanish, and an increasing number also into Arabic, Chinese and Russian.

Address: 4 Albert Embankment, London SE1 7SR
Telephone: 0171 735 7611
Fax: 0171 587 3241
Email: publications.sales@imo.org
Website: www.imo.org

I

International Masters Publishers

An international direct marketing company specialising in high-quality continuity series. Our family information and education department embraces a range of publications designed to broaden knowledge in an entertaining and accessible way. Our cookery publications cater for every kind of cook, from the busy mother to the gourmet. Home and hobby publications are designed to help people make the most of their increasing leisure time. Our health products promote a healthy lifestyle as well as addressing more indepth medical issues. All of our fact files and books combine clear step-by-step photography and concise factual text with expert hints and tips. We are constantly updating our products and developing new ones.

Editor(s): Kay Turner, Kim Cooper, Cornelia Philipp, Mark Cockerton, Leslie Robb, Debbie Myatt
Address: Winchester House, 259-269 Old Marylebone Road, London NW1 5RW
Telephone: 0171 753 9200
Fax: 0171 723 9191
Unsolicited Manuscripts: No

INTES International (UK) Ltd

English language editions of one of the most popular adventure/humour comic books in the world: The Greatest Adventures Of Spike And Suzy is suitable for children aged 7-12 years.

Editor(s): Ellie Shepherd
Address: 384 Lanark Road, Edinburgh EH13 0LX
Telephone: 0131 477 2223
Fax: 0131 441 4680
Email: RShep31245@aol.com
Website: www.cs.vu.nl/~hartskam/swenghome.html
Imprints: INTES International

IOM Communications

IOM Communications publishes books on materials science and engineering. The books include textbooks and reference works covering metals, ceramics. polymers and composite materials. IOM Communications is a wholly owned subsidary of The Institute of Materials, the learned and professional body for materials scientists and engineers.

Editor(s): Peter Danckwerts
Address: 1 Carlton House Terrace, London SW1Y 5DB
Telephone: 0171 451 7305
Fax: 0171 839 2289
Email: Bill_Jackson@materials.org.uk
Website: www.materials.org.uk
Parent Company: The Institute of Materials
Payment Details: Royalties on sales
Unsolicited Manuscripts: To Peter Danckwerts

Irish Academic Press

Book publisher interested in following subject areas: Irish history, military history, Irish culture and heritage, arts and literature. Two new series: New Directions In Irish History and Women In Irish History. New manuscript and reprint ideas in the Press' subject areas welcomed.

Editor(s): Linda Longmore
Address: Northumberland House, 44 Northumberland Road, Ballsbridge, Dublin 4, Ireland
Telephone: 353 1 6688244
Fax: 353 1 6601610
Email: info@iap.ie
Website: www.iap.ie
Imprints: Irish Academic Press, Irish University Press
Unsolicited Manuscripts: Yes - send to Editor

I

Iron Press

Iron Press enters its 26th year with as strong a committment as ever to the principles of small press publishing. Still unimpressed with literary competitions, marketing junkets or overhyped nonentities, Iron continues its policy of discovering the best new talent in the North East region, the rest of the country and sometimes the world. We bring out three or four new titles a year - single collections of poetry and fiction, international anthologies and contemporary plays.

Editor(s): Peter Mortimer
Address: 5 Marden Terrace, Cullercoats, North Shields, Tyne & Wear NE30 4PD
Telephone: 0191 253 1901
Fax: Same as phone
Imprints: Iron Press
Payment Details: By agreement
Unsolicited Manuscripts: Contact Editor first

Isis Publishing Ltd

Publishers of large-print and audio books.

Editor(s): Veronica Babington Smith
Address: 7 Centremead, Osney Mead, Oxford OX2 0ES
Telephone: 01865 250333
Fax: 01865 790358
Email: audiobooks@isis-publishing.co.uk
Imprints: Isis Large Print, Isis Audio Books

Islamic Texts Society

The Islamic Texts Society publishes books from the Islamic heritage mostly in the form of translations of original Arabic texts. Subjects covered: Qur'an, Hadith, philosophy, science etc.

Editor(s): Fatima Azzam
Address: 22a Brooklands Avenue, Cambridge CB2 2DQ
Telephone: 01223 314387
Fax: 01223 324342
Email: mail@its.org.uk
Website: www.its.org.uk
Imprints: Islamic Texts Society
Payment Details: Royalties 7.5% of net receipts
Unsolicited Manuscripts: Yes

Ithaca Press

Established 1973, publishes academic books, mainly on the Middle East, in the fields of history, politics and international relations, economics, social anthropology, religion and literature. Extensive backlist. Has expanded in recent years to include subjects of more general interest such as women's studies, legal studies and biography. Ithaca Press Paperbacks was launched in 1996 to reach a wider audience, including in particular students of social sciences. Important Ithaca Press series are Middle East Monographs, co-published with St Anthony's College, Oxford; the Oriental Institute Monographs, co-published with the Oriental Institute; and the Durham Middle East Monographs, co-published with the Centre for Islamic and Middle Eastern Studies, University of Durham. Strong links are also maintained with the School of Oriental and African Studies, University of London.

Editor(s): Emma Hawker (Editorial Manager)
Address: 8 Southern Court, South Street, Reading RG1 4QS
Telephone: 0118 959 7847
Fax: 0118 959 7356
Email: enquiries@garnet-ithaca.demon.co.uk
Parent Company: Garnet Publishing Ltd

Jane's Information Group

Jane's mission is to be the leading supplier of electronic information for the defence, geo-politics, law enforcement and transport markets world-wide. Jane's supplies its information to governments, militaries, universities and industries globally and is the market leader in this area of business to business publishing. Jane's publishes over 200 titles a year and is based in five offices, around the world - two offices in London (UK), Washington, DC and Santa Ana, California (USA), Singapore, Sydney (Australia). Jane's has over 100 individual editors involved in its publications, many of whom have been awarded the highest honours in defence and aviation journalism during their careers. Jane's most well known publications include Jane's Fighting Ships, Jane's Defence Weekly and Jane's All the World's Aircraft. All these publications are available online and along with Jane's other publications are now updated as often as weekly. Visit www.janesonline.com to experience all of Jane's information via the internet.

Editor(s): Over 100 individual editors worldwide
Address: Sentinel House, 163 Brighton Road, Coulsdon, Surrey CR5 2YH
Telephone: 0181 700 3700
Fax: 0181 763 1006
Email: info@janes.co.uk
Website: www.janes.com
Parent Company: The Thomson Corporation
Payment Details: Contract basis
Unsolicited Manuscripts: None

Janus Publishing Company Ltd

Janus Books and Empiricus Books. These are two imprints of Janus Publishing Co Ltd which incorporate both subsidised and non-subsidised publishing. Art, biography and autobiography, crime, economics, fiction, history, humour, music, medical, military and war, nautical, the occult, philosophy, poetry, politics and world affairs, science, science fiction, self-help, religion and theology, travel.

Editor(s): Sandy Leung
Address: 76 Great Titchfield Street, London W1P 7AF
Telephone: 0171 580 7664
Fax: 0171 636 5756
Email: publishers@januspublishing.co.uk
Website: http:/www.januspublishing.co.uk
Imprints: Janus, Empiricus
Parent Company: Junction Books Ltd
Payment Details: Janus - mostly subsidised; Empiricus - no subsidies
Unsolicited Manuscripts: Yes, must be printed and in double space

Jarrold Publishing

Travel guides mostly UK; leisure; gift books, mainly heritage titles. All books have a high photographic content and some artwork.

Editor(s): Sarah Letts
Address: Whitefriars, Norwich, Norfolk NR3 1TR
Parent Company: Jarrold and Sons Ltd
Payment Details: Fees and royalties
Unsolicited Manuscripts: Approach in writing first

J
A H Jolly (Editorial) Ltd

Both a book publisher and a book packager - putting titles together for other publishers. Encompassing in-house editing, design, photography and pre-press. Non-fiction, illustrated, arts-related.

Address: Yelvertoft Manor, Yelvertoft, Northamptonshire NN6 6LF
Telephone: 01788 823868
Fax: 01788 823915
Payment Details: By individual arrangement
Unsolicited Manuscripts: Synopsis only

John Jones Publishing Ltd

Publishes paperback books for the tourist market in Wales and on the Celtic and Tudor periods. Publishes about 5 books a year. Most on the list are re-publications.

Editor(s): J Jones
Address: Unit 12 Clwydfru Business Centre, Ruthin, North Wales LL15 1NJ
Telephone: 01824 705272 / 704856
Fax: 01824 705272
Email: mail@johnjonespublishing.ltd.uk
Website: www.johnjonespublishing.ltd.uk
Imprints: John Jones Publishing
Payment Details: Royalties
Unsolicited Manuscripts: Enquiring letter first with SAE

Jordan Publishing Ltd

Jordan Publishing have now been producing practical legal books for over 100 years. During that time our Jordans imprint has established a respected reputation for a whole range of company law, commercial law, property, agricultural law, charities, private client work, education, crime and specialist insolvency titles. Under our Family Law imprint there are an extensive range of journals, law reports and reference works. A prime source of legal update and information for family lawyers.

Address: 21 St Thomas Street, Bristol BS1 6JS
Telephone: 0117 9230600
Fax: 0117 9250486
Email: ryoung@jordanpublishing.co.uk
Website: www.jordanpublishing.co.uk
Imprints: Jordans, Family Law
Unsolicited Manuscripts: Yes

Richard Joseph Publishers Ltd

Publishers of directories of antiquarian and secondhand book dealers in many countries around the world. Also published are directories of dealers in prints and maps, ephemera and collectables. A few titles also published about secondhand books.

Editor(s): Jackie Farrow
Address: Unit 2, Monks Walk, Farnham, Surrey GU9 8HT
Telephone: 01252 734347
Fax: 01252 734307
Email: rjoe01@aol.com
Website: http://members.aol.com/rjoe01/sheppards.htm
Imprints: Sheppard's
Unsolicited Manuscripts: Not accepted unless directly related

𝒦

S Karger AG

Founded in 1890, Karger is an independent medical publisher based in Basel, Switzerland. We publish 80 journals and about 60 new books a year, primarily in highly specialised medical research.

Editor(s): Peter Lawson
Address: 58 Grove Hill Road, Tunbridge Wells TN1 1SP
Telephone: 01892 533534
Fax: 01892 533735
Email: lawson_karger@compuserve.com
Website: www.karger.com
Imprints: Karger
Parent Company: S Karger AG, Basel
Unsolicited Manuscripts: No

Karnak House

Specialists in African and Caribbean studies only. Subjects published are history, education, linguistics, languages, egyptology, prehistory, anthropology, sociology and politics. Fiction only - no memoirs, biographies or autobiographies.

Editor(s): A S Saakana
Address: 300 Westbourne Park Road, London W11 1EH
Telephone: 0171 243 3620
Fax: Same as phone
Imprints: Karnak House
Unsolicited Manuscripts: Yes but synopsis and sample chapter only, plus SAE

Richard Kay (Publications)

Publishes books the majority of which have a Lincolnshire association; also a few with a more general historical interest, and a few titles of medico-political and economico-political concern. Books in and about Lincolnshire dialect including a 10,000-word dictionary. Life in Lincolnshire and Vernacular History series. Local history - academic and nostalgic.

Editor(s): Richard Allday
Address: 80 Sleaford Road, Boston, Lincolnshire PE21 8EU
Telephone: 01205 353231
Imprints: Richard Kay, History Of Boston Project
Payment Details: Royalties where apppropriate paid annually
Unsolicited Manuscripts: Initial letter preferred

Keepdate Publishing

Traditional and new media publishers.

Editor(s): Managing Editor: J Hinves
Address: 21 Portland Terrace, Newcastle Upon Tyne NE2 1QQ
Telephone: 0191 2819444
Fax: 0191 2813105
Website: www.newsworth.com

𝒦
Kegan Paul International Ltd

We are probably the leading publishers of books on all aspects of the Middle East, Asia, Africa, Japan, the Pacific and South America, from the most general to the most specialist.

Editor(s): Editorial Director: Kaori O'Connor
Address: PO Box 256, 121 Bedford Court Mansions, Bedford Avenue, London WC1B 3SW
Telephone: 0171 580 5511
Fax: 0171 436 0899
Email: books@keganpau.demon.co.uk
Website: www.demon.co.uk/keganpaul/
Unsolicited Manuscripts: Yes

Kenilworth Press Ltd

Leading publisher of instructional equestrian books, including the official books of the British Horse Society, and the famous Threshold Picture Guides.

Editor(s): Lesley Gowers
Address: Addington, Buckingham, MK18 2JR
Telephone: 01296 715101
Fax: 01296 715148
Email: mail@kenilworthpress.co.uk
Imprints: Kenilworth, Threshold
Payment Details: Royalties
Unsolicited Manuscripts: Yes

Kensington West Productions

Publishes sports, leisure, photography, business and children's titles. Children's imprint 3 R's Books specialises in titles that are both fun and educational.

Editor(s): Julian West
Address: 5 Cattle Market, Hexham, Northumberland NE46 1NJ
Telephone: 01434 609933
Fax: 01434 600066
Email: kwp@kensingtonwest.demon.co.uk
Website: www.@kensingtonwest.demon.co.uk
Imprints: Kensington West Productions, 3 R's Books
Unsolicited Manuscripts: No, please send outline of proposal by post

The King's England Press

Formed in 1989 to reprint Arther Mee's King's England series of 1930s guidebooks to the English counties. Due this year are Surrey and Cambridgeshire. Also available - Notts, Derbys, Durham, Essex, Herts, Lincs, Warwicks, Staffs, Leics & Rutland, West Yorks. Press also publishes children's poetry by Gez Walsh (The Spot On My Bum) and Andrew Collett (Always Eat Your Bogies), plus other books on local history and folklore. See website or send for free catalogue.

Editor(s): Steve Rudd
Address: 21 Commercial Road, Goldthorpe Industrial Estate, Goldthorpe, Rotherham S63 9BL
Telephone: 01226 270258
Fax: 01709 897787
Email: sales@kingsengland.demon.co.uk
Website: www.kingsengland.demon.co.uk

K

Laurence King Publishing

Publisher of fine illustrated books on graphic design, architecture, interior design, decorative arts and textiles.

Editor(s): Philip Cooper, Jo Lightfoot, Jane Tobin, Laura Church
Address: 71 Great Russell Street, London WC1B 3BN
Telephone: 0171 831 6351
Fax: 0171 831 8356
Email: enquiries@calmann-king.co.uk
Website: www.laurence-king.com
Parent Company: Calmann & King Ltd
Payment Details: Royalties paid twice-yearly
Unsolicited Manuscripts: Yes

Kingfisher Publications

Non-fiction: children 0-16 years. Exciting, visual books, coupled with solid information that should be provided in a stimulating way to satisfy young enquiring minds. Fiction: children 0-16 years. Rich variety of titles with opportunities to share the joy of reading with every child.

Editor(s): Gill Denton (non-fiction), Ann-Janine Murtagh (fiction)
Address: New Penderel House, 283-288 High Holborn, London WC1V 7HZ
Imprints: Kingfisher Non-Fiction, Kingfisher Fiction
Parent Company: Vivendi
Unsolicited Manuscripts: No

Jessica Kingsley Publishers

Professional and academic level books on special needs, arts therapies, social work, psychiatry, psychology. Books for professionals and parents on autism, Asperger's syndrome and related conditions. An independent company founded in 1987, now publishing 90 books a year.

Editor(s): Jessica Kingsley, Helen Parry, Amy Lankaster-Owen
Address: 116 Pentonville Road, London N1 9JB
Telephone: 020 7833 2307
Fax: 020 7837 2917
Email: post@jkp.com
Website: www.jkp.com
Payment Details: Royalties
Unsolicited Manuscripts: No, but proposals for books in our subject areas welcome - send outline, contents and author CV

Kluwer Academic-Plenum Publishers

Plenum Publishing is now part of Kluwer Academic Publishers. The UK company, based in London, provides an editorial base for new journals and books at postgraduate, research and professional levels in life sciences, physical sciences and social sciences.

Editor(s): Ken Derham, Joanna Lawrence
Address: New Loom House, 101 Back Church Lane, London E1 1LU
Telephone: 0207 264 1910
Fax: 0207 264 1919
Email: mail@plenum.co.uk
Website: www.plenum.co.uk
Imprints: Plenum Press, Kluwer Academic-Plenum Publishers
Parent Company: Kluwer Academic-Plenum Publishers, New York
Payment Details: Royalty on sales negotiable according to type of book
Unsolicited Manuscripts: Yes

𝒦
Knockabout Comics

Humorous comic strip collections, graphic novels, cartoon collections. Also drug information books.

Editor(s): George Rayburn
Address: Unit 24, 10 Acklam Road, London W10 5QZ
Telephone: 0181 969 2945
Fax: 0181 968 7614
Email: knockcomic@aol.com
Website: knockabout.com
Imprints: Knockabout, Jester Books, Hassle Free Press
Parent Company: Toskanex Ltd
Unsolicited Manuscripts: No

Kogan Page Ltd

Business and management, marketing, HRM, training and development, careers, study skills, personal development, personal finance, education for schools and HE, health care management, transport and logistics.

Editor(s): Philip Mudd, Pauline Goodwin
Address: 120 Pentonville Road, London N1 9JN
Telephone: 0171 278 0433
Fax: 0171 837 6348
Email: kpinfo@kogan-page.co.uk
Website: www.kogan-page.co.uk
Payment Details: Royalties or flat fee
Unsolicited Manuscripts: No - proposal required

Kyle Cathie Ltd

An independent company formed in 1990 to publish highly illustrated non-fiction, specialising in cookery, gardening, health and beauty, design, style, reference. Authors include Sue Lawrence, Bob Flewerdew, Jekka McVicar, Paul Gayler, Marilyn Glenville, John Cushrie, Alison Price, Marylyn Abbott, Jane Lapotaine, Darina Allen. Bestsellers in 1999 include Natural Alternatives to Dieting, Bareface Chic, Sue Lawrence on Salads, Perfect Order.

Editor(s): Kyle Cathie, Caroline Taggart, Kate Oldfield, Sophie Bessemer
Address: 20 Vauxhall Bridge Road, London SW1V 2SA
Telephone: 0171 840 8400
Fax: 0171 821 9258
Email: kcathie@aol.com
Parent Company: Independent
Payment Details: Royalties paid twice yearly
Unsolicited Manuscripts: On relevant subjects, synopses only, return postage

Landfall Publications

About 30 books published so far, all with a Cornish interest. Main series is Landfall Walks Books, 14 volumes by Bob Acton giving directions for round walks with copious information on points of interest. Another ongoing series is Exploring Cornish Mines, and industrial archaeology is the focus of several other publications. Also publish books by Viv Acton, including two popular ones about Cornwall during World War 2, plus other local history books by this author and others.

Address: Landfall, Penpol, Devoran, Truro TR3 6NR
Telephone: 01872 862581
Email: bob.acton@virgin.net
Unsolicited Manuscripts: No

$\mathcal{L}$

Landy Publishing

Publishes local history for Lancashire townships. Also Lancashire dialect poetry.

Address: 3 Staining Rise, Staining, Blackpool FY3 0BU
Telephone: 01253 895678
Fax: Same as phone
Payment Details: By arrangement
Unsolicited Manuscripts: No. Phone or write first

Lapwing Publications

Poetry publisher publishing the following: Northern Irish authors living in Northern Ireland; Northern Irish authors living in UK and EEC; Irish authors living in Eire; Irish authors living in UK and EEC; Irish authors with a strong link with or home in Northern Ireland. Small print runs, A5 (21cm), saddle-stitched, paperbound (3 sheet card), spot colour covers.

Editor(s): Dennis Greig, Rene Greig
Address: c/o 1 Ballysillan Drive, Belfast BT14 8HQ
Telephone: 01232 391240
Fax: Same as phone
Payment Details: Authors' copies, 10% of print run
Unsolicited Manuscripts: Yes, always, up to 20 poems

The Latchmere Press

Provide practical case studies on how to stimulate and maintain success in purposeful teaching and learning. Our Quality In Education series of books feature articles written by seasoned professionals who have succeeded at the chalkface - and whose successes have been recognised nationally. Titles: Striving For Quality In Schools (£9.95); Maintaining Excellence In Schools (£10.95); The Disabled Child, The Family And The Professional (£11.95); Literacy And Numeracy: Crusade For Standards (£10.95); Partnerships For School Effectiveness (£13.95).

Editor(s): Tony Evans, Carol Kay, Angela Cornforth
Address: 6 Dundalk Road, London SE4 2JL
Telephone: 0171 639 7282
Fax: 0181 853 0724

Law Pack Publishing Ltd

Self-help law for the layman, self-help in general, tax and careers titles. Books, kits, software and forms.

Editor(s): Jamie Ross
Address: 10-16 Cole Street, London SE1 4YH
Telephone: 0171 357 0367
Fax: 0171 357 0347
Email: mailbox@lawpack.co.uk
Website: www.lawpack.co.uk
Imprints: Take Note
Unsolicited Manuscripts: Yes

L

Law Society Publishing

A commercial publishing business existing within The Law Society of England and Wales. Publish practical handbooks, guides and legal reference material designed to enable solicitors and other law practitioners to carry out their work more effectively. Main publishing areas: litigation (including ADR/PI), commerce, employment law, human rights, practice management, IT, professional conduct, property and conveyancing, crime, environmental law, family and social welfare, partnerships, wills and probate and legal reference.

Editor(s): Steven Reed, Angela Atcheson, Ben Mullane
Address: 113 Chancery Lane, London WC1A 1PL
Telephone: 0171 320 5876
Fax: 0171 404 1124
Email: steven.reed@lawsociety.org.uk
Website: www.publishing.lawsociety.org.uk
Imprints: Law Society Publishing
Parent Company: The Law Society of England and Wales
Payment Details: Royalties (negotiable)
Unsolicited Manuscripts: Yes

Lawrence And Wishart Ltd

Independent left publisher, specialising in politics and cultural studies, also publishing in the areas of history and education.

Editor(s): Sally Davison, Bertie Vitry
Address: 99A Wallis Road, London, E9 5LN
Telephone: 0181 533 2506
Fax: 0181 533 7369
Email: editorial@l-w-bks.demon.co.uk
Website: l-w-bks.co.uk
Unsolicited Manuscripts: Welcome if on our interests, no fiction - send SAE, written communication only

LDA - Learning Development Aids

Publishers of educational materials for Primary schools and special needs.

Editor(s): Jo Browning-Wroe
Address: Abbeygate House, East Road, Cambridge CB1 1DB
Telephone: 01223 357788
Fax: 01223 460557
Email: ldaorders@compuserve.com
Parent Company: Living and Learning/Tribune Education

Learning Materials Ltd

A popular company with teachers, devoted to publishing materials for children with special educational needs, giving excellent support in literacy and numeracy. The majority of books are photocopiable and provide much-needed differentiation within the classroom. In addition to English and mathematics, subjects covered include history, science, thinking skills and life skills. Several taped series are available to help in the development of listening skills. New publications for the year 2000 include: Support for Grammar, Write Away!

Editor(s): Barbara Mitchelhill
Address: Dixon Street, Wolverhampton WV2 2BX
Telephone: 01902 454026
Fax: 01902 457596
Email: Learning.Materials@btinternet.com
Website: http://www.btinternet.com/~learning.materials
Payment Details: By negotiation
Unsolicited Manuscripts: Enquire first

ℒ
Learning Together

Practice tests for 9-12 year olds in reasoning (verbal and non-verbal), English, maths and science. Target group is end of Key Stage 2.

Editor(s): Stephen McConkey, Tom Maltman
Address: 18 Shandon Park, Belfast BT5 6NW
Telephone: 01232 402086
Fax: 01232 425852

Legal Action Group

An independent self-financing education trust founded in 1972. Its purpose is to promote equal access to justice. It publishes a monthly journal Legal Action, the quarterly Community Care Law Reports and a range of law and practice books for legal practitioners and advisers.

Address: 242 Pentonville Road, London N1 9UN
Telephone: 0171 833 2931
Fax: 0171 837 6094
Email: lag@lag.org.uk
Website: www.lag.org.uk
Payment Details: Royalties twice-yearly
Unsolicited Manuscripts: Considered, but prefer synopsis and draft chapter

Lennard Publishing

General non-fiction but only where projects are underwritten by sponsorship or a guaranteed order for a large proportion of the print run.

Editor(s): Adrian Stephenson
Address: Windmill Cottage, Mackerye End, Harpenden, Herts AL5 5DR
Telephone: 01582 715866
Fax: 01582 715121
Email: lennard@lenqap.demon.co.uk
Parent Company: Lennard Associates Ltd
Payment Details: By negotiation
Unsolicited Manuscripts: No

Letts Educational

Educational books for use at home and in school for 3-18 year olds. We also publish undergraduate textbooks in business and computing, and books to help trainee teachers meet requirements of the new ITTNC.

Address: Aldine House, Aldine Place, London W12 8AW
Telephone: 0181 740 2266
Fax: 0181 743 8451
Email: mail@lettsed.co.uk
Parent Company: BPP Holdings Plc
Payment Details: Royalties
Unsolicited Manuscripts: No

John Libbey & Co Ltd

John Libbey & Co Ltd offer a fast, flexible and comprehensive publishing service. The company has achieved a reputation for well produced, timely publications - made available at realistic prices. Many titles are published with leading researchers, professional institutions and pharmaceutical companies, and based on proceeding conferences. Our specialised subjects are; epilepsy, obesity, nutrition, neurology and nuclear medicine. We also publish books and journals in cinema, film and animation. We welcome your inquiries about our company and our products.

Address: 13 Smiths Yard, Summerley Street, London SW18 4HR
Telephone: 0181 9472777
Fax: 0181 9472664
Email: johnlibbey@aol.com
Website: www.johnlibbey.com
Imprints: John Libbey, Eurotext

L

Libertarian Alliance

The Libertarian Alliance is a radical pro-free market and civil libertarian group. It campaigns for social and economic freedom by means of regular conferences and seminars, speeches to university, political, civic, business and trade union groups, and frequent appearances on television and radio. It also gives evidence and presentations to government and parliamentary inquiries. Publishes a quarterly magazine Free Life, and a wide range of serial publications - leaflets, pamphlets and monographs - on all aspects of economic, political, social, moral and sexual freedom from classical liberal, libertarian, free market and anarcho-capitalist persepectives. There are currently over 400 items in print.

Address: 25 Chapter Chambers, Esterbrooke Street, London SW1P 4NN
Telephone: 0171 821 5502
Fax: 0171 834 2031
Email: la@capital.demon.co.uk
Website: www.freespace.virgin.net/old.whig/fl.htm
Unsolicited Manuscripts: Yes

Library Association Publishing

With over 200 titles in print Library Association Publishing is one of the largest publishers worldwide in the specialist field of library and information science. At the forefront of library and information development, Library Association Publishing has a comprehensive list covering all the major areas of professional activity.

Editor(s): Publisher: Helen Carley, Commissioning Editor: Beth Barber
Address: 7 Ridgmount Street, London WC1E 7AE
Telephone: 0171 636 7543
Fax: 0171 636 3627
Email: lapublishing@la-hq.org.uk
Website: http://www.la-hq.org.uk/lapublishing
Parent Company: The Library Association
Payment Details: Negotiable
Unsolicited Manuscripts: Yes

Libris

Literary publisher specialising in German-language literature in English translation, and in studies of German literature and its authors.

Editor(s): Nicholas M Jacobs
Address: 10 Burghley Road, London NW5 1UE
Telephone: 0171 482 2390
Fax: 0171 485 4220
Imprints: Libris
Payment Details: By negotiation
Unsolicited Manuscripts: No

Lion Publishing

Publishes Christian books for general readers, both children and adults.

Editor(s): Rebecca Winter, Maurice Lyon, Sarah Medina, Su Box, Lois Rock
Address: Peter's Way, Sandy Lane West, Oxford OX4 5HG
Telephone: 01865 747550
Fax: 01865 747568
Email: custserv@lion-publishing.co.uk
Website: www.lion-publishing
Payment Details: Royalties paid twice a year
Unsolicited Manuscripts: To Celia Walden

L
Little, Brown & Company (UK)

General fiction and non-fiction hardback and paperback. Non-fiction includes - biographies and autobiographies, politics, current affairs, popular science and history. Fiction includes - thrillers, crime, SF and fantasy, women's fiction and literary fiction.

Editor(s): Alan Samson, Barbara Boote, Hilary Hale, Richard Beswick, Lennie Goodings, Imogen Taylor, Julia Charles, Tim Holman
Address: Brettenham House, Lancaster Place, London WC2E 7EN
Telephone: 0171 911 8000
Fax: 0171 911 8100
Email: email.uk@littlebrown.com
Imprints: Little Brown, Warner, Abacus, Virago, Orbit
Parent Company: Time Warner Inc
Payment Details: None
Unsolicited Manuscripts: Prefer not

The Littman Library Of Jewish Civilization

The Littman Library of Jewish Civilization exists to publish books within the field of Jewish studies, to prepare and manufacture these books to the highest editorial and production standards, and to market them as effectively as possible throughout the world. All the books published are scholarly works which explain and peretuate the jewish heritage. Following its established guidelines, the Littman Library publishes work of scholarship that reflect objectivity, fresh research, and new insight. The Library also publishes translations of Hebrew classics so as to make the jewish religious and literary heritage more accessible to english speaking readers. In addition it publishes academic works from Hebrew and other languages which reflect new research in the subject.

Editor(s): Connie Webber
Address: PO Box 645, Oxford OX2 6AS
Telephone: 01235 868104
Fax: As phone
Email: connie01@globalnet.co.uk
Unsolicited Manuscripts: Yes

Liverpool University Press

Academic and scholarly books in the fields of archaeology, architecture, art and art history, contemporary culture and society, history (all periods and areas of the world), literary criticism (English, American, French, Iberian, Latin American), environmental studies, science fiction criticism, poetry studies, sociology, veterinary science.

Editor(s): Publisher: Robin Bloxsidge
Address: 4 Cambridge Street, Liverpool L69 3BX
Telephone: 0151 794 2231
Fax: 0151 794 2235
Email: robblo@liv.ac.uk
Website: www.liverpool-unipress.co.uk
Imprints: Liverpool University Press
Parent Company: The University of Liverpool
Payment Details: Royalties paid annually; advances negotiable
Unsolicited Manuscripts: Yes

LLP Limited

Publishers and information providers to the international shipping, transportation, legal, insurance, energy and financial markets. Publish reference and professional books and directories for these markets. 200 backlist titles and up to 50 new titles each year.

Address: 69-77 Paul Street, London EC2A 4LQ
Telephone: 0171 553 1000
Fax: 0171 553 1107
Website: www.llplimited.com
Parent Company: Informa Group Plc
Unsolicited Manuscripts: To Reference Publishing Division

L

Logaston Press

Concentrates on publishing books on history, social history and archaeology concerning central or South Wales, Welsh Borders, and/or West Midlands. Looking, especially, for authors to help develop series on history of pubs, and Monuments in Landscape series. Discuss ideas/synopsis first before considering chapters/manuscript.

Editor(s): Andy Johnson, Ron Shoesmith
Address: Logaston, Woonton, Almeley, Herefordshire HR3 6QH
Telephone: 01544 327344
Imprints: Logaston Press
Payment Details: By mutual agreement, normally on publication
Unsolicited Manuscripts: Send outline idea first, manuscript by request only

Y Lolfa

Welsh - language and English - language for adults and children. Children's books: original. Age groups: all. Particular interest in contemporary welsh writing; original series for children; music; books for learners and tourists, politics and general books on Wales. Around 20% of titles are commissioned.

Editor(s): Lefi Gruffudd (General Editor)
Address: Talybont, Ceredigion SY24 5AP
Telephone: 01970 832 304
Fax: 01970 832 782
Email: ylolfa@ylolfa.com
Website: www.ylolfa.com

Lonely Planet Publications

Independent travel guidebook publisher. Over 460 books including regional, country and city guides, first time, pocket, food and restaurant guides, pictorial travel books, atlases, sheet city maps, phasebooks, walking, cycling, wildlife and diving guides, travel literature and books on healthy travel.

Editor(s): Katharine Leck
Address: 10a Spring Place, London NW5 3BH
Telephone: 0171 428 4800
Fax: 0171 428 4828
Email: go@lonelyplanet.co.uk
Website: www.lonelyplanet_com/
Parent Company: Lonely Planet Publications Australia
Payment Details: Dependent on contract
Unsolicited Manuscripts: No

Richard R Long

Publication of short runs of national curriculum science guides and safety signs. Offers service to education to publish similar books.

Editor(s): Richard R Long, Jo Long
Address: Lindum Lodge, 37 Nettleham Road, Lincoln LN2 1RW
Telephone: 01522 522836
Imprints: Richard R Long

𝓛
LTP (Language Teaching Publications)

LTP is an independent publisher specialising in innovative materials for the ELT market. LTP has an exceptional business English and teacher training list which continues to grow alongside general English products. Established titles include The Lexical Approach; Implementing The Lexical Approach; Dictionary Of Selected Collocations; Business Matters and The Working Week. New titles in 1999 include Idioms Organiser; Teaching Collocation; Grammar With Laughter.

Editor(s): M Lewis, J Hill
Address: 114a Church Road, Hove, E Sussex BN3 2EB
Telephone: 01273 736344
Fax: 01273 775361
Email: lanteapub@aol.com
Unsolicited Manuscripts: Accepted with contents page, rationale, 3 sample units/ chapters

Lucis Press Ltd

Lucis Press publishes books of esoteric philosophy, a continuation of the Ageless Wisdom presented as a guide to the merging of spiritual values and goals with the challenges of modern living. The teaching of the Tibetan Master, Djwhal Khul, written by Alice Bailey, encompasses a wide range of subjects including the new psychology of the soul, education, discipleship, astrology, healing, intuition, karma and telepathy. Other author's titles include the Agni Yoga series.

Editor(s): Sarah McKechnie
Address: 3 Whitehall Court, Suite 54, London SW1A 2EF
Telephone: 0171 839 4512
Fax: 0171 839 5575
Email: london@lucistrust.org
Website: www.lucistrust.org/
Parent Company: Lucis Publishing, New York

Lucky Duck Publishing

Specialise in books for teachers and parents which present a positive approach to behaviour management. Our catalogue includes books, videos and teaching materials about self-esteem, bullying, circle time, circle of friends, emotional curriculum, parenting skills and equal opportunities. We have published a number of first-time authors, and provide a supportive editorial service to assist in the production of user-friendly materials. Visit the website for more information.

Editor(s): George Robinson, Barbara Maines
Address: 34 Wellington Park, Clifton, Bristol BS8 2UW
Telephone: 0117 9732881
Fax: Same as phone
Email: publishing@luckyduck.co.uk
Website: www.luckyduck.co.uk
Payment Details: 10% of net sales
Unsolicited Manuscripts: No

Lund Humphries Publishers

Publishers of books on fine art, architecture, decorative arts, design and photography. Specialise in co-publications with museums and galleries. Publishers for the Henry Moore Foundation, and distributors for a number of museums worldwide.

Editor(s): Editorial Director: Lucy Myers
Address: Park House, 1 Russell Gardens, London NW11 9NN
Telephone: 0181 458 6314
Fax: 0181 905 5245
Email: lhpubs@aol.com
Unsolicited Manuscripts: Yes

L

Léirmheas

Publishers of Irish historical and political material and some other items of Irish interest (1 book of poetry).

Editor(s): Daltún O Ceallaigh
Address: PO Box 3278, Dublin 6, Ireland
Telephone: 353 1 4976944
Email: dcg@tinet.ie
Imprints: Léirmheas

Macmillan Children's Books

Publishes novels, board games, picture books, non-fiction (illustrated and non-illustrated), poetry and novelty books in paperback and hardback. No unsolicited material.

Editor(s): Managing Director: Kate Wilson; Full-colour Publishing Director: Alison Green; Black and White Publishing Director: Marion Lloyd
Address: 25 Eccleston Place, London SW1W 9NF
Telephone: 0171 881 8000
Fax: 0171 881 8001
Website: www.panmacmillan.co.uk
Imprints: Macmillan, Pan, Campbell Books
Parent Company: Macmillan Publishers Ltd
Unsolicited Manuscripts: No unsolicited material

Macmillan Publishers Ltd

Macmillan Publishers, founded in 1843, publish approximately 1400 titles a year. Unsolicited proposals and synopses are welcome in all divisions of the company, which are: Macmillan Press Ltd, publishing textbooks and monographs; Macmillan Education, publishing international education titles; Macmillan Heineman ELT, publishing ELT titles; Macmillan, publishing biographies, autobiographies, crafts, hobbies, economics, gift books, health and beauty, history, humour, natural history, travel, philosphy, politics and world affairs, psychology, theatre and drama, gardening, cookery, encyclopedias; Pan, publishing fiction and non- fiction paperbacks; Papermac, publishing serious non-fiction; Picador, publishing literary and general fiction and non-fiction; Sidgwick & Jackson, publishing military and war and music; Macmillan Children's Books and Campbell Books, publishing novels, board books, picture books; Macmillan Reference Ltd, publishing works of reference in academic, professional and vocational subjects; Boxtree, publishing books linked to, and about, television, film, popular culture, humour and sport.

Address: 25 Eccleston Place, London SW1W 9NF
Telephone: 0171 881 8000
Fax: 0171 881 8001
Imprints: Macmillan, Pan, Papermac, Sidgwick & Jackson
Parent Company: Holtzbrinck
Payment Details: Royalties are paid annually or twice-yearly depending on contract
Unsolicited Manuscripts: Yes

Macmillan Reference Ltd

Art, music, politics, current affairs, economics, finance, science.

Editor(s): Gina Fullerlove, Margot Levy, Sara Lloyd
Address: 25 Eccleston Place, London SW1W 9NF
Telephone: 0171 881 8000
Fax: 0171 881 8001
Website: www.macmillan-reference.co.uk
Imprints: Grove's Dictionaries
Parent Company: Macmillan Ltd
Payment Details: Vary
Unsolicited Manuscripts: Yes

M

Magi Publications

Children's picture books, 4-7 years, pre-school and novelty books 0-4 years.

Editor(s): Linda Jennings
Address: 22 Manchester Street, London W1M 5PG
Telephone: 0171 486 0925
Fax: 0171 486 0926
Email: info@magi.publication.demon.co.uk.
Website: www.littletiger.okukbooks.com
Imprints: Little Tiger Press
Payment Details: To be agreed with author
Unsolicited Manuscripts: Yes, welcomed, but please phone first

Magna Large Print Books

Family saga, doctor/nurse, mystery, suspense/adventure, romance, romantic/suspense, westerns, thrillers, general fiction, historical romance and a small amount of non-fiction. Please note: we only publish large-print books which have already been published in ordinary print.

Editor(s): Diane Allen
Address: Magna House, Long Preston, Nr Skipton, North Yorkshire BD23 4ND
Telephone: 01729 840225
Fax: 01729 840683
Imprints: Magna, Dales and Story Sound
Parent Company: The Ulverscroft Group
Unsolicited Manuscripts: No

Mainstream Publishing Co Ltd

Mainstream publishes a wide variety of non-fiction books covering sport, health, biography, autobiography, current affairs, art, photography and illustrated books. The company was founded by its current directors in 1978 and now publishes 80-90 titles per year. Manuscripts should not be submitted in the first instance - a covering letter and detailed synopsis will do.

Editor(s): Bill Campbell
Address: 7 Albany Street, Edinburgh EH1 3UG
Telephone: 0131 557 2959
Fax: 0131 556 8720
Email: mainstream.pub@btinternet.com
Imprints: Mainstream
Unsolicited Manuscripts: No

Management Books 2000 Ltd

Management guides, handbooks and directories, covering all types of business book from career development to technical reference. Also interested in general non-fiction titles of particular topical relevance.

Editor(s): Nigel Dale-Harris
Address: Cowcombe House, Cowcombe Hill, Chalford, Gloucester GL6 8HP
Telephone: 01285 760722
Fax: 01285 760708
Email: m.b.200@virgin.net
Website: www.mb2000.com
Imprints: Management Books 2000, Mercury Business Books
Payment Details: Advance/Royalties
Unsolicited Manuscripts: Yes

M
Management Pocketbooks Ltd

Pocket-size (A6 landscape), succinct, factual text, and high visual content distinguish Management Pocketbooks. More than 40 titles in the series, which broadly fall into the following categories: training, personal development, management, sales and marketing, and finance. Flagship The Trainer's Pocketbook has sold over 40,000 copies. The pages of a Pocketbook resemble an overhead transparency: a heading denotes the subject of the page; the text is often presented as bullet-points; acronyms, mnemonics and other memory trigger devices are used; and illustrations are included wherever possible. Thumb logos enable reader to identify the chapter they are reading. Many of the Pocketbook authors are trainers and present their own training materials in a similar way. The books are £6.99 and when discounted (for multiple copies) they can be used as inexpensive course material, either before, during or after the training event. ISBN series prefix 1 870471.

Editor(s): Ros Baynes, Sue Kerr, Adrian Hunt
Address: 14 East Street, Alresford, Hants SO24 9EE
Telephone: 01962 735573
Fax: 01962 733637
Email: pocketbks@aol.com
Website: http://members.aol.com/pocketbks
Payment Details: 10% of net receipts
Unsolicited Manuscripts: To Ros Baynes

Institute Of Management

Publisher of books, checklists, CD-ROMs, on over 200 management-related topics. I M publishes independently and in association with Hodder & Stoughton and Butterworth Heinemann.

Editor(s): D Darke
Address: Management House, Cottingham Road, Corby NN17 1TT
Telephone: 01536 204222
Fax: 01536 201651
Email: publications@imgt.org.uk
Website: www.inst-mgt.org.uk

Manchester University Press

Art history, history, theology and religion (Editor: Graham). Economics and business studies, international law, politics (Editor: Viinikka). Architecture, design, film and media, foreign language texts, literary studies, music, philosophy and theory, photography (Editor: Frost). We also publish a number of journals.

Editor(s): Vanessa Graham (history), Nicola Viinikka (economics), Matthew Frost (humanities)
Address: Oxford Road, Manchester M13 9NR
Telephone: 0161 273 5539
Fax: 0161 274 3346
Email: mup@man.ac.uk
Website: www.man.ac.uk/mup
Imprints: Mandolin
Payment Details: Royalties
Unsolicited Manuscripts: Yes

Maney Publishing

Maney is one of the few remaining independent publishers of quality in an era of declining production standards and the increasing concentration of publishing in the hands of international conglomerates. Since 1945 Maney has offered academic societies, their editors and authors outstanding service in the publication of their books and journals: that process continues with the development of our journal publishing imprint Maney Publishing and our monograph imprint Northern Universities Press. We publish in the areas of archaeology, architecture, history, decorative arts, literature and language and more recently the biomedical sciences.

Editor(s): Publishing Director: Michael Gallico
Address: Hudson Road, Leeds LS9 7DL
Telephone: 0113 249 7481
Fax: 0133 248 6983
Email: maney@maney.co.uk
Website: www.maney.co.uk
Imprints: Northern Universities Press, Maney Publishing
Parent Company: W S Maney & Son Ltd
Unsolicited Manuscripts: Yes

M

Mango Publishing

Focuses on the Caribbean - especially literature and poetry from Caribbean heritage writers, particularly women. Anything with a Caribbean connection is considered.

Editor(s): Joan Anim-Addo
Address: P O Box 13378, London SE27 0ZN
Telephone: 0181 480 7771
Fax: Same as phone
Email: j.anim-addo@virgin.net
Imprints: Mango Publishing
Payment Details: By arrangement
Unsolicited Manuscripts: Yes

Manson Publishing Ltd

Books for professionals and students in medicine, veterinary medicine, biological and agricultural sciences and earth sciences. All our books are distributed through Blackwell Science Ltd.

Address: 73 Corringham Road, London NW11 7DL
Telephone: 020 8905 5150
Fax: 020 8201 9233
Email: manson@man-pub.demon.co.uk
Imprints: Manson Publishing Ltd, The Veterinary Press
Unsolicited Manuscripts: No

Map Collectors Publications Ltd

Specialist publishers and booksellers of books concerned with antique map collecting and the history of cartography.

Editor(s): Mrs V Scott, Mrs J French
Address: 48 High Street, Tring, Herts HP23 5BH
Telephone: 01442 824977
Fax: 01442 827712
Email: gp86@dial.pipex.com
Website: http://www.mapcollector.com
Payment Details: On request
Unsolicited Manuscripts: No

Peter Marcan Publications

Small publisher of information directories: Outlets For Specialist New Books In The UK; The Marcan Handbook Of Arts Organisations; Greater London History And Heritage Handbook; Art Historians And Specialists In The UK. Also pictorial albums and reprints on London history and topography.

Address: PO Box 3158, London SE1 4RA
Telephone: 0171 357 0368

Marcham Manor Press

Specialist publisher interested in PhD level academic publications in the field of history and church history c1520-1690 and c1750-1900.

Editor(s): Gervase Duffield
Address: Appleford, Abingdon, Oxon OX14 4PB
Telephone: 01235 848319
Imprints: Marcham Books, Sutton Courtenay Press
Parent Company: Appleford Publishing Group
Unsolicited Manuscripts: Only in our field

M
Market House Books Ltd

Compilers and packagers of reference books, including the Collins English Dictionary, the Macmillan Encyclopedia, the Larousse 6-volume Thematic Encyclopedia, the Oxford Paperback Encyclopedia and over 150 other reference books. Established 1970.

Editor(s): Alan Isaacs, John Daintith, Elizabeth Martin
Address: Market House, Market Square, Aylesbury, Bucks HP20 1TN
Telephone: 01296 484911
Fax: 01296 437073
Email: mhb-aylesbury@compuserve.com
Unsolicited Manuscripts: For reference books only

Marshall Cavendish Books

International packagers of popular illustrated books. Subject areas include crafts, gardening, cookery, home improvement, sex, health, children's/family reference and the arts. Established international publisher of high quality reference series Cultures Of The World, Festivals Of The World, Culture Shock! Also publishes a general trade list: natural history, coffee-table albums, cookery, professional business and biographies of Asian leaders.

Editor(s): Publishing Manager: Shova Loh
Address: 119 Wardour Street, London W1V 3TD
Telephone: 0171 565 6047
Fax: 0171 734 1936
Email: te@corp.tpl.com.sg
Website: www.timesone.com.sg/te
Imprints: Marshall Cavendish Books, Marshall Cavendish Continuity Sets, Times Editions, Times Books International, Les Editions Du Pacifique
Parent Company: Times Publishing Group

Marshalle Publications

Alternative or complementary medicine, biblical diseases and medicines, homeopathy, murder and poisoning by arsenic, history of the Hebrews from 12C BC. History, short stories, Westcountry stories including Tamerton Treacle Mines. Amusing incidents.

Editor(s): Mervyn Madge
Address: Chelfham House, Saltburn Road, Plymouth PL5 1PB
Telephone: 01752 361832

Martin Books

Food, drink, cookery, beauty, health, homes and interiors, gardening, general leisure, interest.

Editor(s): Susanna Clarke, Anna Hitchin
Address: Grafton House, 64 Maids Causeway, Cambridge CB5 8DD
Telephone: 01223 366733
Fax: 01223 461428
Parent Company: Simon & Schuster UK Ltd
Unsolicited Manuscripts: No

M
Association Of Teachers Of Mathematics (ATM)

ATM aims to promote ideas and encourage the sharing of teaching and learning strategies in relation to mathematics. Members receive regular journals: Mathematics Teaching (4 issues a year, concerned with classroom approaches to mathematics teaching) and Micromath (3 issues a year, focuses on integrating ICT into mathematics classroom practice). Journals feature news, discussion and classroom ideas. ATM also publish resources for all ages. Publications include a comprehensive range of books and teaching materials. Recent publications: Questions And Prompts For Mathematics Thinking (£7.95); Teaching, Learning And Primary Mathematics (£12.50); Developing Number 'Sofware' (£49.95). Free catalogue on request.

Editor(s): D Ball and B Ball (Mathematics Teaching), Sue and Peter Johston Wilder (Micromath)
Address: 7 Shaftesbury Street, Derby DE23 8YB
Telephone: 01332 346599
Fax: 01332 204357
Email: atm_maths@compuserve.com
Website: http://acorn.educ.nottingham.ac.uk//SchEd/pages/atm/

Mathew Price Ltd

Education through delight. Co-edition specialists for fiction and non-fiction for 1 to 10-year-olds. Board books, novelties, picture books and natural history.

Address: The Old Glove Factory, Bristol Road, Sherborne, Dorset DT9 4HP
Telephone: 01935 816010
Fax: 01935 816310
Email: mathewp@mathew-price.com
Unsolicited Manuscripts: To Sue Davies

Kevin Mayhew Ltd

Non-denominational christian publishing company producing books, music, hymn books, worship resources and church requisites.

Editor(s): Helen Elliot (books), Rachel Judd (music)
Address: Maypole Farm, Buxhall, Stowmarket, Suffolk IP14 3BW
Telephone: 01449 737978
Fax: 01449 737834
Email: info@kevinmayhewltd.com
Imprints: Kevin Mayhew, Palm Tree Press
Unsolicited Manuscripts: To music or editorial dept

B McCall Barbour

Publishers of Christian books, greeting cards, calendars and gift items etc. Also wholesale distributors for Bibles, books etc, from various other publishers. British agents for Zondervan Publishers, Living Stories Inc, AMG Publishers, Riverside/ World Bibles, Dake's Bibles, Kirkbride Bibles, Sword of the Lord Publishers and Schoettle Publishers as well as Thomas Nelson Bibles and Books. Singspiration Music and Peterson Music also sole distributors. This firm is a family business established in 1900 and is strictly evangelical.

Editor(s): T C Danson-Smith
Address: 28 George IV Bridge, Edinburgh EH1 1ES
Telephone: 0131 225 4816
Fax: Same as phone
Payment Details: By arrangement
Unsolicited Manuscripts: No

M
Medici

Publishes illustrated children's picture books drawing on the themes of art, nature and biblical stories.

Address: Grafton House, Hyde Estate Road, London NW9 6JZ
Telephone: 0181 205 2500
Fax: 0181 205 2552
Unsolicited Manuscripts: No - send synopses with specimen illustrations only

Mehring Books

Mehring Books produce high quality editions of socialist books and pamphlets. Titles cover a wide range of subjects, from history and philosophy to culture, science and contemporary politics. Recent publications include, 'Art as the cognition of life', by Alexsandr Voronsky - outstanding Marxist literary critic and writer on art, aesthetics and culture. Voronsky was editor of the most important literary journal in the 1920s USSR and an opponent of Stalin. Also '1937 - Stalin's year of terror' by noted Russian historian Vadim Z Rogovin. 'Human BSE - Anatomy of a health disaster', contains submissions by Professor Richard Lacey and the families of nvCJD victims. Also available: 'A State Murder Exposed - The Truth about the Killing of Joy Gardner'. Please visit our website or ask for our free catalogue.

Address: P O Box 1306, Sheffield S9 3UW
Telephone: 0114 2440055
Fax: 0114 2440224
Email: sales@mehringbooks.co.uk
Website: www.mehringbooks.co.uk
Imprints: Mehring Books

M

Melrose Press Ltd

The International Biographical Centre of Cambridge has been producing a full range of biographical directories for more than thirty years. These directories cover vast interest and geographical areas and are specially designed to provide easy access to detailed biographical information from many varied, prominent individuals. All IBC titles are compiled without political, racial or religious bias and are of genuine international interest.

Editor(s): Jon Gifford
Address: St Thomas Place, Ely, Cambs CB7 4GG
Imprints: International Biographical Centre (IBC)
Unsolicited Manuscripts: Yes biographical data only

The Menard Press

The Menard Press celebrated its thirtieth birthday in 1999 with a group of new books, including new translations of Rilke and Nerval, and Itinerary, the intellectual autobiography of the great Mexican poet Octavio Paz, its third book by a Nobel Prize winner. The Menard Press, which specialises in literary translation (mainly of poetry), is a smaller version of presses such as Carcanet and Bloodaxe but it rarely publishes texts submitted in the usual way, rather it seeks out work of the kind its faithful readers have come to expect over many years of sporadically intensive activity. Around half of the 150 published books are still in print. In addition to translated poetry and other literary texts it has published major essays on the nuclear issue, and a number of testimonies by survivors of Nazism. Its worldwide trade distributors are Central Books, apart from North America, where Small Press Distribution is used.

Editor(s): Anthony Rudolf
Address: The Menard Press (Anthony Rudolf), 8 The Oaks, Woodside Avenue, London N12 8AR
Telephone: 0181 446 5571
Fax: Same as phone
Imprints: The Menard Press
Unsolicited Manuscripts: No

ℳ
Mercat Press

Non-fiction Scottish interest titles, no novels or poetry.

Editor(s): Tom Johnstone, Seán Costello
Address: 53 South Bridge, Edinburgh EH1 1YS
Fax: 0131 557 8149
Email: sean.costello@jthin.co.uk (or) tom.johnstone@jthin.co.uk
Website: www.jthin.co.uk/merchome.htm
Imprints: Mercat Press
Parent Company: James Thin Ltd
Payment Details: Annual royalty on copies sold
Unsolicited Manuscripts: Yes - preferably sample chapters and synopsis

Mercier Press/Marino Books

One Cork-based imprint (Mercier) and one Dublin-based imprint (Marino). Mercier specialises in history, folklore, heritage and Irish studies, politics. Marino in fiction, popular, business, biography.

Editor(s): Mary Feehan (Mercier), Jo O'Donoghue (Marino)
Address: 5 French Church Street, Cork, Ireland
Telephone: (01)6615299 / (021)275040
Fax: (01)6618583 / (021)274969
Email: books@mercier.ie
Website: www.indigo.ie/usrs/mercier/
Imprints: Mercier, Marino
Parent Company: Mercier Press
Unsolicited Manuscripts: Send complete ms and return postage (not UK postage)

Merlin Press Ltd

Radical history and social studies. Letters and synopses only please.

Editor(s): P Eve
Address: 2 Rendlesham Mews, Rendlesham, Woodbridge, Suffolk IP12 2SZ
Telephone: 01394 461313
Fax: 01394 461314
Email: merlinpres@aol.com
Imprints: Seafarer Books, Greenprint
Payment Details: Royalties on copies sold
Unsolicited Manuscripts: No

Merrell Holberton Publishers Ltd

Publishers of books on fine art, decorative art, photography, architecture, textiles and design.

Editor(s): Julian Honer
Address: 42 Southwark Street, London SE1 1UN
Telephone: 0171 403 2047
Fax: 0171 407 1333
Email: merrholb@dircon.co.uk
Imprints: Merrell Holberton
Unsolicited Manuscripts: All correspondence to Hugh Merrell, Publisher

Merrick & Day

Publishers of specialised books on curtain design and interior make-up techniques for designers and curtain makers.

Address: Southfield, Redbourne, Gainsborough, Lincs DN21 4QR
Telephone: 01652 648814
Fax: 01652 648104
Email: merrick.day@drapes.u-net.com
Website: www.drapes.u-net.com

M
Merrow Publishing Co Ltd

Publishers of textile books. Titles include Handbook Of Textile Fibres Vol 1 and 2 and Weaving: Conversion Of Yarn To Fabric.

Editor(s): J G Cook
Address: 22 Abbey Road, Darlington DL3 8LR
Telephone: 01325 351661
Fax: Same as phone
Unsolicited Manuscripts: No

Merton Priory Press Ltd

A small independent publisher of academic and mid-market British history, especially local history and industrial history. About six new titles a year. Proposals from young academic historians seeking publication of their first book welcome.

Editor(s): Philip Riden
Address: 67 Merthyr Road, Whitchurch, Cardiff CF14 1DD
Telephone: 02920 521956
Fax: 02920 623599
Imprints: Merton Priory Press
Parent Company: Independent
Payment Details: Royalties half-yearly, normally 10% retail
Unsolicited Manuscripts: Please send synopsis first

Methodist Publishing House

Popular religious hymn books, serious theology, religious music and drama, Bible study material and the DISCIPLE Bible study course.

Editor(s): Brian Thornton, Susan Hibbins
Address: 20 Ivatt Way, Peterborough PE3 7PG
Imprints: Foundery Press
Parent Company: The Methodist Church
Payment Details: Subject to negotiation
Unsolicited Manuscripts: Yes

Metra Martech

Metra Martech specialises in economic, technical and management reports. Typically these sell in low quantities (100s) and with a high price. People who buy and read the reports are senior managers, planners, technical directors and special interest libraries all over the world. Title examples: Business Opportunities In China; Use Of Countertrade; European Centres Of Expertise In Advanced Materials; Sensors Technology Research; The German Building Market. Authors should either be experts in their own right, or able and willing to grasp the subject and create a report out of our background research. We publish about 3 titles a year. The main business of the company is management consultancy and specialist market research. We have a multilingual team.

Editor(s): Peter Gorle
Address: Glenthorne House, Hammersmith Grove, London W6 0LG
Telephone: 0181 563 0666
Fax: 0181 563 0040
Email: research@metra-martech.com
Website: www.metra-martech.com
Imprints: Metra, Metra Martech, Martech Publications
Parent Company: Relion Plc
Payment Details: Negotiable

Metro Publishing Ltd

Two imprints: Metro Books - non-fiction: lifestyle, health, self-help, popular psychology, childcare, travel, popular science, humour, cookery, gardening, biography. Richard Cohen Books - literary non-fiction: biography, autobiography, popular science. Was 1998 Small Publisher of the Year.

Editor(s): Freelance
Address: 19 Gerrard Street, London W1V 7LA
Telephone: 0171 734 1411
Fax: 0171 734 1811
Email: metro@metro-books.demon.co.uk
Imprints: Metro Books, Richard Cohen Books
Unsolicited Manuscripts: With SAE

M

Micelle Press

Technical books and monographs on the science of cosmetics, toiletries, fragrances, detergents and emulsions, and the ingredients and techniques used in the preparation of these products. Natural materials - their sources and applications.

Editor(s): Janet Barber
Address: 10-12 Ullswater Crescent, Weymouth, Dorset DT3 5HE
Telephone: 01305 781574
Fax: Same as phone
Email: tony@wdi.co.uk
Website: www.wdi.co.uk/micelle
Imprints: Micelle Press
Payment Details: By negotiation
Unsolicited Manuscripts: Send synopsis or sample chapter first

Middleton Press

Specialists in railway, tramway and trolleybus photographic albums for England. Also military subjects in southeast England.

Editor(s): J C V Mitchell
Address: Easebourne Lane, Midhurst, West Sussex GU29 9AZ
Telephone: 01730 813169
Fax: 01730 812601
Imprints: MP
Payment Details: Negotiated
Unsolicited Manuscripts: No

Midland Publishing Ltd

Aviation and railways.

Address: 24 The Hollow, Earl Shilton, Leicester LE9 7NA
Telephone: 01455 847256
Fax: 01455 841805
Email: midlandbooks@compuserve.com
Parent Company: Ian Allan Group Ltd
Unsolicited Manuscripts: No

MidNag (Mid Northumberland Arts Group)

Publishing programme centres on literature and visual arts.

Editor(s): Managing Editor: G S Payne
Address: Pick Sharpeners' Shop, Woodhorn Colliery Museum, Ashington, Northumberland NE63 9YS
Telephone: 01607 853962
Fax: 01670 810958
Imprints: MidNag
Parent Company: Mid Northumberland Arts Group
Payment Details: On application
Unsolicited Manuscripts: No

M
Milestone Publications

Milestone Publications is the publishing and bookselling division of Goss & Crested China Ltd. We only publish books on Goss & Crested china and English heraldic porcelain.

Editor(s): Nicholas Pine
Address: 62 Murray Road, Horndean, Waterlooville, Hants PO8 9JL
Telephone: 01705 597440
Fax: 01705 591975
Email: info@gosschinaclub.demon.co.uk
Website: www.gosschinaclub.demon.co.uk
Imprints: Milestone, Milestone Publications
Parent Company: Goss & Crested China Ltd
Unsolicited Manuscripts: Should never be sent

Milestones London Publishers

Show room: Muslim Bookshop. Booksellers, publisher and distributor, we stock hundreds of titles on Islamic studies covering a wide range of subjects including children's books and many more. We also stock video, CD, audio tapes, CD ROM titles, stickers and posters. We also supply other titles including educational books for schools and colleges.

Address: 233 Seven Sisters Road, London, N4 2DA
Telephone: 0171 272 5170
Fax: 0171 272 3214
Parent Company: Muslim Information Centre

Miller's Publications Ltd

Editor(s): Elizabeth Norfolk, Madeleine Marsh, Mick Walker, Dave Selby
Address: The Cellars, 5 High Street, Tenterden, Kent TN30 6BN
Telephone: 01580 768411
Fax: 01580 766100
Email: info-mp@millers.uk.com
Website: www.millers.uk.com
Parent Company: Octopus Publishing Group Ltd

Harvey Miller Publishers

History of art, reference works; particularly medieval art and history, and 17th century studies.

Editor(s): Marc Jordan, Elly Miller, Jean-Claude Peissel, Sarah Kane
Address: K101 Tower Bridge Business Complex, 100 Clements Road, London SE16 4DG
Telephone: 0171 252 1531
Fax: 0171 252 3510
Email: sarah.kane@gbhap.com
Website: www.gbhap.com
Parent Company: G+B Arts International
Unsolicited Manuscripts: No

J Garnet Miller Ltd

Plays and theatre books.

Address: 10 Station Road, Industrial Estate, Colwall WR13 6RN
Telephone: 01684 540154
Fax: Same as phone
Parent Company: Cressrelles Publishing Co
Unsolicited Manuscripts: Yes

M

Mind Publications

Mental health, self-help, psychiatric drug information, complementary therapies, advocacy and mental health legislation.

Editor(s): Anny Brackx
Address: Granta House, 15-19 Broadway, Stratford, London E15 4BQ
Parent Company: Mind
Unsolicited Manuscripts: No

Minerva Press Ltd

Founded in 1997, the Minerva imprint dates back to 1792. Publishes fiction and non-fiction; biography, poetry, children's and religious books. Specialises in new authors; publishes around 250 titles a year. No 'adult' or sexually explicit material. Unsolicited manuscripts, synopses and ideas for books welcome.

Address: 6th Floor, Canberra House, 315-317 Regent Street, London W1R 7YB
Telephone: 0171 580 4114
Fax: 0171 580 9256
Email: mail@minerva-press.co.uk
Website: www.minerva-press.co.uk
Parent Company: Hybeck Holdings Ltd
Payment Details: Royalties twice-yearly
Unsolicited Manuscripts: Yes

Mitchell Beazley

Antiques, the arts, crafts, interior design, architecture, gardening, sex and health, wine, cookery and reference books.

Address: 2-4 Heron Quays, London E14 4JP
Telephone: 0171 531 8400
Fax: 0171 531 8650
Website: www.mitchell-beazley.co.uk
Parent Company: Octopus Publishing Group Ltd

Monarch Books

We publish about 25 Christian books per year, ranging from theology and apologetics to psychology, biography, the spiritual life and education. We do not handle fiction, poetry or children's literature. Most of our books are from UK authors and we welcome new authors and ideas.

Editor(s): Tony Collins
Address: Broadway House, The Broadway, Crowborough, East Sussex TN6 1HQ
Telephone: 01892 652364
Fax: 01892 663329
Email: monarch@dial.pipex.com
Imprints: Monarch, Marc
Payment Details: We pay full royalties
Unsolicited Manuscripts: Yes

Moorley's Print & Publishing Ltd

All following the Christian faith only: drama scripts; school assemblies; adult verse; children's recitations; prayers and meditations; humorous monologues; Bible study notes for small groups. Commissioned publications undertaken on most subjects.

Editor(s): John R Moorley
Address: 23 Park Road, Ilkeston, Derbyshire DE7 5DA
Telephone: 0115 932 0643
Fax: 0115 932 0643
Email: 106545.413@compuserve.com
Imprints: Moorley's, Pawprint Music
Payment Details: Royalties on sales
Unsolicited Manuscripts: No - prior correspondence required

ℳ
Motor Racing Publications Ltd

Specialist publishers of well-researched and highly illustrated books for competition, performance and classic car enthusiasts, including marque and model histories, biographies and technical and practical books. Subjects published range from Mini to Rolls-Royce, Jeep to Land Rover, MG to Porsche and Cylinder Head Modification to Turbocharging. Publishing proposals welcomed for 'How To' books on competition and road car tuning and modification. Editorial, production and complete publishing service offered to companies or individuals requiring corporate, promotional or personal books.

Editor(s): John Blunsden and John Plummer
Address: Unit 6, The Pilton Estate, 46 Pitlake, Croydon CR0 3RY
Telephone: 020 8681 3363
Fax: 020 8760 5117
Email: mrp.books@virgin.net
Website: www.oberon.co.uk/mrp
Imprints: MRP and The Fitzjames Press
Parent Company: Motor Racing Publications Ltd
Payment Details: Royalties paid twice yearly
Unsolicited Manuscripts: Accepted but initial contact with synopsis recommended

Multi-Sensory Learning

Special needs titles including a fully structured, integrated and cumulative literacy skills programme.

Editor(s): Philippa Attwood
Address: Earlstrees Court, Earlstrees Road, Corby, Northants NN17 4HH
Telephone: 01536 399003
Fax: 01536 399012
Email: firstbest9@aol.com
Parent Company: First And Best In Education
Payment Details: Royalties
Unsolicited Manuscripts: No

Multilingual Matters Ltd

Academic publishers in the fields of applied linguistics, translation studies and tourism. Also parents and teachers' guides and general information on bilingualism.

Address: Frankfurt Lodge, Clevedon Hall, Victoria Road, Clevedon BS21 7HH
Telephone: 01275 876519
Fax: 01275 343096
Email: multi@multilingual-matters.com
Website: www.multilingual-matters.com
Imprints: Channel View Books

John Murray (Publishers) Ltd

School books, success study books, history, biography, travel, art and architecture, politics, current affairs, war and military.

Editor(s): Grant McIntyre, Caroline Knox, Gail Pirkis
Address: 50 Albemarle Street, London W1X 4BD
Telephone: 0171 493 4361
Fax: 0171 499 1792
Payment Details: Royalties paid twice-yearly
Unsolicited Manuscripts: No

Peter Nahum At The Leicester Galleries Ltd

Illustrated art books and pamphlets. Example of titles: Burne-Jones, The Pre-Raphaelites And Their Century; Michael Rothenstein's Boxes; Fairy Folk In Fairy Land (William Allingham's fairy poem illustrated by Peter Nahum); Burne-Jones - A Quest For Love.

Editor(s): Peter Nahum
Address: 5 Ryder Street, London SW1Y 6PY
Telephone: 0171 930 6059
Fax: 0171 930 4678
Email: peternahum@netserv.net
Parent Company: The Leicester Galleries

𝒩
National Academy Press

Publishes the reports issued by the National Academy of Science, the National Academy of Engineering, the Institute of Medicine and the National Research Council, all operating under a charter granted by the Congress of the United States of America. Subjects: science, technology, engineering, medicine and health.

Address: 12 Hid's Copse Road, Cumnor Hill, Oxford OX2 9JJ
Telephone: 01865 865466
Fax: 01865 862763
Email: nap@opp.i-way.co.uk
Website: www.nas.edu
Imprints: Joseph Henry Press
Parent Company: National Academy Press
Unsolicited Manuscripts: No

The National Archives Of Scotland

The National Archives of Scotland preserves and makes available the historical records of Scotland. Its collections span the 12th - 20th centuries and range from the records of Scottish government prior to the Union of 1707, court and legal records, local authority and church records, private archives, family papers, records of institutions, businesses and industrial firms as well as thousands of maps and plans. Our publications are designed to make the holdings of the NAS more accessible to amateur and professional searchers alike. They include indexes and texts of the older groups of records, educational publications for schools, guides for specific researchers and source lists. Many are published under the NAS imprint, others have been published by The Stationery Office and its predecessor, HMSO.

Address: HM General Register House, Edinburgh EH1 3YY
Telephone: 0131 535 1314
Fax: 0131 535 1360
Email: research@nas.gov.uk
Website: www.nas.gov.uk (From April 2000)
Unsolicited Manuscripts: We do not accept unsolicited manuscripts

$\mathcal{N}$

The National Assembly For Wales

The Statistical Directorate in the National Assembly for Wales produces a range of statistical publications covering topics such as population, education, agriculture, transport, local government finance, road accidents, health, housing and social services. For a copy of the leaflet 'Statistical Publications', that provides a list of the publications that are produced, along with the expected publication dates and prices, please telephone the National Assembly for Wales at the number below.

Address: Statistical Directorate, Publications Unit, Cathays Park, Cardiff CF10 3NQ
Telephone: 01222 825054
Fax: 01222 825350
Email: stats.pubs@wales.gsi.gov.uk
Imprints: Statistical Directorate
Parent Company: Government Statistical Service
Unsolicited Manuscripts: No

National Children's Bureau

National Children's Bureau (NCB) works to identify and promote the well-being and interests of all children and young people across every aspect of their lives. It encourages professionals and policy makers to see the needs of the whole child and emphasises the importance of multidisciplinary, cross-agency partnerships. NCB undertakes high quality research; identifies, develops and promotes good practice; plays an active role in policy development and advocacy at both central and local levels of government; disseminates information to professionals, policy makers, parents, and children and young people; and ensures the views of children and young people are taken into account.

Address: 8 Wakley Street, London EC1V 7QE
Telephone: 0171 843 6000
Fax: 0171 278 9512
Email: booksales@ncb.org.uk
Website: www.ncb.org.uk
Imprints: National Children's Bureau Enterprises
Parent Company: NCB
Unsolicited Manuscripts: Rarely - publication proposal form needs to be completed

𝒩
National Christian Education Council

Bible reading notes, group Bible study notes, worship anthologies, prayer anthologies, Teddy Horsley series for young children, Holiday Club material, all-age worship and learning material and a Christian education journal. Books on different aspects of family life.

Editor(s): Elizabeth Bruce
Address: 1020 Bristol Road, Selly Oak, Birmingham B29 6LB
Telephone: 0121 472 4242
Fax: 0121 472 7575
Email: ncec@ncec.org.uk
Website: www.ncec.org.uk
Imprints: NCEC, IBRA (International Bible Reading Association)
Unsolicited Manuscripts: Yes

National Coaching Foundation (NCF)

The NCF publishes material in various formats for the education and information of sports coaches. Most material produced is distributed by Coachwise, the trading arm of the NCF, but also by governing bodies of sport. The NCF welcomes authors writing on sports science or coaching issues in generic or sports-specific contexts. The NCF also commissions authors with special interest in these areas for in-house projects.

Editor(s): Bill Galvin, Anne Simpkin, Nicola Cooke
Address: 114 Cardigan Road, Headingley, Leeds LS6 3BJ
Telephone: 0113 2744802
Fax: 0113 2755019
Email: bgalvin@ncf.org.uk
Website: www.ncf.org.uk
Parent Company: National Coaching Foundation
Payment Details: Negotiable
Unsolicited Manuscripts: To Bill Galvin, Head of Publications

National Council For Voluntary Organisations (NCVO)

Produces books for the voluntary sector. Major publications include: Voluntary Agencies Directory 1999 - over 2000 contact details for english voluntary organisations. Good Guide Series - Good Employment Guide, Good Financial Management Guide, Good Trustee Guide. Also a range of publications covering the voluntary sector in areas such as Europe, Trusteeship and Rural.

Address: Hamilton House, Earlstrees Court, Earlstrees Road, Corby NN17 4AX
Telephone: 01536 399016
Fax: 01536 399012
Email: HHmailing@aol.com
Website: www.ncvo-vol.org.uk
Imprints: NCVO Publications
Parent Company: NCVO
Unsolicited Manuscripts: No thank you

National Extension College (NEC)

Distance learning courses, NVQ training materials, open learning packs, training resources, consultancy and staff development packs. NEC is a self-financing educational trust and is one of the UK's most successful open learning providers.

Address: 18 Brooklands Avenue, Cambridge CB2 2HN
Telephone: 01223 450200
Fax: 01223 313586
Email: info@nec.ac.uk
Website: www.nec.ac.uk
Imprints: NEC
Unsolicited Manuscripts: No

N

National Library Of Scotland

Publishes bibliographies, facsimiles, catalogues, literary and historical books mainly of Scottish interest. Tends to publish in partnership with commercial publishing houses.

Editor(s): Head of Public Programmes: Kenneth Gibson
Address: George 1V Bridge, Edinburgh EH1 1EW
Telephone: 0131 226 4531
Fax: 0131 622 4803
Email: enquiries@nls.uk
Website: www.nls.uk
Unsolicited Manuscripts: Send outline and covering letter in first instance

National Portrait Gallery

Publishers of books on art, biography and cultural history; exhibition catalogues and educational material; as well as posters, postcards and unusual gifts and stationery.

Editor(s): Publishing Manager: Jacky Colliss Harvey; Sales and Marketing: Pallavi Vadhia; Editorial and Marketing Assistant: Susie Foster
Address: Publications Department, 2 St Martin's Place, London WC2H 0HE
Telephone: 0171 306 0055 ext 266 or 0171 3112 2482
Fax: 0171 306 0092
Email: pvadhia@npg.org.uk
Website: www.npg.org.uk

The Natural History Museum - Publishing Division

Popular natural history, academic and scholarly; biology and zoology; fine art and art history; geography and geology; scientific and technical.

Editor(s): Head of Publishing: June Hogg; Editorial Manager: Trudy Brannan; Production Manager: Lynn Millhouse; Assistant Editor: Catharine Baden-Daintree
Address: Cromwell Road, London SW7 5BD
Telephone: 020 7942 5060
Fax: 020 7942 5010
Email: publishing@nhm.ac.uk
Website: www.nhm.ac.uk/publishing/
Imprints: The Natural History Museum
Unsolicited Manuscripts: No

Need2Know

Need2Know publishes a distinctive series of self-help non-fiction for the general reader. Subjects fall within the consumer/health/personal relationship areas. Current titles include A Parent's Guide To Dyslexia, Make The Most Of Your Retirement, The Facts About The Menopause, Make The Most Of Being A Carer, It's Up To You - Your Blueprint For A Better Life. We are open to ideas and proposals for new titles, especially from experts/practitioners in their subject.

Editor(s): Kerrie Pateman
Address: Remus House, Coltsfoot Drive, Woodston, Peterborough PE2 9JX
Telephone: 01733 898103
Fax: 01733 313524
Email: kerriepateman@lineone.net
Parent Company: Forward Press Ltd
Payment Details: Advance, 15% royalties
Unsolicited Manuscripts: Yes

N

Network Educational Press Ltd

The company focuses its activity on the quality of teaching and learning in mainstream education, working with teachers and their managers in three ways: publishing high-quality, accessible and practical books; producing quality educational conferences; providing in-service training for teachers. All these activities draw upon current practical research, particularly that on how the brain functions, and then present the outcomes in ways that can be applied directly to the classroom. Examples of titles: Accelerated Learning In Practice (Smith); Accelerated Learning In The Classroom (Smith); Effective Learning Activities (Dickinson); Raising Boys' Achievement (Pickering); Effective Provision For Able And Talented Children (Teare); Making Pupil Data Powerful (Pringle and Cold); Improving Personal Effectiveness for Managers in Schools (Johnston); Best Behaviour (Rolf et al); Imagine That... (Bowkett); Effective Careers Education and Guidance (Edwards and Barnes); The Effective School Governor (Marriott); Closing the Learning Gap (Hughes); Lessons are for Learning (Hughes); Accelerated Learning in the Primary School (Smith).

Editor(s): Gina Walker, Carol Thompson, Chris Griffin, Carol Etherington, Sara Peach
Address: Box 635, Stafford ST16 1BF
Telephone: 01785 225515
Fax: 01785 228566
Email: enquiries@networkpress.co.uk
Website: www.networkpress.co.uk
Imprints: School Effectiveness Series, Accelerated Learning Series
Unsolicited Manuscripts: Yes, considered

New Beacon Books

A small specialist publisher specialising in books about Black Britain, the Caribbean and Africa. Founded 1966.

Editor(s): John La Rose
Address: 76 Stroud Green Road, London N4 3EN
Telephone: 0171 272 4889
Fax: 0171 281 4662
Unsolicited Manuscripts: No

New City

Publishers of religious books.

Editor(s): Callan Slipper
Address: 57 Twyford Avenue, London W3 9PZ
Telephone: 0181 993 6944
Fax: Same as phone
Email: new.city@telinco.co.uk
Unsolicited Manuscripts: To Editor

New Clarion Press

Workers' co-operative publishing non-fiction books on current affairs and social policy for the intelligent general reader and college market. Our publications are written from a reformist perspective. We do not yet publish fiction, but are open to persuasion.

Editor(s): Chris Bessant
Address: 5 Church Row, Gretton, Cheltenham GL54 5HG
Telephone: 01242 620623
Fax: Same as phone
Email: newclarionpress.co.uk
Payment Details: Royalty
Unsolicited Manuscripts: Synopsis in first instance

ℵ

New Era Publications UK Ltd

New Era Publications publish the fiction and non-fiction works of L Ron Hubbard. Mr Hubbard is 'one of the most acclaimed and widely read authors of all time' (Magazine and Booksellers USA). He is also one of the most prolific, with over 117 million copies of his hundreds of literary works in print.

Address: Saint Hill Manor, East Grinstead, West Sussex RH19 4JY
Telephone: 01342 314 846
Fax: 01342 314 857
Website: www.newerapublications.com
Parent Company: New Era Publications International
Unsolicited Manuscripts: We are interested in SF/Fantasy short stories which can be entered into the 'Writers of the Future' contest

New Fiction

The New Fiction imprint was launched in 1992 to provide a platform for the work of short story writers and promote it to a wider audience. Editorial Criteria: We are looking for stories that are well-written and provide a 'good read'. The following questions, which we ask ourselves when considering stories for publication, will give you an idea of the specific things we look for. Beginning: Does the story start at an interesting point in the action, that encourages the reader's curiosity and emotions? Characterisation: Are the characters believable? Are they revealed by what they do and say rather than explanation from the author? Content: Does the story keep your attention? If the story is based on fact - are the facts right? If applicable, does the story fulfil the criteria of the genre? Dialogue: Is the dialogue natural? Does the way a character says something fit that character? Writing: Does the writing convey meaning clearly and concisely? Ending: Is the ending believable, satisfying and logical in the context of the story? Contact the address below for submission guidelines.

Editor(s): Heather Killingray
Address: New Fiction, Remus House, Coltsfoot Drive, Woodston, Peterborough PE2 9JX
Telephone: 01733 898101
Fax: 01733 313524
Parent Company: Forward Press Ltd
Payment Details: Royalties 7.5% of total sales receipts, as calculated 1 year after publication, will be split equally between authors published in the book

New Holland Publishers (UK) Ltd

International co-edition publishers of illustrated reference books for the international market. Subjects published: interiors; DIY and home decoration; soft furnishings; outdoor DIY and gardening; needlecrafts; crafts (including mosaics, stained glass, ceramics, etc); food and drink; cake decorating; art and design; gift books. Our international travel and wildlife programme covers numerous destinations and includes: travel guides, maps and atlases; large-format illustrated travel titles; walking guides; diving, climbing and golf guides; large-format underwater and sports titles; natural history field and pocket guides; large-format wildlife and 'wildplaces' titles.

Editor(s): Rosemary Wilkinson, Tim Jollands
Address: 24 Nutford Place, London W1H 6DQ
Telephone: 0171 724 7773
Fax: 0171 724 6184
Email: postmaster@nhpub.co.uk
Imprints: New Holland, Struik, Southern, Zebra
Parent Company: Millennium Entertainment Group Africa (MEGA)
Payment Details: By negotiation
Unsolicited Manuscripts: Yes

New Island Books

Founded in 1992, New Island Books has successfully continued the innovative and often polemical publishing tradition of its predecessor, The Raven Arts Press. Publishers of Fiction, Biography, Drama and Current Affairs, recent successes have included Our Father... A Tribute To Dermot Morgan by Don, Bobby and Ben Morgan; Are You Somebody by Nuala O'Faolain and The Truth About the Irish by Terry Eagleton.

Editor(s): Managing Editor: Ciara Considine, Executive Editor: Dermot Bolger
Address: New Island Books Ltd, 2 Brookside, Dundrum Road, Dublin 14, Ireland
Telephone: 3531 2989937
Fax: 3531 2982783
Imprints: New Island Books, Brookside
Payment Details: Own standard contract / royalties paid twice yearly
Unsolicited Manuscripts: Fiction/Non-Fiction - synopsis and sample of writing plus SAE

𝒩
New Living Publishers

Pentecostal/evangelical publisher. Only publish own material. Four books are in print at this time. Paths of Righteousness in Psalm 23, ISBN-85756-094-9 Price £6.99. The Growing Pains of Peter, ISBN-1-899721-00-2 Price £9.99. In Sickness and in Health, ISBN-1-899721-01-0 Price £7.99. Dying is Living, ISBN-899721-02-9 Price £7.99. New publication in the year 2000, Buried Talents, price £8.99. An exposition of the character of Jonah. All are available from New Living Publishers at the address given. Terry Atkinson is the author of all the above books.

Address: 164 Radcliffe New Road, Whitefield, Manchester M45 7TU
Telephone: 0161 7661166
Fax: Same as phone
Email: theway@ministry61.freeserve.co.uk
Unsolicited Manuscripts: No

New Playwrights' Network

Publishes plays for amateur performance.

Editor(s): L G Smith
Address: 10 Station Road, Colwall, Herefordshire WR13 6RN
Telephone: 01684 540154
Fax: Same as phone

New World Press

High-quality general non-fiction and educational books, covering literature, science, culture, philosophy, spirituality. Write to Sales Department for current lists. Bi-monthly journal New World covering similar subjects and short stories. In addition to the scope of books indicated, a new bi-monthly magazine with cutting-edge essays on science, philosophy, culture and spirituality.

Editor(s): Matt Fopson
Address: PO Box 919, Sutton SM2 6ZU
Telephone: 0208 643 3967
Fax: 0208 286 0468
Email: editor@nwpress.co.uk
Website: nwpress.co.uk
Imprints: New World, Knightscross
Unsolicited Manuscripts: No unsolicited mss. Typewritten synopses considered; please allow 6-8 weeks for a response

Nexus Special Interests

Hobby and leisure in the core subject areas of modelling, model engineering, radio control modelling, workshop practice, home brewing and military modelling.

Address: Nexus House, Azalea Drive, Swanley, Kent BR8 8HU
Telephone: 01322 660070
Fax: 01322 616309
Parent Company: Nexus Media
Payment Details: Standard authors' contract advance and royalties
Unsolicited Manuscripts: Yes

N
NIACE

The National Organisation for Adult Learning publishes books and journals on policy and practice in adult education. Our aim is to promote adult learning for all people, regardless of age, race, gender, disability, social or economic background. We do this by organising conferences, through publishing, research and development work. We seek to influence government, business, trade unions, adult education providers.

Editor(s): Senior Publications Officer: Virman Man
Address: 21 De Monfort Street, Leicester LE1 7GE
Telephone: 0116 204 4200
Fax: 0116 285 4514
Email: niace@niace.org.uk
Website: www.niace.org.uk
Imprints: NIACE
Parent Company: NIACE
Payment Details: By negotiation

NMS Publishing Ltd

Scottish history and culture, biography, Scottish literary anthologies, international art, archaeology, geology, museum studies science and technology.

Editor(s): Helen Kemp
Address: Royal Museum, Chambers Street, Edinburgh EH1 1JF
Telephone: 0131 247 4026
Fax: 0131 247 4012
Email: cara@nms.ac.uk
Website: www.nms.ac.uk
Payment Details: Royalties
Unsolicited Manuscripts: Synopsis and sample chapter only

No Exit Press

Leading independent publisher of crime and noir fiction.

Address: 18 Coleswood Road, Harpenden, Herts AL5 1EQ
Telephone: 01582 761264
Fax: 01582 712244
Email: info@noexit.co.uk
Website: www.noexit.co.uk
Unsolicited Manuscripts: No

North York Moors National Park Authority

Publish booklets on walking in the North York Moors as well as booklets on local history and natural history of interest to visitors to the area. Also publish planning documents and strategies relevant to the area and research papers relating to archaeology, the environment, etc.

Editor(s): Jill Renney
Address: The Old Vicarage, Bondgate, Helmsley, York YO62 5BP
Telephone: 01439 770657
Fax: 01439 770691
Email: j.renney@northyorkmoors.npa.gov.uk
Website: www.northyorkmoors-npa.gov.uk

$\mathcal{N}$
Northcote House Publishers Ltd

Established in 1985, publishes up to 30 titles each year in the fields of: literary criticism (Writers & Work series); education and education management (Resources In Education); careers and self-development (Starting Out...); and a small number of educational dance and drama titles. In addition to the above, a series of studies of specific works of literature is in preparation, aimed at A level and higher education students in both English and Modern Languages.

Editor(s): Brian Hulme
Address: Horndon House, Horndon, Tavistock, Devon PL19 9NQ
Telephone: 01822 810066
Fax: 01822 810034
Imprints: Writers And Their Work
Parent Company: Northcote House Publishers Ltd
Payment Details: Annual royalty by contract
Unsolicited Manuscripts: Well argued proposals in the above subjects with good marketing credentials welcome

W W Norton & Co

Independent publisher of quality trade and academic books. Subject areas include biology; business books; history; music; nautical; biography; poetry; politics and current affairs; sport; photography; and art and architecture. Norton's college list includes textbooks in literature and criticism; classical studies; music; history; economics; psychology and science.

Editor(s): All editorial work undertaken in the US
Address: 10 Coptic Street, London WC1A 1PU
Telephone: 0171 323 1579
Fax: 0171 436 4553
Email: office@wwnorton.co.uk
Website: www.wwnorton.com
Imprints: Liveright Publishing Corporation, The Countryman Press
Parent Company: W W Norton & Co Inc, 500 Fifth Avenue, New York NY10110

Norwood Publishers

Norwood Publishers is a small independent publishers. Books published serve schools and the educational market in general.

Address: 3 Chapel Street, Norwood Green, Halifax, West Yorkshire HA3 8QU
Telephone: 01274 602454

Nottingham University Press

Agriculture, medicine, geography, food science, law, sports and engineering. Other subject areas also considered.

Editor(s): D J A Cole
Address: Manor Farm, Main Street, Thrumpton, Nottingham NG11 0AX
Telephone: 0115 9831011
Fax: 0115 9831003
Email: editor@nup.com
Website: www.nup.com
Imprints: Castle Publications
Unsolicited Manuscripts: Yes

Oak Tree Press

Ireland's leading publisher of business and professional titles. Specialising in management, human reources, accountancy and marketing.

Editor(s): David Givens - Commissioning Editor
Address: Merrion Building, Lower Merrion Street, Dublin 2, Ireland
Telephone: 353 1 6761600
Fax: 353 1 6761644
Email: oaktreep@iol.ie
Website: www.oaktreepress.com
Parent Company: Cork Publishing Ltd
Unsolicited Manuscripts: Proposals and sample chapter

O
Oakwood Press & Oakwood Video Library

Established 1931. Family-owned company specialising in transport topics - buses, trams, canals, and especially railways. Producing books of interest to railway historians and enthusiasts alike. Catalogue available.

Editor(s): Various
Address: PO Box 13, Usk NP15 1YS
Telephone: 01291 650444
Fax: 01291 650484
Email: oakwood-press@dial.pipex.com
Website: http://dial.pipex.com/oakwood-press
Unsolicited Manuscripts: Yes

Oasis Books

Publishers of short fiction and poetry - no novels. Look for work that takes linguistic and imaginative risks and which would not normally find a home with mainstream publishers. Our programme for 1999 is full. Also publish Oasis Magazine - 6 issues a year - looks for a wide range of excellent writing that concentrates on originality of thought, expression and imagination.

Editor(s): Ian Robinson
Address: 12 Stevenage Road, London SW6 6ES
Telephone: 0171 736 5059
Imprints: Oasis Books
Payment Details: Copies only
Unsolicited Manuscripts: Yes but not for 1999

O

Oberon Books

Theatre books, play texts and translation of plays.

Editor(s): James Hogan, Cathy Herbert, Humphrey Gudgeon
Address: 521 Caledonian Road, London N7 9RH
Telephone: 0171 6073637
Fax: 0171 6073629
Email: oberon.books@btinternet.com
Imprints: Oberon Modern Playwrights, Absolute Classics
Unsolicited Manuscripts: Yes

OCLC Europe, The Middle East & Africa

The Dewey Decimal Classification systems (DDC) is a general knowledge organisation tool that is continuously revised to keep pace with knowledge. The sytem was conceived by Melvil Dewey in 1873 and first published by Forest Press, which in 1888 became a division of OCLC Online Computer Library Center, Inc. The Dewey Decimal Classification is published in two editions, full and abridged. The Classification is kept up-to-date between editions through monthly posting of new and changed entries on the Dewey home page, and annual publication of additions and corrections in Dewey Decimal Classification Additions, Notes and Decisions (DC&). The full edition is also published in an enhanced electronic version, Dewey for Windows. Eash update disc of Dewey for Windows incorporates the changes announced in DC&.

Editor(s): Editor: Joan S Mitchell, Assistant Editors: Julianne Beall, Winton E Matthews Jr, Gregory R New
Address: OCLC Europe, 7th Floor, Tricorn House, 51-53 Hagley Road, Edgbaston, Birmingham B16 8TP
Telephone: 0121 456 4656
Fax: 0121 456 4680
Email: europe@oclc.org
Website: www.oclc.org/europe
Imprints: Forest Press, Albany, New York, 1996
Parent Company: OCLC INC

O

The Octagon Press

Philosophy, psychology, Sufism, eastern classics and travel. We do not accept any manuscripts which we have not ourselves commissioned under any circumstances.

Editor(s): G R Schrager
Address: PO Box 227, London N6 4EW
Telephone: 0181 348 9392
Fax: 0181 341 5971
Email: octagon@octagonpress.com
Website: www.octagonpress.com
Unsolicited Manuscripts: No

Octopus Publishing Group

The group comprises the following, with specialist areas as noted: Hamlyn Octopus (cookery, gardening, craft, sport, film tie-ins, rock 'n' roll); Mitchell Beazley (antiques, gardening, craft and interiors, wine); Millers (antiques and collectibles); Conran Octopus (lifestyle, cookery, gardening); Philips (atlases, maps, encyclopaedias); Bounty (promotional publishing); Brimax. All are adult illustrated reference publishers, with the exception of Brimax, a publisher of illustrated children's books.

Editor(s): Publishers: Laura Bamford (Hamlyn); Jane Aspden (Mitchell Beazley/ Millers); Carolyn Proud (Conran Octopus); John Gaisford (Philips); Mark Newman (Bounty/Brimax)
Address: 2-4 Heron Quays, London E14 4JP
Telephone: 0171 531 8400
Fax: 0171 531 8650
Website: www.octopus-publishing.co.uk
Parent Company: Octopus Publishing Group
Unsolicited Manuscripts: Yes

Old Bailey Press

Old Bailey Press publishes a comprehensive range of law books for students and practitioners alike. Publications include Cracknell's Statutes; 150 Leading Cases Series; 101 Questions and Answers Series, The Law in Practice Series and the Practitioner's Handbook, a 720-page compendium of recent developments in ten areas of mainstream legal practice.

Editor(s): Helen O'Shea
Address: 200 Greyhound Road, London W14 9RY
Telephone: 020 7385 3377
Fax: 020 7381 3377
Email: obp@hltpublication.co.uk
Website: hlt@holborncollege.ac.uk
Imprints: Old Bailey Press/HLT Publications
Parent Company: The HLT Group Ltd

The Oleander Press

Language and literature; travel; games and pastimes; reference; biography; Cambridge town, gown and county; Arabia past and present. Before sending a synopsis or idea (with SAE), read our manual The Small Publisher, with account of how The Oleander Press grew yet stayed small, and the sequel, The Oleander Press: 37 Years As A Small Publisher in The National Small Press Centre Handbook (1997), pp. 75-78. Latest titles are Contemporary Designer Bookbinders: A Worldwide Illustrated Directory (£30), Dennis Baron's De Vere Is Shakespeare: Evidence From The Biography And Wordplay (£9.95), and a reworking of The Oresteia by William Whallon to incorporate a version of the lost satyr play (£9.95).

Address: 17 Stansgate Avenue, Cambridge CB2 2QZ
Unsolicited Manuscripts: No

O

Ollav Healer Publications

Self-publishing company with the following publications: A Path Directed (Life of James Cassidy, WW1 veteran and Belfast City missionary 1892-1970); Cousins (local history booklet); Clarendon, Belfast (locally set historical fiction); Circumstantial Evidence (evidence supporting biblical facts).

Editor(s): D Cassidy
Address: 9 Brunswick Park, Bangor, Co Down BT20 3DR
Telephone: 01247 473362
Unsolicited Manuscripts: No

Omnibus Press

The world's largest publisher of books about music, ranging from biographies to picture books and from classical and jazz to rock and pop. Distributors for Gramophone, RED, Firefly, Rogan House and others.

Editor(s): Chris Charlesworth
Address: 8-9 Frith Street, London W1V 5TZ
Telephone: 0171 4341170
Fax: 0171 4343310
Email: music@musicsales.co.uk
Website: omnibuspress.com
Imprints: Omnibus Press/Wise Publications/Ozone/Bobcat/Amsco
Parent Company: Music Sales Ltd
Unsolicited Manuscripts: To Chris Charlesworth

On Stream Publications Ltd

Publishers of non-fiction books including food and wine, health, academic, local history and commissioned comercial company histories and promotional literature. Editing and proof-reading services for books not published by us and design service for books and promotions.

Editor(s): Roz Crowley
Address: Cloghroe, Blarney, Co Cork, Ireland
Telephone: 353 21 385798
Fax: Same as phone
Email: onstream@indigo.ie
Website: http://indigo.ie/~onstream
Imprints: Forum Publications
Parent Company: On Stream Publications Ltd
Payment Details: Royalites paid twice yearly
Unsolicited Manuscripts: No

Oneworld Publications

An independent publishing house specialising in books on world religions, comparative religion, mysticism, psychology and inspirational writing. Large enough to benefit from worldwide distribution by Penguin Books, we are also small enough to ensure that we publish only quality titles by authors who are leaders in their field. Consistently producing cutting-edge texts by leading academics, Oneworld is frequently acclaimed for its work in increasing interfaith understanding and religious tolerance, while our inspirational and self-help books continue to attract favourable reviews.

Editor(s): Juliet Mabey
Address: 185 Banbury Road, Oxford OX2 7AR
Telephone: 01865 310597
Fax: 01865 310598
Email: oneworld@cix.co.uk
Website: www.oneworld-publications.com
Unsolicited Manuscripts: Yes

O

Onlywomen Press Ltd

The radical edge of feminist, lesbian literature: fiction, political theory, poetry, literary criticism, lesbian romance and crime novels.

Editor(s): Apply first to company as a whole
Address: 40 St Lawrence Terrace, London W10 5ST
Telephone: 0181 960 7122
Fax: 0181 960 2817
Email: onlywomen_press@compuserve.com
Imprints: Zest (lesbian romance), onlywomencrime (lesbian crime novels), Liaison (feminist theory and research)
Payment Details: By publishing contract
Unsolicited Manuscripts: Yes

Open Books Publishing Ltd

Packagers of gardening books and general publishers.

Editor(s): Patrick Taylor
Address: Willow Cottage, Cudworth, Nr Ilminster, Somerset TA19 0PS
Telephone: 01460 52565
Fax: Same as phone
Email: patrickta@aol.com
Imprints: Somerset House
Unsolicited Manuscripts: Always write first

Open Gate Press

Founded in 1988 by a group of psychoanalysts, social psychiatrists and artists to provide a forum for psychoanalytic social studies - a branch of psychoanalysis which Freud hoped would be a major contribution to the 'liberation of humanity from the pathology of civilisations'. Despite some attempts since Freud's time to apply psychoanalysis to social problems, his hopes have not been fulfilled, and the raison d'etre of Open Gate Press is to remedy this. The company publishes a series Psychoanalysis And Society as well as writings by experts in various fields of the social sciences, with the objective of arousing the interest of a wide public. The aim of the publishers is also to bring life to the increasingly moribund state of philosophy. Finally, the publishers are keen to promote debate on a wide variety of environmental issues.

Editor(s): Jeannie Cohen, Elisabeth Petersdorff
Address: 51 Achilles Road, London NW6 1DZ
Telephone: 020 7431 4391
Fax: 020 7431 5129
Email: books@opengatepress.co.uk
Website: www.opengatepress.co.uk
Imprints: Open Gate Press, Centaur Press, Linden Press
Parent Company: Open Gate Press
Payment Details: Royalties twice-yearly
Unsolicited Manuscripts: Synopses and ideas for books welcome

Open University Press

Subjects published in the areas of health and social welfare, counselling and psychotherapy, psychology, women's studies, sociology, cultural studies, politics, criminology, education and higher education.

Editor(s): Jacinta Evans
Address: Celtic Court, 22 Ballmoor, Buckingham MK18 1XW
Telephone: 01280 823388
Fax: 01280 823233
Email: enquiries@openup.co.uk
Website: www.openup.co.uk
Imprints: Open University Press
Unsolicited Manuscripts: No

O

Orchard Books

Children's fiction : board books, picture books. Gift books. Young and older fiction.

Editor(s): Francesca Dow
Address: 96 Leonard Street, London EC2A 4XD
Telephone: 0171 739 2929
Fax: 0171 739 2318
Email: ob@wattspub.co.uk
Parent Company: Watts Publishing Group Ltd
Payment Details: By negotiation
Unsolicited Manuscripts: Yes

Ordnance Survey

National map makers of Great Britain.

Address: Romsey Road, Maybush, Southampton SO16 4GU
Telephone: 08456 050505
Fax: 01703 792452
Email: custinfo@ordsvy.gov.uk
Website: www.ordsvy.gov.uk

Oriel Stringer

Publishers of ornithological books covering the breeding biology of wild birds and their nesting sites.

Editor(s): M J Dawson
Address: 66 Tivoli Crescent, Brighton BN1 5ND
Telephone: 01273 723413

Orion Children's Books

Fiction, age range 0-14+.

Editor(s): Managing Director and Publisher: Judith Elliott
Address: Orion House, 5 Upper St Martin's Lane, London WC2H 9EA
Imprints: Orion Children's Books, Dolphin Paperbacks
Parent Company: Orion Publishing Group
Unsolicited Manuscripts: No

Osborne Books Ltd

Publishers of business education and accounting texts for secondary and tertiary sectors under the Osborne Books imprint. Also publishers of local history and general historical books under the Osborne Heritage imprint.

Editor(s): Michael Fardon
Address: Unit 1b, Everoak Estate, Bromyard Road, St Johns, Worcester WR2 5HN
Telephone: 01905 748071
Fax: 01905 748952
Email: books@osborne.u-net.com
Website: www.osbornebooks.co.uk
Imprints: Osborne Books, Osborne Heritage
Payment Details: By negotiation
Unsolicited Manuscripts: To Editor

O

Osprey Publishing Ltd

World leader in publishing illustrated military history books including the Men-At-Arms and Campaign series. Also publish aviation including Aircraft of the Aces series and automotive titles. Over 600 titles in print.

Editor(s): Lee Johnson, Shaun Barrington, Tony Holmes
Address: Elms Court, Chapel Way, Botley, Oxford OX2 9LP
Telephone: 01865 727022
Fax: 01865 727017
Email: osprey@osprey-publishing.co.uk
Website: http://www.osprey-publishing.co.uk
Imprints: Osprey
Unsolicited Manuscripts: Detailed synopses only

Otter Publications

Specialising in layperson's texts on motoring, law and business. Published book on a particular form of sports massage called soft tissue release, and sports science is an area we would like to develop.

Editor(s): Jonathan Hutchings
Address: 9 Roman Way, Fishbourne, Chichester PO19 3QN
Telephone: 01243 539106
Fax: 01243 839669
Imprints: Otter Publications
Payment Details: 10% royalty on net receipts
Unsolicited Manuscripts: Yes

Peter Owen

Literary (non-genre) adult fiction list, including work in translation. Biographies and memoirs of writers, artists, celebrities, etc. Only very rarely do we publish memoirs of lesser-known people. We also publish general non-fiction including history, literary criticism, arts subjects (not highly illustrated), social science, current affairs, philosophy, psychology and entertainment. Note that all manuscripts or, preferably, synopses and sample chapters, should be accompanied by return postage. No poetry.

Editor(s): Antonia Owen
Address: 73 Kenway Road, London SW5 0RE
Telephone: 0171 373 5628
Fax: 0171 373 6760
Email: admin@peterowen.u-net.com
Unsolicited Manuscripts: Only with prior request and SAE

Oxfam Publishing

Publishes and distributes books and other resource materials for development practitioners, policy makers, academics, schools, children and young people, as part of its programme of advocacy, education and information.

Editor(s): Catherine Robinson, Anke Lueddecke
Address: 274 Banbury Road, Oxford OX2 7DZ
Telephone: 01865 313774
Fax: 01865 313790
Email: publish@oxfam.org.uk
Website: www.oxfam.org.uk
Parent Company: Oxfam GB
Payment Details: Varied
Unsolicited Manuscripts: No

O

Oxford University Press

A department of the University of Oxford. Furthers the University's objective of excellence in research, scholarship and education by publishing worldwide. It is the world's largest university press, publishing more than 4,000 titles a year. It has a presence in more than 50 countries, employing some 3,500 staff. Turnover in 1997/98 was £282 million.

Address: Great Clarendon Street, Oxford OX2 6DP
Telephone: 01865 556767
Fax: 01865 556646
Email: enquiry@oup.co.uk
Website: www.oup.com
Parent Company: University of Oxford

Parkway Publishing

Books on Middle East, mainly Egypt. Non-fiction: facsimile editions of famous travel books. Examples: 1000 Miles Up The Nile by Amelia Edwards; Letters From Egypt by Florence Nightingale.

Address: 4-5 Academy Buildings, Fanshaw Street, London N1 6LQ
Telephone: 0171 613 5533
Fax: 0171 613 4433
Email: pwbookex@dircon.co.uk

Parthian Books

New Welsh fiction and drama in English. Translations of the Welsh Language Fiction. Previous titles include Work, Sex & Rugby; I Kissed Her Little Sister; A Trilogy of Appropriation.

Editor(s): Richard Davies
Address: 53 Colum Road, Cardiff CF10 3EF
Telephone: 01222 341314
Fax: Same as phone
Payment Details: 10% net sales
Unsolicited Manuscripts: No. Synopsis with sample chapters

PASS Publications
(Private Academic & Scientific Studies Ltd)

Publish a series of 10 books for GCE A level in pure mathematics, comprehensively covering the syllabus of most examination boards. They uniquely include (in Part 2) complete solutions to all exercises at the end of each chapter. Can be purchased separately or as a set (set price £95). Publish detailed solutions for the Edexel exams (1994 and continuing) in pure mathematics, mechanics and statistics; produced every year in April and September for the January and June exams respectively. Also available for technicians are Electrical And Electronic Principles 1 & 2 (£12.95, £14.95) and Engineering Maths (2 books, £9.95 for both). Modular Textbooks, Pure Mathematics. P1, P2, P3, P4 (£13.95, £15.95, £14.95, £18.95 respectively) for 12 copies of P1, or P2, or P3 or P4 50% discount.

Editor(s): Anthony Nicolaides
Address: 11 Baring Road, London SE12 0JP
Telephone: 0181 857 4752
Fax: 0181 857 9427

PasTest

Revision books relating to post-graduate and undergraduate medical exams.

Editor(s): Sue Harrison
Address: Egerton Court, Parkgate Estate, Knutsford, Cheshire WA16 8DX
Telephone: 01565 752000
Fax: 01565 650264
Email: sue@pastest.co.uk
Website: www.pastest.co.uk
Payment Details: Negotiable
Unsolicited Manuscripts: Yes

P

Paternoster Publishing

Paternoster publishes books to advance the Christian faith and encourage a bibical world view and lifestyle.

Editor(s): Mark Finnie
Address: PO Box 300, Kingstown, Carlisle CA3 0QS
Imprints: Paternoster, Solway
Parent Company: Send the Light
Payment Details: Royalty 10-14% net receipts
Unsolicited Manuscripts: Yes

Paupers' Press

Publish booklets containing 10,000-15,000-word essays, mostly on literary criticism. Occasionally produce full-length books - but only to accommodate an exceptional manuscript. Publish up to 6 new titles a year, which are distributed in the US by Borgo Press. Also operate as a centre for Colin Wilson studies, publishing his work and essays on it by well-known Wilson scholars. Examples of titles: Sex And The Intelligent Teenager by Colin Wilson; Witchcraft And Misogyny by Samantha Giles; Woody Allen's Trilogy Of Terror by Christina Byrnes; So Far So Linear: responses to the work of Jeanette Winterson by Christopher Pressler. We also distribute selected titles for the US publishers Borgo Press and Robert Briggs Associates.

Editor(s): Colin Stanley
Address: 27 Melbourne Road, West Bridgeford, Nottingham NG2 5DJ
Telephone: 0115 9815063
Fax: Same as phone
Email: stan2727uk@aol.com
Website: http://members.aol.com/stan2727uk/pauper.htm
Imprints: Paupers' Press
Unsolicited Manuscripts: No. Write in first instance outlining content of essay

Pavilion Books Limited

A substantial and varied list of high quality colour illustrated non-fiction books geared to international co edition markets. Subjects covered include art, photography, travel, biography, humour and gift books.

Editor(s): Editorial Directors: Colin Webb, Pamela Webb, Vivien James
Address: London House, Great Eastern Wharf, Pargate Road, London SW11 4NQ
Telephone: 0171 350 1230
Fax: 0171 350 1261
Parent Company: C & B Publishing Plc
Payment Details: Negotiable
Unsolicited Manuscripts: Yes - in writing only

Pavilion Publishing (Brighton) Ltd

Leading publisher in health and social care training materials, handbooks, research findings, journals. Subjects include: mental health, learning disability, older people, adult protection, looked after children, forensic practice.

Editor(s): Edwina Rowling (Managing Editor)
Address: 8 St George's Place, Brighton BN6 8SU
Telephone: 01273 623222
Fax: 01273 622582
Email: edwinar@pavpub.com
Website: www.pavpub.com
Payment Details: Negotiable royalty
Unsolicited Manuscripts: Yes

PBN Publications

Publish transcripts of local (Sussex) archives which are of particular interest to family and local historians. Publications are either in book form or on microfiche.

Address: 22 Abbey Road, Eastbourne BN20 8TE
Telephone: 01323 731206

P

Pearson Education

Pearson Education is the newly created company following the merger of Addison Wesley Longman, Financial Times Managment and Simon & Schuster's Educational Businesses. Pearson Education publishes across the curriculum from pre-school to postgraduate and professionals throughout the world.

Address: Pearson Education, Edinburgh Gate, Harlow, Essex CM20 2JE
Telephone: 01279 623928
Fax: 01279 414130
Email: firstname.lastname@pearsoned-ema.com
Website: www.pearsoned-ema.com
Imprints: Longman, Addison-Wesley, Financial Times Prentice Hall, Prentice Hall, Logotron
Parent Company: Pearson Plc

Pearson Publishing

Educational resources for primary and secondary schools. All subjects including school management and policy titles. Resources include photocopiable resources, student handbooks, revision guides, software, IT training materials. Titles can be ordered via website. Sample sheets can also be downloaded.

Editor(s): Maura Rutter, Donna Bones
Address: Chesterton Mill, French's Road, Cambridge CB4 3NP
Telephone: 01223 350555
Fax: 01223 356484
Email: infor@pearson.co.uk
Website: www.pearson.co.uk
Payment Details: Royalties on publisher's net receipts, sometimes royalty advances paid
Unsolicited Manuscripts: To George Pearson

J M Pearson & Son (Publishers) Ltd

Founded 1981; specialise in canal and railway related materials; all titles produced in-house.

Address: Tatenhill Common, Burton-on-Trent DE13 9RS
Telephone: 01283 713674
Fax: Same as phone
Email: jpearson@netcomuk.
Website: www.page-net.co.uk/pearsons
Unsolicited Manuscripts: No

Peartree Publications

Christian musicals and educational piano music.

Editor(s): Roger M Stepney
Address: 61 Peartree Lane, Little Common, Bexhill-On-Sea, East Sussex TN39 4RQ
Unsolicited Manuscripts: No

Peepal Tree Press

Began publishing in 1986. Peepal Tree focuses on the Caribbean and its Diaspora, and also publishes writing from the South Asian Diaspora and Africa. Its books seek to express the popular resources of transplanted and transforming cultures. Has now published over 100 quality literary paperback titles, with fiction, poetry and literary, cultural and historical studies. We publish around 15 English language titles a year, with writers from Guyana, Jamaica, Trinidad, Nigeria, Bangladesh, Montserrat, St Lucia, America, Canada, the UK, India and Barbados.

Editor(s): Jeremy Poynting
Address: 17 Kings Avenue, Leeds LS6 1QS
Telephone: 0113 2451703
Fax: 0113 2459616
Email: hannah@peepal.demon.co.uk
Payment Details: Generally 10% net
Unsolicited Manuscripts: Telephone first for submission guidelines

P

Pen & Sword Books Ltd

Military history especially WW1, WW2, Falklands and Napoleonic. Local history, highly illustrated focusing on nostalgia. Battlefield guides containing then and now pictures. Regimental histories all regiments and squadrons considered, even if disbanded.

Editor(s): Tom Hartman, Brian Elliott, Nigel Cave, Henry Wilson
Address: 47 Church Street, Barnsley S70 2AS
Telephone: 01226 734 222
Fax: 01226 734 438
Email: charles@pen-and-sword.demon.co.uk
Website: www.yorkshire-web.co.uk/ps
Imprints: Wharncliffe, Leo Cooper
Parent Company: Barnsley Chronicle Holdings Ltd
Payment Details: Royalties are paid twice a year
Unsolicited Manuscripts: Yes. Please send a synopsis

Penhaligon Page

Penhaligon Page provides a showcase for today's poets. It incorporates the diverse styles and structures throughout our publications that the poetry world encounters. We are giving you the chance to become part of our voice, and join together with other poets. Poems no longer than 30 lines on any theme are considered.

Editor(s): Rebecca Mee
Address: Penhaligon Page, Remus House, Coltsfoot Drive, Woodston, Peterborough PE2 9JX
Telephone: 01733 898 104
Fax: 01733 313 524
Imprints: Poetry Today, Eden Press
Parent Company: Penhaligon Page Ltd

Pentathol Publishing

No new material needed at present.

Editor(s): A E Cowen
Address: PO Box 92, 40 Gibson Street, Wrexham LL13 7NS
Unsolicited Manuscripts: No

The Pentland Press Limited

The Pentland Press welcomes new, unknown authors. We specialise in books the large publishing houses deem uncommercial. Small enough to retain a traditional family approach but large enough to publish over one hundred books every year. We are always interested to hear from authors who have written books in the following areas: autobiography, naval, military, aviation, biography, history, politics, religion, philosophy, self-help, literature, poetry and fiction. A preliminary letter is required before submitting manuscripts.

Address: 1 Hutton Close, South Church, Bishop Auckland, Durham DL14 6XB
Telephone: 01388 776555
Fax: 01388 776766
Email: manuscripts@pentlandpress.co.uk
Website: pentlandpress.co.uk
Unsolicited Manuscripts: Yes

Peridot Press Ltd

Peridot Press publishes easy-to-read, regularly updated reference books including The Gap Year Guidebook and The Specialist Speakers Directory. Main readers are sixth-formers, their parents, schools and small business. We do not usually take unsolicited manuscripts but we employ people for short-term research and database work.

Address: 2 Blenheim Crescent, London W11 1NN
Telephone: 0171 221 7404
Website: www.peridot.co.uk
Imprints: Peridot

P

Permanent Publications

Publishers of Permaculture Magazine and specialist books on environmental issues, sustainable design and permaculture.

Editor(s): Madeleine Harland, A M Glanville-Hearson
Address: The Sustainability Centre, East Meon, Hants GU32 1HR
Telephone: 01730 823311
Fax: 01730 823322
Email: hello@permaculture.co.uk
Website: www.permaculture.co.uk
Imprints: Permanent Publications
Parent Company: Hyden House Ltd
Unsolicited Manuscripts: No

Perpetuity Press

Specialist books and journals in the field of risk, security, crime prevention, policing and community safety. Journals include the Security Journal, Risk Management: An International Journal and Crime Prevention And Community Safety: An International Journal. Books include Crime At Work; Learning From Disasters: a management approach; Crime and Security: managing the risk to safe shopping; and Zero Tolerance Policing. Subjects covered by our publications include the following: CCTV; fraud; civil recovery; staff dishonesty; retail crime; abuse and violence within the workplace; risk management; business continuity planning; repeat victimisation; computer security; product contamination; robbery; crises and disaster management; financial risk; contingency planning; human error and vulnerability; environmental threats; crime against businesses. All our publications are jargon free and will help you to identify and develop successful strategies for managing security, risk and crime prevention by evaluating existing measures and assessing new policies and initiatives.

Editor(s): Karen Gill
Address: PO Box 376, Leicester LE2 3ZZ
Telephone: 0116 221 7778
Fax: 0116 270 7742
Email: info@perpetuitypress.co.uk
Website: www.perpetuitypress.co.uk
Unsolicited Manuscripts: Yes

Perseus Books Group

Social sciences and humanities, especially politics, international relations, area studies, sociology, religion, history, philosophy and cultural studies.

Editor(s): Sue Miller
Address: 12 Hid's Copse Road, Cumnor Hill, Oxford OX2 9JJ
Imprints: Basic Books, Counterpoint, Civitas, Public Affairs, Westview Press, Perseus Books
Unsolicited Manuscripts: Yes

Petroc Press

Educational books and other media for doctors, GPs, junior doctors in training as well as qualified professionals.

Editor(s): P L Clarke
Address: 3b Thames Court, High Street, Goring-on-Thames, Reading RG8 9AQ
Telephone: 01491 875252
Fax: 01491 875200
Email: petroc@librapharm.co.uk
Website: www.librapharm.co.uk
Imprints: Petroc Press
Parent Company: Librapharm Ltd
Payment Details: Royalties paid annually
Unsolicited Manuscripts: Yes

Phaidon Press Ltd

Publishes books on art, architecture, design, photography, decorative arts, fashion and music.

Editor(s): Deputy Publisher: Amanda Renshaw
Address: Regent's Wharf, All Saints Street, London N1 9PA
Telephone: 0171 843 1000
Fax: 0171 843 1010
Email: tspruyt@phaidon.com
Unsolicited Manuscripts: No

P

Pharmaceutical Press

Publishes information on all aspects of medicine for an international audience of pharmacists, GPs, nurses and other health professionals.

Editor(s): Paul Weller
Address: 1 Lambeth High Street, London SE1 7JN (Orders to: PO Box 151, Wallingford, Oxon OX10 8QU)
Telephone: 0171 735 9141
Fax: 0171 735 5085
Email: pweller@rpsgb.org.uk
Website: www.pharmpress.com
Parent Company: Royal Pharmaceutical Society of Great Britain
Unsolicited Manuscripts: Yes

Phillimore & Co Ltd

British local and family history, genealogy, heraldry and institutional history.

Editor(s): Noel Osborne, Simon Thraves
Address: Shopwyke Manor Barn, Chichester, West Sussex PO20 6BG
Telephone: 01243 787636
Fax: 01243 787639
Email: bookshop@phillimore.co.uk
Website: www.phillimore.co.uk
Payment Details: Royalties by negotiation
Unsolicited Manuscripts: Yes with return postage

Piatkus Books

Founded 1979 by Judy Piatkus. The company is customer-led and is committed to publishing excellent non-fiction and top quality fiction, both commercial and literary. Specialises in publishing books and authors 'who we feel enthusiastic and committed to as we like to build for long-term author success as well as short-term!' Publishes fiction, biography and autobiography, health, mind body and spirit, popular psychology, self-help, business and management, cookery, and other books that tempt us. In 1996 launched a list of mass-market non-fiction and fiction titles. About 120 titles a year (60 of which are fiction).

Editor(s): Non-fiction: Gill Bailey, Fiction: Judy Piatkus
Address: 5 Windmill Street, London W1P 1HF
Telephone: 0171 631 0710
Fax: 0171 436 7137
Email: info@piatkus.co.uk
Website: www.piatkus.co.uk
Parent Company: Independently owned
Payment Details: Royalties are paid twice yearly
Unsolicited Manuscripts: Piatkus are expanding their range of books and welcome synopses and first 3 chapters

Pica Press

Ornithology and natural history.

Editor(s): Nigel Redman
Address: The Banks, Mountfield, Nr Robertsbridge TN32 5JY
Telephone: 01580 880561
Fax: 01580 880541
Email: nigel.redman@pica-press.co.uk
Parent Company: Helm Information Ltd
Payment Details: Advances against royalties and flat fees
Unsolicited Manuscripts: Yes

P

Picador

Outstanding international fiction and non-fiction, travel, current affairs, history, science, humour, literary fiction, literary biography. In hardback and paperback.

Editor(s): Publisher: Peter Straus; Deputy Publisher: Maria Rejt; Senior Editorial Director: Ursula Doyle; Senior Editor: Richard Milner; Editor: Mary Mount
Address: 25 Eccleston Place, London SW1W 9NF
Parent Company: Macmillan
Unsolicited Manuscripts: No

Piccadilly Press

Children's picture books, very simple character-based storybooks (very limited range) for ages 2-6 years. Teenage books (10-15 years old) fiction and non-fiction, fast paced and humorous. Parenting Books a series on 'how to help your child'.

Editor(s): Judith Evans
Address: 5 Castle Road, London NW1 8PR
Payment Details: Depending on the ms
Unsolicited Manuscripts: Yes, but not the whole ms, letter and chapter will be OK

Pira International

Pira International is the leading independent centre for research, consultancy, publishing, training and information services for the pulp and paper, packaging, printing and publishing industries. Pira's publishing division produces an extensive range of titles covering the packaging, pulp and paper, prepress and printing, and graphic communications and publishing industries. Pira publications provide you with everything you need to know, ranging from market analysis and information, to details of the latest technology and techniques. Pira reviews give details of the latest industrial developments and our conference proceedings bring you up to date with what expects in the field are currently thinking. Alternatively, if its market analysis and financial information you require, Pira market reports provide incisive information and are accompanied by Pira's independent commentary.

Editor(s): Marie Rushton - Publishing Director
Address: Randalls Road, Leatherhead, Surrey KT22 7RU
Telephone: 01372 802000
Fax: 01372 802079
Email: publications@pira.co.uk
Website: www.pira.co.uk
Unsolicited Manuscripts: Ingmar Folkmans

Pisces Angling Publication

Books on fishing. Recent titles include My Way With The Pole by Tom Pickering and Colin Dyson (£12.95 hardback; £9.95 softback) and Fantastic Feeder Fishing by Archie Braddock (£9.95).

Address: 8 Stumperlowe Close, Sheffield S10 3PP
Telephone: 0114 2304038

P
Pitkin Unichrome Ltd

Highly illustrated souvenir guides for the tourist industry, specialising in cathedrals, churches, historic cities, great events and famous people.

Editor(s): Managing Editor: Shelley Grimwood; Editor: Jenni Davis
Address: Healey House, Dene Road, Andover SP10 2AA
Telephone: 01264 409200
Fax: 01264 334110
Email: guides@pitkin-unichrome.com
Website: www.britguides.com
Parent Company: Johnsons News Group
Unsolicited Manuscripts: No

The Playwrights Publishing Company

One-act and full length plays, comedy and drama, for amateur groups, professional and schools - reading fee charged - SAE required.

Editor(s): Tony and Liz Breeze
Address: 70 Nottingham Road, Burton Joyce, Nottinghamshire NG14 5AL
Telephone: 01159 313356
Imprints: Ventus Books
Unsolicited Manuscripts: With reading fee (£15 one act/£30 full length)

Plexus Publishing Limited

Publishers of high quality illustrated books with an emphasis on the following subjects: biography, popular music, rock 'n' roll, popular culture, art, photography and cinema.

Editor(s): Sandra Wake
Address: 55A Clapham Common Southside, Clapham, London SW4 9BX
Telephone: 0171 622 2440
Fax: 0171 622 2441
Email: plexus@plexusuk.demon.co.uk
Unsolicited Manuscripts: Yes

P

Plunkett Foundation

The Foundation is an independent charitable trust which supports the development of co-operatives and rural enterprises, both in the UK and overseas. Founded in 1919, the Foundation supports itself through membership fees, donations, and fees earned from work carried out. This includes project development and management, training, information provision and publications. Produce two annual publications, The World Of Co-operative Enterprise and Directory Of Agricultural Co-operatives, and a limited range of other co-operative titles.

Editor(s): Publications Manager
Address: 23 Hanborough Business Park, Long Hanborough, Oxford OX8 8LH
Telephone: 01993 883636
Fax: 01993 883576
Email: info@plunkett.co.uk
Payment Details: No payment
Unsolicited Manuscripts: Considered only for World Of Co-operative Enterprise - must be on related topics and no more than 3000 words

Pluto Press Ltd

Pluto Press, established in 1970, is one of the UK's leading independent publishers. We are committed to publishing the best and critical writing across the social sciences and humanities. Our authors include Noam Chomsky, Sheila Rowbotham, Pierre Bourdieu, Jean Baudrillard, Hal Foster, Augusto Boal, Susan George, Israel Shahak, Antonio Gramsci, Frantz Fanon and bell hooks. Pluto Press currently publishes over 60 titles a year and has an extensive backlist of over 400 titles. We have global profile supported by our team of representatives and agents. Warehouses in the UK, USA, Canada, Australia and South Africa ensure rapid delivery of our books anywhere in the world.

Editor(s): Roger van Zwanenberg, Anne Beech
Address: Pluto Press, 345 Archway Road, London N6 5AA
Telephone: 0181 348 2724
Fax: 0181 348 9133
Email: pluto@plutobks. demon.co.uk
Website: www.plutobooks.com
Unsolicited Manuscripts: Yes

P
The Poetry Business

A small independent literary publisher of contemporary poetry and fiction. List includes Michael Schmidt, Dorothy Nimmo and Michael Laskey. Run an annual book and pamphlet competition - apply for details. Also publish The North magazine: new poetry, reviews and articles.

Editor(s): Peter Sansom, Janet Fisher
Address: The Studio, Byram Arcade, Westgate, Huddersfield HD1 1ND
Telephone: 01484 434840
Fax: 01484 426566
Email: poetbus@pop3.poptel.org.uk
Imprints: Smith/Doorstop Books
Payment Details: Royalties
Unsolicited Manuscripts: Sample 12 poems only please

Poetry Now

Publishes anthologies of more modern verse, likes to deal with topical, provocative issues but will also consider poetry on any subject. New poets always welcome, there are no entry fees and we publish a wide range of poetry. Poetry Now also publishes a quarterly magazine featuring workshops, competition news, profiles and articles of interest. In each issue there is also poetry published on five different subjects, changing each issue. We are always looking for guest editors (must have had poetry published), article writers, etc. If you contact us by email, please include postal address.

Editor(s): Heather Killingray
Address: Remus House, Coltsfoot Drive, Woodston, Peterborough PE2 9JX
Telephone: 01733 898101
Fax: 01733 313524
Email: suzy@forwardpress.co.uk
Imprints: Poetry Now, Strongwords (18-25 year olds), Women's Words (Female poets only)
Parent Company: Forward Press Ltd
Payment Details: Small payments which vary depending on publication - call for details
Unsolicited Manuscripts: Single poems only

Poetry Now Young Writers

Poetry written by young people aged between 8 and 18 years inclusive. Two series of books published per year: April - September 8 - 11 year olds, October - March 11 - 18 year olds. Poems usually submitted through schools, but individual entries are accepted. Poems can be written on any subject and in any style, but must not exceed 30 lines in length. If you choose to contact us by email, please include postal address.

Editor(s): Managing Ed: Sarah Andrew, Asst Managing Eds: Carl Golder; Simon Harwin, Magazine Eds: Allison Dowse; Lynsey Hawkins, Eds: Lucy Jeacock; Jucy Jenkins; Emma Marsden; Dave Thomas
Address: Remus House, Colstfoot Drive, Woodston, Peterborough PE2 9JX
Telephone: 01733 890066
Fax: 01733 313524
Email: suzy@forwardpress.co.uk
Parent Company: Forward Press Ltd
Payment Details: Prizes:- Per Series: 1 x £1000 5 x £250 10 x £100 awarded to schools. Per Book: 1 x £20 4 x £5 Book Tokens awarded to the writers of the five best poems
Unsolicited Manuscripts: Yes

Polar Publishing

Design, print and produce quality sports publications (football, cricket). Catalogue available.

Editor(s): Julian Baskcomb
Address: 2 Uxbridge Road, Leicester LE4 7ST
Telephone: 0116 261 0800
Fax: 0116 261 0559
Imprints: Polar Publishing
Parent Company: Polar Print Group
Payment Details: Individual agreements
Unsolicited Manuscripts: Yes

P

The Policy Press

Social policy and social exclusion. Immigration and migration. Social services and community care. Disability issues. Deafness. Ageing and later life. Health. Family policy, child welfare and domestic violence. Governance. Labour markets, training and lifelong learning. Housing. Construction. Urban policy. Policy and Politics journal (quarterly).

Editor(s): Dawn Louise Pudney
Address: 34 Tyndall's Park Road, Bristol BS8 1PY
Telephone: 0117 954 6800
Fax: 0117 973 7308
Email: tpp@bristol.ac.uk
Website: www.bristol.ac.uk/Publications/TPP/
Unsolicited Manuscripts: Will only accept proposals

Polygon

New fiction, Scottish culture, general interest, poetry, travel, Gaelic, guides, oral history and folklore.

Editor(s): Commissioning Editor: Alison Bowden
Address: 22 George Square, Edinburgh EH8 9LF
Parent Company: Edinburgh University Press
Unsolicited Manuscripts: No

Pomegranate Europe Ltd

Pomegranate Europe is renowned for publishing an extensive range of quality paper products. The prolific variety of images include classic and contemporary, fresh and popular, artists and photographers. The extent of subjects are equally dynamic and diverse. From culture and nature to leisure and humour. Our excellent standard of images, from source to print, is maintained through collaboration with the world's major institutions, libraries and galleries.

Editor(s): Katie Burke
Address: Fullbridge House, Fullbridge, Maldon, Essex CM9 4LE
Telephone: 01621 851 646
Fax: 01621 852 426
Email: sales@pomeurope.demon.co.uk
Website: www.pomegranate.com
Parent Company: Pomegranate Communications

Populace Press

Small independent publisher specialising in children's titles. We serve as a springboard for career authors, and also encourage one-off writers of all ages. Publications are not restricted to book format only; as a new publisher we look to the Internet as an excellent medium for future development of storytelling.

Editor(s): Mary Cooke
Address: 31 Malmesbury Road, Chippenham, Wilts SN15 1PS
Telephone: 01249 461131
Fax: Same as phone
Email: populacepress@mailhost.net
Website: www.mailhost.net/~populacepress
Payment Details: No advances. Quarterly for 1st eighteen months, then annual royalties
Unsolicited Manuscripts: Yes

P

David Porteous Editions

Non-fiction publishers of high quality colour illustrated books on hobbies and leisure pursuits for the UK and international markets. Subjects include watercolour painting, papercrafts, cross stitch, salt dough, papier mache and other crafts.

Address: PO Box 5, Chudleigh, Newton Abbot, Devon TQ13 0YZ
Telephone: 01626 853310
Fax: 01626 853663
Payment Details: Royalties
Unsolicited Manuscripts: No - letter/synopsis first

Power Publications

Publishers of local history, cycle guides, pub walking guides, pub guides and penstemons.

Editor(s): Mike Power/Gill Coomson
Address: 1 Clayford Avenue, Ferndown, Dorset BH22 9PQ
Telephone: 01202 875223
Fax: Same as phone
Unsolicited Manuscripts: Yes

T & A D Poyser

Ornithology and natural history for the academic and advanced amateur audience. Includes treatment of individual species and subjects of an ecological and behavioural nature; field guides and species-finding guides.

Editor(s): Andrew Richford
Address: 24-28 Oval Road, London NW1 7DX
Parent Company: Academic Press
Payment Details: Royalty on net receipts
Unsolicited Manuscripts: Yes, but outlines sufficient for preliminary appraisal/not full ms

Praxis Books

A small press, producing only one or two titles per year. Shared costs, shared proceeds. Proposals will be considered - enclose 2-3 sample chapters and full synopsis, plus ideas as to how the book might be marketed. Assessment service details on request. No new fiction.

Editor(s): Rebecca Smith
Address: Sheridan, Broomers Hill Lane, Pulborough, West Sussex RH20 2DU
Email: 100543.3270@compuserve.com
Website: www.beckysmith.demon.co.uk
Imprints: Praxis Books
Payment Details: Shared costs, shared proceeds
Unsolicited Manuscripts: Yes, with return postage

PRC Publishing Ltd

Promotional publishing, hardback non-fiction covering most areas - lifestyle, history, military, art, architecture, wildlife etc.

Editor(s): Simon Forty, Martin Howard
Address: Kiln House, 210 New Kings Road London SW6 4NZ
Telephone: 0171 736 5666
Fax: 0171 736 5777
Email: martin@prcpub.com
Website: www.prcpub.com
Imprints: PRC, Parkgate
Parent Company: Collins & Brown
Payment Details: Negotiable
Unsolicited Manuscripts: Yes

P

Prentice Hall

Publishes books and CD-ROMS for teaching and learning English as a foreign language at all levels. Particular strengths are business English, English for specific purposes and English for academic purposes.

Address: Campus 400, Maylands Avenue, Hemel Hempstead HP2 7EZ
Telephone: 01442 881891
Fax: 01442 882288
Email: orders@prenhall.co.uk
Website: www.pheurope.co.uk

Prestel Publishing Ltd

Publishers of books on art, architecture, photography, ethnographic art, decorative art.

Editor(s): Philippa Hurd
Address: 4 Bloomsbury Place, London WC1A 2QA
Telephone: 0171 323 5004
Fax: 0171 636 8004
Parent Company: Prestel Verlag
Unsolicited Manuscripts: Yes

Prim-Ed Publishing Ltd

Specialises in producing an extensive range of high quality, photocopiable classroom resources, including hundreds of titles/activities especially suitable for the Literacy Hour. Authored by teachers, our titles provide tried and tested classroom activities which are designed to cut preparation time whilst maintaining a high level of content quality and task value. Clear instructions, page layouts and relevant graphics are features of our titles which help to stimulate increased motivation, interest and concentration. Prim-Ed have also launched a range of double-sided, laminated wall maps and a wide selection of CDs suitable for nursery, primary, secondary school age and home use to complement the well-established and successful copymasters.

Address: 5a Kelsey Close, Attleborough Fields Industrial Estate, Nuneaton CV11 6RS
Telephone: 01203 322860
Fax: 01203 322861
Email: sales@prim-ed.com
Website: www.prim-ed.com/

Prion Books Ltd

Publish books on food and drink, humour, beauty, health, psychology, military, martial arts, popular culture, film and cinema. Also reprint biographical, fiction and historical titles.

Editor(s): Andrew Goodfellow
Address: Imperial Works, Perren Street, London NW5 3ED
Telephone: 0171 482 4248
Fax: 0171 482 4203
Email: books@prion.co.uk
Imprints: Prion
Unsolicited Manuscripts: Yes, with return postage

P
Pritam Books

Books on teaching Pujabi, Urdu, English speakers of Punjabi for school and FE colleges. Punjabi and Urdu bilingual dictionaries in english: Sikhism, Indian Musical Instruments, Phase books (in English, Punjabi, Hindustani, Bengali).

Address: 102 Sandwell Road, Handsworth, Birmingham B21 8PS
Telephone: 0121 523 7429

Profile Books Ltd

General trade non-fiction publishers. Two imprints: Profile which publishes biography, travel, general history, cultural studies, The Economist Books which publishes business and management titles in association with The Economist Magazine.

Editor(s): Andrew Franklin, Stephen Brough
Address: 58a Hatton Gardens, London EC1N 8LX
Telephone: 0171 404 3001
Fax: 0171 404 3003
Email: info@profilebooks.co.uk
Website: www.profilebooks.co.uk
Imprints: Profile, The Economist Books
Unsolicited Manuscripts: Ring first before sending

Prospero Books

Prospero fills a valuable niche helping authors to publish their own books by providing all the expertise and services needed to convert a manuscript into a finished book. Manuscripts can be on any subject, and books are produced in the format and quantity chosen by the author. Advice is given on sales, marketing and publicity.

Editor(s): Barbara Grunwell
Address: 46 West Street, Chichester, West Sussex PO19 1RP
Telephone: 01243 782700
Fax: 01243 786300
Email: prospero@summersdale.com
Payment Details: Authors own all copies of their own books, and retain 100% of any income
Unsolicited Manuscripts: Yes

Psychology Press

This imprint was created specifically to serve the needs of researchers, professionals and students concerned with the science of human and animal behaviour. It publishes at all levels, including primary research journals, monographs, professional books, student texts and credible scientifically valid popular books. Psychology Press intends to publish psychology in its broadest sense, encompassing work of psychological significance by people in related areas, such as biology, neuroscience, linguistics, sociology, artificial intelligence, as well as the work of mainstream psychologists. Its publications will be of interest to any discipline which is concerned in any way with the science of human and animal behaviour.

Address: 27 Church Road, Hove, East Sussex BN3 3FA
Telephone: 01273 207 411
Fax: 01273 205 612
Email: information@psypress.co.uk
Website: www.tandf.co.uk/homepages/pphome.htm
Parent Company: Taylor & Francis Ltd

P
The Psychotherapy Centre

An established therapy, training, referral and publishing centre, helping people to understand themselves, live their lives more effectively, and resolve their emotional problems, relationship behaviour and psychogenic conditions. Some of its numerous publications, such as 'Emotional Problems: Different Ways Of Dealing With Them'; 'Enjoy Parenthood' and 'Selecting A Therapist' are written in-house by the practitioners. For some others, such as 'Group Therapy: We Tried It', or 'Two Therapies And After', well-written, accurate, informative and interesting write-ups of personal experiences are welcome - though there is unlikely to be any payment unless the publication takes off and becomes a best-seller.

Address: 1 Wythburn Place, London W1H 5WL
Telephone: 0171 723 6173
Payment Details: No payment apart from free copies
Unsolicited Manuscripts: Quality accounts of personal experiences of problems and therapies are considered

Public Record Office

The Public Record Office is the national archives of the United Kingdom. Publishes a wide range of historical titles; specialities are family history, military history, primary source material and academic titles.

Editor(s): Anne Kilminster, Sheila Knight
Address: Ruskin Avenue, Kew, Surrey TW9 4DU
Telephone: 0181 392 5206
Fax: 0181 392 5266
Email: bookshop@pro.gov.uk
Website: www.pro.gov.uk/
Imprints: Public Record Office, PRO Publications
Unsolicited Manuscripts: To Anne Kilminster

The Publishing Training Centre At Book House

Publish training materials, and offer a mail order service (Book Publishing Books) for training materials and books about publishing. Also offer a wide range of courses on all aspects of the publishing industry. Most are available in London and Oxford although some can be studied via distance learning. Courses cover the following broad subject areas: editorial; computing; electronic publishing; journals publishing; management; marketing; production; rights and contracts. Basic Proofreading, Basic Editing and Effective Copywriting are all available by distance learning. Course guide or mail order catalogue available on application.

Address: 45 East Hill, Wandsworth, London SW18 2QZ
Telephone: 0181 874 2718
Fax: 0181 870 8985
Email: publishingtraining@bookhouse.co.uk
Website: www.train4publishing.co.uk

Quadrille

Founded in 1994 with the objective of creating a small list of innovative books with serious front list potential while simultaneously establishing a core backlist. Publishes high-quality illustrated non-fiction in the chosen fields of cookery, gardening, interiors, crafts, magic and health.

Address: 5th Floor, Alhambra House, 27-31 Charing Cross Road, London WC2H 0LJ
Telephone: 0171 839 7117
Fax: 0171 839 7118
Email: enquiries@quadrille.co.uk
Unsolicited Manuscripts: Non-fiction synopses and ideas welcome

Q

Quadrillion Publishing Ltd

Publisher of mass-market illustrated non-fiction titles. Subject areas: cookery, crafts, popular history, gardening, pop culture, transport, gift. Some 100 new titles published each year. Own list and distribution in US (with sales and marketing) based in New York. Published in US under CLB imprint. Also publish an extensive children's list under the Zig-Zag imprint; subjects: reference and early-learning series for ages 2-12. Pepperpot is a gift and stationery range distributed under the Pepperpot Island brand in the UK and US.

Address: Godalming Business Centre, Woolsack Way, Godalming, Surrey GU7 1XW
Telephone: 01483 426277
Fax: 01483 426947
Email: wss@quad-pub.co.uk
Imprints: CLB, Zig-Zag, Pepperpot
Payment Details: Outright purchase of copyright; flat fee: additional payment for foreign rights sales
Unsolicited Manuscripts: Synopsis and covering letter only

Quartet Books Ltd

Literary fiction, literature in translation, popular non-fiction, literary and music biography, music - popular, rock and jazz.

Editor(s): Jeremy Beale, Stella Kane
Address: 27 Goodge Street, London W1P 2LD
Telephone: 0171 636 3992
Fax: 0171 637 1866
Email: quartetbooks@easynet.co.uk
Imprints: Robin Clark
Parent Company: Namara Group
Payment Details: Royalties paid twice yearly
Unsolicited Manuscripts: Yes

Quartz Editions

Publishers and packagers of highly illustrated books for the international children's market in the main. Predominantly non-fiction and educational. Most titles are in extensive series.

Address: Premier House, 112 Station Road, Edgware HA8 7BJ
Telephone: 0181 951 5656
Fax: 0181 381 2588
Imprints: Quartz

Queen Anne Press

Sporting yearbooks, official coaching manuals and sponsored sports titles.

Editor(s): Adrian Stephenson
Address: Windmill Cottage, Mackerye End, Harpenden, Herts AL5 5DR
Telephone: 01582 715866
Fax: 01582 715121
Email: queenanne@lenqap.demon.co.uk
Parent Company: Lennard Associates Ltd
Payment Details: By negotiation
Unsolicited Manuscripts: No

Quiller Press Ltd

Founded in January 1981, Quiller has a high reputation for non-fiction - art books, travel, sport, biography, food and drink, architecture amongst other subjects. As a paricular niche, Quiller Press publishes for companies, organisations and charities and has developed sophisticated direct selling techniques. For more information send for catalogue and/or leaflet giving details of past projects and our modus operandi. Distribution is through CBS at Paddock Wood and representation to the book trade is through ABS, Maidstone, who have 8 reps on the road. Overseas we are represented in USA, Australia, Europe, Scandinavia and other parts of the world via dedicated book distributors.

Editor(s): J J Greenwood
Address: 46 Lillie Road, London SW6 1TN
Telephone: 0171 499 6529
Fax: 0171 381 8941
Email: orders@combook.co.uk
Imprints: Quiller Press
Payment Details: Royalties
Unsolicited Manuscripts: No

Quintet Publishing

Packagers of illustrated non-fiction: food; craft; transport and travel; art and collectables; sport; health and fitness; history and general interest; natural history and pets; house and garden.

Editor(s): Commissioning Editor: Anna Southgate
Address: The Fitzpatrick Building, 188 York Way, London N7 9QR
Telephone: 0171 700 2001
Fax: 0171 700 5785
Email: annas@quarto.com
Parent Company: The Quarto Group Inc
Unsolicited Manuscripts: Illustrated non-fiction only

Radcliffe Medical Press Ltd

Publishers of high quality management and clinical books and electronic media for primary and secondary care. Radcliffe has an unrivalled list of practical books for general practitioners, dealing with the many management and organisational issues they face in the rapidly changing National Health Service. In addition, we publish titles on specific clinical areas, and thoughtful works on varied topics such as patients' rights, euthanasia, public health and child welfare.

Editor(s): Gillian Nineham, Jamie Etherington, Heidi Allen
Address: 18 Marcham Road, Abingdon, Oxon OX14 1AA
Telephone: 01235 528820
Fax: 01235 528830
Email: medical@radpress.win-uk.net
Website: www.radcliffe-Oxford.com
Unsolicited Manuscripts: Yes

Ragged Bears Publishing Ltd

Publisher's of quality children's books and book related products.

Editor(s): Henrietta Stickland
Address: Milborne Wick, Sherborne, Dorset DT9 4PW
Telephone: 01963 251600
Fax: 01963 250889
Email: henrietta@raggedbears.co.uk
Imprints: Ragged Bears Publishing
Parent Company: Ragged Bears Ltd
Unsolicited Manuscripts: Yes we do receive them - do send SAEs

Ramsay Head Press

Books of Scottish interest, autobiographies, biographies, fiction, poetry, academic, art, architecture, language books and literary criticism.

Editor(s): Conrad Wilson
Address: 15 Gloucester Place, Edinburgh EH3 6EE
Telephone: 0131 225 5646
Fax: Same as phone

Ransom Publishing Ltd

Ransom Publishing is a young innovative multimedia publisher who develop their own titles and license in titles developed by overseas partners. Ransom has developed a reputation for publishing high quality multimedia titles of strong educational value in both formal education and the home environment, covering a wide range of subjects for children and adults. Ransom market and distribute their products in the major world markets for multimedia and license their titles for translation and localisations in many countries and in many languages. Ransom are one of the fastest growing multimedia publishers in the UK. They are unusual in that thay have a strong base in both educational markets and consumer (retail) markets, plus direct marketing arm which supports trade sales. Ransom titles are stocked by most major retailers and their retail presence is growing rapidly. In addition, Ransom titles are actively promoted by all major UK distributors, mail order companies, book clubs and school suppliers.

Editor(s): Barry Kruger
Address: Ransom House, Unit 1, Brook Street, Watlington OX9 5PS
Telephone: 01491 613711
Fax: 01491 613733
Email: Ransom@Ransompublishing.co.uk
Website: www.ransom.co.uk

Ravenswood Publications Ltd

Niche publisher for the academic and practitioner markets in public service finance, management and law. Current area of specialist interest is local authority leisure and recreation management. Authors will be required to contribute to the marketing database for their publication. At present publishing in hard copy only, but open to offers on electronic output. PLS is mandated for collection of photocopy fees and for digitisation of printed materials.

Address: 35 Windsor Road, London N7 6JG
Telephone: 0171 272 5032
Fax: Same as phone
Email: denise.naylor@virgin.net
Unsolicited Manuscripts: Contact first to check subject, or send CV only

Reader's Digest Children's Publishing Ltd

Early learning, information and reference (0-12 years). Very strong emphasis on novelty formats and unusual editorial approaches. Innovative production techniques and book-plus-toy formats are features. No picture storybooks.

Editor(s): Managing Editor: Cathy Jones
Address: King's Court, Parsonnage Lane, Bath BA1 1ER
Telephone: 01225 463401
Fax: 01225 460942
Website: jill.eade@readersdigest.co.uk
Imprints: Reader's Digest Children's Books
Parent Company: Reader's Digest
Unsolicited Manuscripts: No

Ʀ
Reading And Language Information Centre

The Reading and Language Information Centre specialises in short, practical publications on matters of topical interest to teachers.

Editor(s): Viv Edwards
Address: The University of Reading, Bulmershe Court, Reading, Berks RG6 1HY
Telephone: 0118 931 8820
Fax: 0118 931 6801
Email: reading-centre@reading.ac.uk
Website: www.rdg.ac.uk/AcaDepts/eh/ReadLang/home.html
Payment Details: 7½% royalties.
Unsolicited Manuscripts: Yes

Reaktion Books Ltd

Founded in Edinburgh in 1985 and moved to its London location in 1988. Reaktion Books publishes art history, design, architecture, history, cultural studies, Asian studies, politics, geography, film and photography. 20 new titles in 1999 including Liquid city by Marc Atkins and Iain Sinclair, Robinson in Space by Patric Keiller, Tintoretto: Tradition and Identity by Tom Nichols and At the Edge of the World by Jean Mohr and John Berger.

Editor(s): Michael R Leaman
Address: 79 Farringdon Road, London EC1M 3JU
Telephone: 0171 404 9930
Fax: 0171 404 9931
Email: info@reaktionbooks.co.uk
Website: www.reaktionbooks.co.uk
Payment Details: Royalties paid twice-yearly
Unsolicited Manuscripts: No, synopses and ideas welcome

Reardon Publishing (The Cotswold Publisher)

A family-run publishing house founded in 1976, producing publications related to the Cotswold area. Reardon Publishing also acts as a distributor for other publishers and so we are able to offer a wide range of Cotswold books, maps, walking cards, videos and postcards in our specialised subjects of walking, driving, cycling, folklore and tourism in both the Cotswolds and associated counties. Titles include, for example, The Cotswold Way Guide, Video And Map, Cotswold Rideabout, The Haunted Cotswolds, Cotswold Driveabout. Send £1 for illustrated booklist and mail order details.

Editor(s): Nicholas Reardon, Peter T Reardon
Address: 56 Upper Norwood Street, Leckhampton, Cheltenham GL53 0DU
Telephone: 01242 231800
Website: www.reardon.co.uk
Imprints: Walkabout series, Driveabout series and Rideabout series of guide books and walkcards
Payment Details: Royalties paid twice-yearly
Unsolicited Manuscripts: Yes, with return postage

Reflections Of A Bygone Age

Books using old picture postcards as illustrations highlighting localities and themes including local history, transport, sport, politics plus Picture Postcard Annual and Postcard Collecting: a beginner's guide to picture postcard collecting. Also Collect Modern Postcard catalogues (3 editions).

Editor(s): B G Lund
Address: 15 Debdale Lane, Keyworth, Notts NG12 5HT
Telephone: 0115 937 4079
Fax: 0115 937 6197
Email: reflections@argonet.co.uk
Website: www.postcard.co.uk/ppm

R
Regency House Publishing Ltd

Publishers and packagers of mass market non-fiction titles suitable for international co-editions, specialising in art, craft, cookery, transport.

Editor(s): Nicolette Trodd
Address: 3 Mill Lane, Broxbourne, Herts EN10 7AZ
Telephone: 01992 479988
Fax: 01992 479966
Imprints: Regency House, Troddy Books
Payment Details: To be arranged
Unsolicited Manuscripts: No

Research Studies Press Ltd

Research Studies Press Ltd is an independent British publisher. We publish mostly academic and professional books in growing areas of science and technology, principally in the fields of engineering (particularly electronic, electrical, mechanical and materials engineering), computing, botany and forestry.

Editor(s): Guy Robinson
Address: 15-16 Coach House Cloisters, 10 Hitchin Street, Baldock, Herts SG7 6AE
Telephone: 01462 895060
Fax: 01462 892546
Email: vaw@rspltd.demon.co.uk
Website: www.research-studies-press.co.uk
Unsolicited Manuscripts: No (all m/s are approved by series editors)

Rex Natura Ltd

Commercial arm of the Rex Foundation Wildlife Trust, with a brief to publish books, both fiction and non-fiction, and related artwork, resulting from the wildlife research of the Rex Foundation. The research is predominantly undertaken in the field in Africa and Asia, the Foundation's mission being the protection of the cheetah and leopard and their prey-bases, and the dissemination to the public of 'good news' natural history.

Editor(s): L Godsall Bottriell, P Bottriell
Address: PO Box 141, Aylesbury, Bucks HP17 0YD
Telephone: 01442 826678
Fax: 01296 625299
Parent Company: The Rex Foundation
Unsolicited Manuscripts: No

RIBA Publications

Architecture, design and biographies.

Address: Construction House, 56-64 Leonard Street, London EC2A 4LT
Telephone: 0171 251 0791
Fax: 0171 608 2375
Email: riba.publications@ribabooks.com
Website: www.ribabookshop.com
Parent Company: RIBA Companies
Unsolicited Manuscripts: No

R
Richmond House Publishing Co Ltd

Publishes British theatre directory, artistes and agents and a London theatre/concert hall seating plan guide. The first two books are for theatrical reference used by colleges, schools, companies, media and the profession.

Editor(s): British Theatre Directory/Seating Plan Guide - Spencer Block, Artistes and Agents - Lee Rotbart
Address: Douglas House, 3 Richmond Buildings, London W1V 5AE
Telephone: 0171 437 9556
Fax: 0171 287 3463
Email: sales@rhpco.demon.co.uk

RICS Books

RICS Books has been the official bookseller and publisher for The Royal Institution of Chartered Surveyors since 1981 and is the leading supplier of published material to the surveying, construction, property and related professions. As official publisher to the Institution, RICS Books produces a wide range of material for all surveying professionals. The emphasis is on provision of essential information prepared in close collaboration with the RICS which helps members keep abreast of changing legislation, policy and practice.

Address: Surveyor Court, Westwood Business Park, Coventry CV4 8JE
Telephone: 0207 222 7000
Fax: 0207 334 3851
Email: mailorder@rics.org.uk
Website: www.ricsbooks.org.uk
Parent Company: RICS Business Services
Unsolicited Manuscripts: Yes - to Publishing Manager

Rivelin Grapheme Press

A discreet poetry house. No manuscripts please. First approach by letter with bibliography/biography. No agents.

Address: Merlin House, Church Street, Hungerford, Berkshire RG17 0JG
Telephone: 01488 684645
Fax: 01488 683018
Unsolicited Manuscripts: No. First approach by letter

Roadmaster Publishing

Publishers of Motoring and Car Histories, Commercial Vehicles and local interest books about Kent and South East Area.

Editor(s): Malcolm Wright
Address: PO Box 176, Chatham, Kent ME5 9AQ
Telephone: 01634 862843 (ansaphone)
Fax: 01634 201555
Imprints: Roadmaster Publishing
Payment Details: Usually 10% of retail sales cover price 7.5% paper editions
Unsolicited Manuscripts: Yes, but only in above areas of interest please

Robinson Publishing

Fantasy anthologies; SF anthologies; horror anthologies; horror fiction; crime anthologies; crime fiction; true crime; mind, body, spirit; health; general non-fiction.

Editor(s): Krystyna Green
Address: 7 Kensington Church Court, London W8 4SP
Telephone: 020 7938 3830
Fax: 020 7938 4214
Email: enquiries@robinsonpublishing.com
Imprints: Robinson, Magpie
Payment Details: Royalties paid half-yearly
Unsolicited Manuscripts: No - freelance editors complete the anthologies. Do not submit romance, fiction, short stories or poetry

R
Robson Books

Publishers of general non-fiction, biographies, sport, politics, humour, military, showbusiness.

Address: 10 Blenheim Court, Brewery Road, London N7 9NT
Telephone: 0171 700 7444
Fax: 0171 700 4552
Imprints: Robson Books
Parent Company: Chrysalis Plc
Payment Details: Normal royalties
Unsolicited Manuscripts: Synopsis and couple of chapters preferred to complete manuscripts - must have SAE

Rosedene Publisher

We publish in-house only. Titles are Time Tested Alternative Remedies, Making Something From Nothing, The Big Search - Overland Journey To India And Back To Great Britain.

Editor(s): R Schwittau
Address: Rosedene Herbal Farm, Buller Hill, Redruth, Cornwall TR1 6SS
Telephone: 01209 219075

Rough Guides Ltd

Rough Guides publish travel guides and phrasebooks, restaurant guides, a major series of music reference titles, a bestselling Internet guide, and are exploring other areas of popular culture. Authors should write, enclosing synopsis and sample chapter, if proposing a new title. Freelance writers are regularly employed in updating travel titles.

Editor(s): Martin Dunford (Travel), Jonathan Buckley (Music/Reference), Mark Ellingham (New Ventures)
Address: 62-70 Shorts Gardens, London WC2H 9AB
Telephone: 0171 556 5000
Fax: 0171 556 5050
Email: mail@roughguides.co.uk
Website: www.roughguides.com

Rowman & Littlefield

Humanities and social sciences especially the classics; philosophy, political theory, sociology and history.

Editor(s): Sue Miller
Address: 12 Hid's Copse Road, Cumnor Hill, Oxford OX2 9JJ
Imprints: Ivan R Dee, Lexington Books, University Press of America
Unsolicited Manuscripts: Yes

Rowton Press Ltd

Leading publisher for horse-racing titles - also publishes sports books.

Editor(s): D Thomas
Address: PO Box 10, Oswestry Salop SY11 1RB
Telephone: 01691 679111
Fax: 01691 679114
Email: odds.on@btinternet.com
Payment Details: By arrangement
Unsolicited Manuscripts: Yes

ℛ
Royal College Of General Practitioners

The Royal College Of General Practitioners (RCGP) is the academic organisation in the UK for general practitioners. Its aim is to encourage and maintain the highest standards of general medical practice and act as the voice of general practitioners on education, training and standard issues. For many, RCGP publications represent the external face of the College. Under its Royal Charter the College is entitled to 'diffuse information on all matters affecting general medical practice' and as a consequence has developed a long and prestigious list of publications. The College is justifiably proud of its varied titles, which range from the latest research and ideas in contemporary medicine to practical guidelines for dealing with specific medical conditions. By identifying new and topical areas of interest, the College has remained at the forefront of medical publishing.

Editor(s): Publishing Manager: Tracy Rees
Address: 14 Princes Gate, Hyde Park, London SW7 1PU
Telephone: 0171 581 3232
Fax: 0171 225 3047
Email: info@rcgp.org.uk
Website: www.rcgp.org.uk

Royal College Of Psychiatrists

The Royal College of Psychiatrists takes very seriously its commitments to publish high quality, excellent value scientific and educational material for the psychiatric community which it serves. In keeping with the College's aims, the emphasis is on publications which advance the science and practice of psychiatry, promote study and research in psychiatry and related subjects, and promote public knowledge of psychiatry.

Editor(s): Professor Greg Wilkinson
Address: 17 Belgrave Square, London SW1X 8PG
Telephone: 0171 235 2351
Fax: 0171 259 6507
Email: djago@rcpsych.ac.uk
Website: www.rcpsych.ac.uk
Imprints: Gaskell, Royal College Of Psychiatrists
Payment Details: Varies
Unsolicited Manuscripts: Yes

The Royal Institute Of International Affairs

The RIIA, also known as Chatham House, was founded in 1920 and is a research and membership organisation functioning independently of government and vested interests. It is impartial and holds no collective opinion on any aspect of international affairs. Its resident research fellows, specialised information resources and range of publications, conferences and meetings span the fields of international politics, economics, security and energy/environmental issues. Publications include scholarly monographs, discussion papers, briefings, co-publications, as well as a quarterly and a monthly journal. Publications have a worldwide reputation for quality, accessibility and topicality.

Editor(s): Margaret May (Books etc); Journals eds: Graham Walker (The World Today), Caroline Soper (International Affairs)
Address: Chatham House, 10 St James's Square, London SW1Y 4LE
Telephone: 0171 957 5700
Fax: 0171 957 5710
Email: aallister@riia.org
Website: ww.riia.org
Imprints: Chatham House Papers (with Cassell Academic/Pinter), International Affairs (quarterly journal - Blackwells), The World Today (monthly magazine - RIIA)
Unsolicited Manuscripts: Only for journals

Royal Society Of Chemistry

An internationally renowned publisher, the RSC produces a range of high quality, competitively priced books on chemistry and allied subjects. These range from texts for undergraduates and graduates, through to reviews, handbooks and conference proceedings.

Address: Thomas Graham House, Science Park, Milton Road, Cambridge CB4 0WF
Telephone: 01223 420066
Fax: 01223 423429
Email: books@rsc.org
Website: www.rsc.org
Unsolicited Manuscripts: May be sent to the Publisher, Print Products at the Cambridge address

ℛ
The Rubicon Press

Ancient history (Egypt, Turkey and Greece); history (kings and queens of Britain), nineteenth century travel, biography and literature. All written by academics for the general reader.

Editor(s): Juanita Homan, Anthea Page
Address: 57 Cornwall Gardens, London SW7 4BE
Telephone: 0171 937 6813
Fax: Same as phone
Unsolicited Manuscripts: Yes if relevant to our areas of publication

Russell House Publishing Ltd

RHP's books and training manuals are designed to help anyone studying or working in these areas to develop their thinking and practice: social policy, social care, helping children and families, work with young people, activities for training and work with young people, combating social exclusion, striving for safer communities, working with offenders. Although principally focussed on policy and practice in the UK, we also publish the journal Social Work In Europe, and other comparative works.

Address: 4 St George's House, Uplyme Road Business Park, Lyme Regis DT7 3LS
Telephone: 01297 443948
Fax: 01297 442722
Email: russellhouse.co.uk
Payment Details: Royalties
Unsolicited Manuscripts: Yes if relevant to our areas of publication

The Rutland Press

Publishers of the RIAS Illustrated Architectural Guides to Scotland series; monographs; technical; Scottish urban design. Aim to publish fully-illustrated guides for all regions of Scotland by 2001.

Address: 15 Rutland Square, Edinburgh EH1 2BE
Telephone: 0131 229 7545
Fax: 0131 228 2188
Email: rutland@rias.org.uk
Website: www.rias.org.uk
Parent Company: Royal Incorporation of Architects in Scotland
Unsolicited Manuscripts: No

Salamander Books

Publishers of non-fiction adult reference books which are primarily full colour illustrated. Subjects include: interiors/crafts/cookery/military history/gardening/transport/music/natural history.

Editor(s): Charlotte Davies
Address: Salamander Books, 8 Blenheim Court, Brewery Road, London N7 9NT
Telephone: 0171 700 7799
Fax: 0171 700 3918
Imprints: Vega, Salamander
Parent Company: Chrysalis Group
Payment Details: Depends on contract
Unsolicited Manuscripts: Not required/accepted

The Salariya Book Company

Children's non-fiction; mainly history, science and natural history.

Address: 25 Marlborough Place, Brighton BN1 1UB
Telephone: 01273 603306
Fax: 01273 693857/621619
Email: salariya@fastnet.co.uk
Unsolicited Manuscripts: Concepts for ages 3-12 considered, SAE essential

S

Saltire Society

Scottish history, poetry and literary studies.

Editor(s): Saltire Society Publications Committee
Address: 9 Fountain Close, 22 High Street, Edinburgh EH1 1TF
Telephone: 0131 556 1836
Fax: 0131 557 1675
Email: saltire@saltire.org.uk
Website: www.saltire-society.demon.co.uk
Payment Details: 7½% royalties
Unsolicited Manuscripts: Yes

Sandhill Press Ltd

Specialise in publishing books of local interest to Northumberland.

Editor(s): Beryl Sanderson
Address: 17 Castle Street, Warkworth, Morpeth, Northumberland NE65 0UW
Telephone: 01665 712483
Fax: 01665 713004
Unsolicited Manuscripts: No

S

Sangam Books Limited

One of the major strengths of the Sangam Books list is its quantity of titles reflecting India, from its long history, art and culture, its philosophy and religion, to its current affairs and contemporary public figures, Islam, Hinduism, Sikhism and Buddhism are studied, as are temples and classical dance. Publishes books on Sociology, Scientific and Technical and on Indian fiction.

Editor(s): Mr Anthony de Souza
Address: 57 London Fruit Exchange, Brushfield Street, London E1 6EP
Telephone: 0171 377 6399
Fax: 0171 375 1230
Email: GOATONY@aol.com
Imprints: Orient Longman, Universities Press, Vikas Books Ltd, UBS Publisher
Parent Company: Orient Longman Ltd, India
Unsolicited Manuscripts: No

Saqi Books

Saqi Books is an independent publisher specialising in the production of high quality books on a wide range of topics related to the Near and Middle East and the Arab World, such as art architecture, history, politics, religion, literature, etc.

Editor(s): Mai Ghoussoub/Jana Gough
Address: 26 Westbourne Grove, London W2 5RH
Telephone: 0171 221 9347
Fax: 0171 229 7492
Email: saqibooks@dial.pipex.com
Imprints: Saqi Books, Echoes
Parent Company: Arab Books Ltd
Unsolicited Manuscripts: Yes

S

Savannah Publications

Specialist works of reference: orders, medals, decorations, navy, army, air force, military biography and military genealogy.

Editor(s): Diana Birch
Address: 90 Dartmouth Road, Forest Hill, London SE23 3HZ
Telephone: 0181 244 4350
Fax: 0181 244 2448
Email: savpub@dircon.co.uk
Imprints: Savannah Publications, JB Hayward & Son
Parent Company: Savannah Publications
Payment Details: By arrangement
Unsolicited Manuscripts: Yes

Save The Children

Save the Children publishes a wide range of materials for professionals, academics and practitioners working with children in the UK and overseas. Free catalogues available.

Address: 17 Grove Lane, London SE5 8RD
Telephone: 0171 703 5400
Fax: 0171 708 2508
Email: publications@scfuk.org.uk
Website: www.savethechildren.org.uk
Imprints: Save the Children
Unsolicited Manuscripts: No

SAWD Books

Local interest books, also cookery, gardening and general non-fiction.

Editor(s): Allison Wainman, David Wainman
Address: Plackett's Hole, Bicknor, Sittingbourne, Kent ME9 8BA
Telephone: 01795 472262
Fax: 01795 422633
Email: wainman@sawd.demon.co.uk
Parent Company: Sawd Publications
Payment Details: Royalties bi-annually
Unsolicited Manuscripts: Synopses considered

Alastair Sawday Publishing

Small independent publishers who specialise in accommodation guides. Countries covered: Britain, France, Spain, Portugal and Ireland. Also Paris Hotels.

Address: 44 Ambra Vale East, Bristol BS8 4RE
Telephone: 0117 929 9921
Fax: 0117 925 4712
Email: asbristol@aol.com

SB Publications

Local history, pictorial local history books, travel guides (GB only) - walking and touring, pictorial transport history, (especially railway and maritime), mythology, unknown, unusual, ghosts and legends. All books should be based on events in the UK.

Editor(s): Stephen Benz, Brigid Chapman, Judy Moore
Address: 19 Grove Road, Seaford, East Sussex BN25 1TP
Telephone: 01323 893498
Fax: 01323 893860
Email: sales@sbpublications.swinternet.co.uk
Website: www.sbpublications.swinternet.co.uk
Payment Details: Royalties, 10% of selling price; paid annually no advances
Unsolicited Manuscripts: Yes with SAE

S

Scandinavia Connection

English-edition Scandinavian books about Scandinavian countries - Norway, Finland, Denmark, Sweden, Iceland.

Address: 26 Woodsford Square, London W14 8DP
Telephone: 0171 602 0657
Fax: 0171 602 8556
Email: books@scandinavia-connection.co.uk
Website: www.scandinavia-connection.co.uk
Parent Company: Max Morgan-Witts Productions Ltd
Unsolicited Manuscripts: No

Scarthin Books

Local studies with a wider scholarly appeal; specialised monographs written for the educated layman.

Editor(s): David Mitchell
Address: The Promenade, Scarthin, Cromford, Derbyshire DE4 3QF
Telephone: 01629 823272
Website: www.scarthinbooks.demon.co.uk
Imprints: Family Walks
Payment Details: Royalties quarterly
Unsolicited Manuscripts: Unsolicited synopses considered

Scholastic Children's Books

Children's books publisher. High quality fiction and original individual titles; best-selling non-fiction; picture books; pre-school and licensed titles.

Address: Commonwealth House, 1-19 New Oxford Street, London WC1A 1NU
Telephone: 0171 421 9000
Fax: 0171 421 9001
Website: www.scholastic.co.uk
Imprints: Point, Hippo, Little Hippo, Scholastic Press
Parent Company: Scholastic USA
Unsolicited Manuscripts: Admin for fiction/non-fiction/pre-school dept

SCI, Society Of Chemical Industry

SCI, an association with members in 65 countries which exists to improve understanding and the exchange of information between researchers, industrialists, financiers and educators. Knowledgeable and impartial, SCI provides access to the latest independent and informed expertise on the application of science for the public benefit. Publishing is a significant part of SCI's range of international activities. As well as commissioned volumes, the Society occasionally publishes conference proceedings from its programme of specialist meetings. SCI produces four learned journals: Journal Of Chemical Technology And Biotechnology, Journal Of The Science Of Food And Agriculture, Pest Management Science, and Polymer International. Industrial and academic research papers are always welcome. SCI also presents original and sound research in its Lecture Paper Series, accessible via the SCI website, http://sci.mond.org. The internationally renowned magazine Chemistry And Industry, respected as a source of news and independent comment on science and industry, is produced twice-monthly by SCI.

Editor(s): Ms J Bolgar (journals, books, Lecture Papers Series), Mr A Crawford (Chemistry And Industry magazine)
Address: International Headquarters, 14-15 Belgrave Square, London SW1X 8PS
Telephone: 020 7598 1500
Fax: 020 7245 1279
Email: secretariat@chemind.demon.co.uk
Website: http://sci.mond.org or http://ci.mond.org
Imprints: Lecture Papers Series
Payment Details: Please telephone for guidance
Unsolicited Manuscripts: Journals and Chemistry And Industry

S

Science Museum Publications

History of science and technology, public understanding of science, museology, railway history, photographic history, reference and museum guide books.

Editor(s): Ela Ginalska
Address: Exhibition Road, London SW7 2DD
Fax: 0171 938 8169
Email: publicat@nmsi.ac.uk
Website: www.nmsi.ac.uk
Imprints: Science Museum
Parent Company: National Museum of Science and Industry
Payment Details: Fee arranged with author
Unsolicited Manuscripts: Yes

SCM Press

Books on progressive Christianity, Judaism and Islam, philosophy, theology, history and ethics.

Editor(s): John Bowden, Margaret Lydamore
Address: 9-17 St Albans Place, London N1 0NX
Parent Company: Hymns Ancient and Modern Ltd
Payment Details: Standard royalty
Unsolicited Manuscripts: Yes with return postage - but better to send outline first

Scottish Braille Press

Printers and publishers of braille and producers of audio, large print, tactile diagrams and material on disc for visually handicapped persons.

Address: Craigmillar Park, Edinburgh EH16 5NB
Telephone: 0131 662 4445
Fax: 0131 662 1968
Email: scot.braille@dial.pipex.com
Website: www.scottish-braille-press.org
Parent Company: The Royal Blind Asylum and School

S

Scottish Council For Voluntary Organisations (SCVO)

SCVO is the umbrella body for voluntary organisations in Scotland. Through our members, elected representatives, paid staff and volunteers, SCVO seeks to promote the interests of voluntary organisations and improve their effectiveness.

Address: 18-19 Claremont Crescent, Edinburgh EH7 4QD
Telephone: 0131 556 3882
Fax: 0131 556 0279
Email: enquiries@scvo.org.uk
Website: www.scvo.org.uk
Unsolicited Manuscripts: No

Scottish Cultural Press And Scottish Children's Press

Scottish Cultural Press and Scottish Children's Press are two separate but allied publishing companies. We publish work by Scots authors or persons resident in Scotland or about scottish culture or with a scottish theme. Scottish Cultural Press publishes history, environmental history, biography, poetry, but no fiction any more. Scottish Children's Press publishes history, poetry, fiction, biography etc for readers from three years old up to early teens.

Editor(s): Brian Pugh and Avril Gray
Address: Unit 4, Leith Walk Business Centre, 130 Leith Walk, Edinburgh EH6 5DT
Telephone: 0131 555 5950
Fax: 0131 555 5018
Email: scp@sol.co.uk
Website: www.taynet.co.uk/users/scp
Parent Company: SCP Publishers Ltd (Scottish Cultural Press) SCP Children's Ltd (Scottish Children's Press)
Unsolicited Manuscripts: No complete manuscript: send synopsis and we will decide whether we want to ask for sample chapters

S
Scottish Library Association

The Scottish Library Association is the professional body representing libraries in Scotland. Its publishing programme includes work on librarianship which are aimed at the profession, as well as bibliographies, scottish interest, local and national history materials for the wider market.

Editor(s): Various
Address: Scottish Library Association, Scottish Centre For Information And Library Services, 1 John Street, Hamilton ML3 7EU
Telephone: 01698 458888
Fax: 01698 458899
Email: sctlb@leapfrog.almac.co.uk
Website: www.slainte.napier.ac.uk
Imprints: Scottish Library Association
Unsolicited Manuscripts: Accepted only if consistent with subject areas described above

Scripture Union

Publisher of Bible reading notes, Sunday school resources, general Christian adult books and children's fiction and picture books.

Editor(s): Tim Carr (church resources), Andrew Clark (Bible resources)
Address: Queensway Union, 207-209 Queensway, Bletchley, Milton Keynes MK2 2EB
Telephone: 01908 856000
Fax: 01908 856111
Email: info@scriptureunion.org
Website: www.scripture.org.uk
Unsolicited Manuscripts: Synopsis and sample chapters to Chris Kembrey

Seafarer Books

Books on traditional sailing, mainly narrative.

Editor(s): Patricia Eve
Address: 102 Redwald Road, Rendlesham, Woodbridge, Suffolk IP12 2TE
Telephone: 01394 420789
Fax: 01394 461314
Email: merlinpres@aol.com
Parent Company: Merlin Press Ltd

Martin Secker & Warburg

Literary fiction and general non-fiction.

Editor(s): Geoff Mulligan, David Milner
Address: Random House, 20 Vauxhall Bridge Road, London SW1V 2SA
Parent Company: Random House
Unsolicited Manuscripts: No

$\mathcal{S}$

Seren Books

General literary publisher specialising in writing in the English language from Wales. Publishing around 30 new titles a year, the list includes poetry, fiction, biography, drama, criticism and art. Most books have a direct connection to Wales through author (birth or residence) or subject matter, though Seren also publishes Border Lines, a series of introductory biographies of writers, artists and composers who lived, worked and found inspiration on both sides of the English-Welsh border. Seren is the imprint of Poetry Wales, a quarterly magazine publishing the best in poetry from Wales and the world.

Editor(s): Amy Wack (poetry/drama), Mick Felton (fiction/biography/criticism/art), John Powell Ward (Border Lines)
Address: First Floor, 2 Wyndham Street, Bridgend CF31 1EF
Telephone: 01656 668018
Fax: 01656 649226
Email: seren@seren.force9.co.uk
Parent Company: Poetry Wales Press Ltd
Payment Details: By negotiation
Unsolicited Manuscripts: With SAE for return

Serpent's Tail Ltd

Inspired by Continental paperback original publishing houses and founded in 1986 to give a voice to writers outside the mainstream. During its first year Serpent's Tail published 12 books, 6 of which were translations. Now publishing 40 books a year, including original British and American fiction, music and popular culture books, crime fiction, tranlations and short story anthologies.

Address: 4 Blackstock Mews, London N4 2BT
Telephone: 0171 354 1949
Fax: 0171 704 6467
Email: info@serpentstail.com
Website: www.serpentstail.com
Payment Details: No payment involved re manuscripts
Unsolicited Manuscripts: After query

Severn House Publishers Limited

Hardcover fiction by well-known authors primarily for library publication.

Editor(s): Marisa McGreevy
Address: 9-15 High Street, Sutton, Surrey SM1 1DF
Telephone: 0181 770 3930
Fax: 0181 770 3850
Email: editorial@severnhouse.com
Website: www.severnhouse.com
Payment Details: Standard royalty terms
Unsolicited Manuscripts: No, via agents only please

Shaw & Sons Limited

Shaw & Sons publish a list of over sixty books covering a wide range of subjects for professionals at various depths, from definitive loose-leaf works to simple quick-reference guides. These texts are predominantly for legal and local government professionals but also include topics for businesses and environmental agencies. At the forefront of Shaws book list are annual directories. These include the renowned Shaw's Directory of Courts in the United Kingdom, which is used by thousands of solicitors, government departments and other agencies each year. Shaw's Local Government Directory is the most comprehensive and best value reference work of its kind, and Shaws have recently taken over publication of the Varsity Directory of Investigators and Process Servers and the 'bible' of the probation service, the NAPO Probation Directory. Shaws are always interested in considering new books for publication and prospective authors should write to the Managing Editor with a synopsis of their proposals.

Editor(s): Crispin Williams
Address: Shaway House, 21 Bourne Park, Bourne Road, Crayford, Kent DA1 4BZ
Telephone: 01322 621100
Fax: 01322 550553
Email: publications@shaws.co.uk
Website: www.shaws.co.uk
Imprints: Shaw
Unsolicited Manuscripts: Yes - to Crispin Williams

S

Sheaf Publishing Ltd

Local interest books, non-fiction only.

Address: 191 Upper Allen Street, Sheffield S3 7GW
Telephone: 0114 273 9067
Unsolicited Manuscripts: No, make prior arrangement

Sheffield Academic Press Ltd

Founded in 1976. Originally known as JSOT Press. Now the leading academic publisher of biblical titles. Recently expanded its list to include archaeology, European studies, literary studies, history and culture, languages, scientific, professional and reference.

Address: Mansion House, 19 Kingfield Road, Sheffield S11 9AS
Telephone: 0114 2554433
Fax: 0114 2554626
Email: admin@sheffac.demon.co.uk
Website: www.shef-ac-press.co.uk
Imprints: Sheffield Academic Press, JSOT Press, Almond Press
Unsolicited Manuscripts: Manuscripts, synopses, ideas and proposals welcome. No fiction

Sheffield Hallam University Press

In-house educational publisher producing educational texts, computer packages, special needs publications and games, CD ROMS etc.

Address: Learning Centre, City Campus, Pond Street, Sheffield S1 1WB
Telephone: 0114 225 4702
Fax: 0114 225 4478
Email: shupress@shu.ac.uk
Imprints: SHU Press
Parent Company: Sheffield Hallam University

Sheldon Press

Publishers of health and self-help books for the popular market. Our health books are written for non-experts, and include titles such as Birth Over 35, The Candida Diet Book and Curing Arthritis The Drug-free Way. Our self-help books are written for a similar readership, and include Crunch Points For Couples, How To Improve Your Confidence and The Good Stress Guide. Our new series of books on natural remedies such as cider vinegar, garlic and antioxidants sets out the real benefits of these products. All our books are reliable, no-nonsense reference books for the general reader.

Editor(s): Joanna Moriarty
Address: Holy Trinity Church, Marylebone Road, London NW1 4DU
Telephone: 020 7387 5282
Fax: 020 7388 2352
Email: jmoriarty@spck.org.uk
Payment Details: By negotiation
Unsolicited Manuscripts: Please send a synopsis and sample chapter

Sheldrake Press

Publishers of highly illustrated non-fiction. Subjects include travel, history, railways, architecture and interior design, cookery, music, gift stationery, art and reference. Titles include The Wild House Guides, The Victorian Hours Book, The Kate Greenaway Baby Book and European Museum Guide.

Editor(s): J S Rigge
Address: 188 Cavendish Road, London SW12 0DA
Telephone: 0181 675 1767
Fax: 0181 675 7736
Email: mail@sheldrakepress.demon.co.uk
Website: www.sheldrakepress.demon.co.uk
Imprints: Museum Media Publishers
Parent Company: Sheldrake Holdings Ltd
Payment Details: Subject to negotiation
Unsolicited Manuscripts: Check first by telephone

S

Shepheard-Walwyn (Publishers) Ltd

We publish in three broad areas - all non-fiction: books originated in calligraphy; history, political economy and philosophy, not in a narrow academic sense, but to help us understand where we are and how, by understanding better, things might be improved; books of Scottish interest.

Editor(s): Anthony Werner
Address: Suite 34, 26 Charing Cross Road, London WC2H 0DH
Telephone: 0171 240 5992
Payment Details: Royalties are paid six-monthly or yearly depending on market potential of book
Unsolicited Manuscripts: Yes, but with return postage - synopsis preferred

Shetland Times Publishing

Publish books on local interest subjects.

Address: Prince Alfred Street, Lerwick, Shetland ZE1 0EP
Telephone: 01595 693622
Fax: 01595 694637
Email: publishing@shetland-times.co.uk
Website: www.shetland-books.co.uk
Imprints: The Shetland Times Ltd
Parent Company: The Shetland Times Ltd

S

The Short Publishing Co Ltd

The company's imprint is Short Books, which publishes The Guide To English Language Teaching Schools And Colleges In Britain. Next planned book is Music Europe, a guide to the leading classical music festivals in Europe. Titles are also published in full on the internet. The company also writes and edits books in EFL under contract to major publishing houses.

Editor(s): Richard Mendelsohn, Katharine Mendelsohn
Address: 18 Quarry Road, Winchester, Hants SO23 0JG
Telephone: 01962 855068
Fax: 01962 856448
Email: shortbooks@easynet.co.uk
Imprints: Short Books
Unsolicited Manuscripts: No

Shropshire Books

Publish books and leaflets about Shropshire to help residents and visitors explore and understand the county. Main subject areas covered so far are walking, cycling, history, archaeology, transport, folklore, wildlife, architecture, agriculture, gardens, literature and many more. Complete booklist available.

Editor(s): Helen Sample
Address: Column House, 7 London Road, Shrewsbury SY2 6NW
Telephone: 01743 255043
Fax: 01743 255050
Email: helen.sample@shropshire-cc.gov.uk
Website: http://www.shropshire-cc.gov.uk/ollie.nsf
Parent Company: Shropshire County Council
Unsolicited Manuscripts: Send to Editor

S

Sigma Press

Walking, cycling, outdoor leisure, local history, sport, dance, travel guides and folklore.

Editor(s): Graham Beech
Address: 1 South Oak Lane, Wilmslow, Cheshire SK9 6AR
Telephone: 01625 531035
Fax: 01625 536800
Email: info@sigmapress.co.uk
Website: www.sigmapress.co.uk
Imprints: Sigma Leisure
Payment Details: By royalty
Unsolicited Manuscripts: Synopsis (and SAE) preferred

Simon & Schuster Ltd

Founded in 1986, Simon & Schuster publish non-fiction; reference, music, travel and biography, fiction; mass market paperbacks, literary fiction and children's books.

Editor(s): Clare Ledingham, Martin Fletcher, Helen Gummer
Address: Africa House, 64-78 Kingsway, Holborn, London WC2B 6AH
Telephone: 0171 316 1900
Fax: 0171 316 0331/2/3
Imprints: Earthlight, Pocket Books, Scribner, Touchstone, Simon & Schuster, Simon & Schuster Children's Books
Parent Company: Viacom

Charles Skilton Ltd

General book publishers including reference, fine art, architecture and fiction.

Editor(s): James Hughes
Address: 2 Caversham Street, London SW3 4AH
Telephone: 0171 351 4995
Fax: Same as phone
Imprints: Luxor Press, Albyn Press, Fortune Press
Parent Company: Skilton
Payment Details: By negotiation
Unsolicited Manuscripts: Introductory letter required first

Skoob Books Ltd

Esoterica and occult, Far Eastern literature in English and well known poetry. We will not be taking in any new material for the foreseeable future, for conventional publication. We are however starting a 'co-operative publishing' venture with an American publisher PenArtPro. This involves an author contribution, please apply for details.

Editor(s): Mark Lovell/Adam Wilson
Address: 76A Oldfield Road, Stoke Newington, London N16 0RS
Fax: 0171 404 4398
Email: books@skoob.com
Imprints: Skoob Seriph, Skoob Esoterica, Skoob Pacifica
Unsolicited Manuscripts: For co-operative publishing, please get in touch first

SLG Press

Short pamphlets and books about the spiritual life, prayer, and things which help towards a greater understanding of Christian tradition.

Address: Convent of The Incarnation, Fairacres, Oxford OX4 1TB
Telephone: 01865 721301
Fax: 01865 790860
Imprints: Fairacres Publications
Payment Details: A portion of the print run in lieu of royalties
Unsolicited Manuscripts: Yes but no poetry please

S

Smith Settle Ltd

Local and regional history (Yorkshire and North of England); general interest; fine and limited editions; customs and folklore; outdoor and leisure.

Editor(s): Ken Smith, Mark Whitley
Address: Ilkley Road, Otley, West Yorkshire LS21 3JP
Telephone: 01943 467958
Fax: 01943 850057
Email: sales@smith-settle.co.uk
Imprints: Westbury Academic Publishing, Yorkshire Journal
Payment Details: By negotiation
Unsolicited Manuscripts: Yes but send synopsis in first instance

Smith-Gordon

Independent science, technology, medicine publisher established 1988. Works internationally, mainly at the postdoctoral level in life sciences: books, journals, newsletters.

Editor(s): E Smith-Gordon
Address: 13 Shalcomb Street, London SW10 0HZ
Telephone: 0171 351 7042
Fax: 0171 351 1250
Email: publisher@smithgordon.com
Unsolicited Manuscripts: Life sciences only, and at author's risk

Colin Smythe Ltd

Primarily publishers of Irish literature and criticism as well as acting as agent for authors and/or their literary estates.

Editor(s): Colin Smythe
Address: PO Box 6, Gerrards Cross, Bucks SL9 8XA
Telephone: 01753 886000
Fax: 01753 886469
Website: www.colin-smythe.com
Imprints: Van Duren, Dolmen Press
Payment Details: Royalties
Unsolicited Manuscripts: No

Snapshot Press

Specialises in haiku and related poetry, publishing individual collections, an annual haiku calendar, and two internationally acclaimed journals, Snapshots (haiku) and Tangled Hair (tanka). It also publishes an annual anthology featuring the best English-language haiku and senryu published in the UK and Ireland during the previous year. The inaugural edition, The New Haiku, was published in 1999. Snapshot Press also publish the winning entries to the Snapshots Collection Competition - an annual competition for unpublished collections of haiku, senryu and/or tanka. (send SAE for details - Closing date 31st July).

Editor(s): John Barlow
Address: PO Box 35, Sefton Park, Liverpool LI7 3EG
Email: jb@snapshotpress.freeserve.co.uk
Website: www.mccoy.co.uk/snapshots
Payment Details: Royalties
Unsolicited Manuscripts: Yes, for journals and competitions. Other material solicited

S

Social Affairs Unit

The SAU is an independent research and educational trust committed to the promotion of lively and wide-ranging debate on social affairs. Its authors - over 200 - have analysed the factors which make for a free and orderly society in which enterprise can flourish. It is committed to international co-operation in ideas - eg The Loss Of Virtue and This Will Hurt published as National Review Books; Gentility Recalled published in co-operation with the Acton Institute and joint Anglo-European projects on food and alcohol policy. Current areas of work include consumer affairs, the critical appraisal of welfare and public spending and problems of freedom and personal responsibility.

Editor(s): Digby Anderson
Address: Suite 5/6 Morley House, 314-322 Regent Street, London W1R 5AB
Telephone: 0171 637 4356
Fax: 0171 436 8530
Email: sausales@compuserve.com

Social Work Monographs

Publish up to 10 new titles each year. A complete checklist containing over 100 titles is available on subjects such as family and child care, child abuse, care of the elderly, mental health, people with disabilities, theory and research and social work with offenders.

Editor(s): A McDonald
Address: School of Social Work, Elizabeth Fry Building, University of East Anglia, Norwich NR4 7TJ
Telephone: 01603 592087
Fax: 01603 593552
Email: j.hancock@uea

Society For General Microbiology

Publisher of three learned scientific journals - Microbiology (monthly), Journal Of General Virology (monthly) and International Journal Of Systematic Bacteriology (quarterly). Also publishes the magazine Microbiology Today, and with Cambridge University Press, the SGM Symposium Series of books on current topics in microbiology. SGM is a limited company and registered charity.

Address: Marllborough House, Basingstoke Road, Spencers Wood, Reading RG7 1AE
Telephone: 0118 988 1800
Fax: 0118 988 5656
Website: www.socgenmicrobiol.org.uk
Payment Details: No payments are made
Unsolicited Manuscripts: Scientific research papers are subject to peer review

Society For Promoting Christian Knowledge (SPCK)

Publishes for the Christian book market. There are books covering all the following areas: prayer and meditation; biography and letters; personal growth and relationships; counselling; healing and pastoral care; church, mission and ministry; social and ethical issues; theology and religious studies; science and religion; biblical studies; church history; liturgical studies and worship resources. SPCK aims to cover a broad spectrum of religious viewpoints, and fulfils its mission through helping people to understand and develop their personal faith. Founded in 1698, it comprises a chain of bookshops and a Worldwide branch, which supports the work of churches around the globe.

Editor(s): Simon Kingston (SPCK), Joanna Moriarty (Sheldon Press), Alison Barr (Triangle & Azure)
Address: SPCK, Holy Trinity Church, Marylebone Road, London NW1 4DU
Telephone: 0171 387 5282
Fax: 0171 388 2352
Email: spck@spck.org.uk
Website: www.spck.org.uk
Imprints: SPCK, Triangle, Lynx Communications, Azure, Sheldon Press
Parent Company: SPCK
Payment Details: Individual agreement
Unsolicited Manuscripts: To imprint editor

S

Society For The Promotion Of Roman Studies

Leading organisation in the UK for those interested in the study of Rome and the Roman Empire. Its scope is wide, covering Roman history, archaeology, literature and art down to about AD700. It has a broadly-based membership, drawn from over forty countries and from all ages and walks of life. The Society publishes two journals, the Journal Of Roman Studies, which contains articles and book reviews dealing with the Roman world in general, and Britannia, which has articles and reviews specifically on Roman Britain; also two monograph series - the JRS and Britannia monographs.

Editor(s): S R F Price (JRS), M G Fulford (Britannia)
Address: Senate House, Malet Street, London WC1E 7HU
Telephone: 0171 862 8727
Fax: 0171 862 8728
Email: romansoc@sas.ac.uk
Website: http://www.sas.ac.uk/icls/roman
Imprints: Society for the Promotion of Roman Studies

Society For The Study Of Medieval Languages And Literature

Publishes the journal Medium Aevum on subjects in the language and literature of medieval European countries, including English. Also publishes an occasional series under the title Medium Aevum Monographs in the same areas, manuscripts (normal length between 50,000 and 70,000 words; for mongraphs, are refereed, and a contribution to publication costs (in the region of £500 to £700) is normally required.

Editor(s): H Cooper (English), University College Oxford; N Palmer (Germanic), St Edmund Hall, Oxford; E Kennedy (Romance), The White Cottage, Byles Green, Upper Bucklebury, Reading RS7 6SG
Address: Hon Treasurer, SSMLL, Magdalen College, Oxford OX1 4AU
Telephone: 01865 276087
Fax: Same as phone
Email: david.pattison@magd.ox.ac.uk
Website: http://units.ox.ac.uk/departments/modlang/ssmll/
Unsolicited Manuscripts: To editors as appropriate

Society For Underwater Technology

Multi-disciplinary international learned society dedicated to the active promotion of the development, dissemination and exchange of ideas, information and technology arising from or related to the underwater environment. Publishes a quarterly learned journal, newsletters and conference proceedings.

Editor(s): D Brown, P C Collar
Address: 80 Coleman Street, London EC2R 5BJ
Telephone: 020 7382 2601
Fax: 020 738 2684
Email: daniel@sutpubs.demon.co.uk
Website: www.sut.org.uk

Society Of Dyers And Colourists

Professional organisation specialising in all aspects of the science and technology of colour and coloration. It publishes a series of books dealing with dyes and pigments, and with the coloration of various substrates, especially textiles.

Address: PO Box 244, Perkin House, 82 Grattan Road, Bradford BD1 2JB
Website: www.sdc.org.uk

Society Of Genealogists

Educational charity. Publishes books related to genealogy and family history. Prospective authors should first contact the Society with a proposal.

Address: 14 Charterhouse Buildings, Goswell Road, London EC1M 7BA
Telephone: 0171 251 8799
Fax: 0171 250 1800
Email: sales@sog.org.uk
Website: www.sog.org.uk
Payment Details: Half-yearly royalties by cheque
Unsolicited Manuscripts: No

S

Society Of Metaphysicians Ltd

Neometaphysics: new fundamental science and its applications. Includes paraphysics, parapsychology, psychic science, estoeric and mystical studies. Evaluation of consciousness: in terms of empathy. Neometaphysics (fundamental laws) and politics...and religion...and the physical sciences. World unity and environmental matters. Journal The NeoMetaphysical Digest invites short articles.

Editor(s): John J Williamson, Alana J Mayne, Eleanor Swift
Address: Archers Court, Stonestile Lane, The Ridge, Hastings, East Sussex TN35 4PG
Telephone: 01424 751577
Fax: Same as phone
Email: newmeta@btinternet.com
Website: www.btinternet.com/~newmeta/index/home.html
Imprints: MRG (Metaphysical Research Group)
Payment Details: By mutual agreement
Unsolicited Manuscripts: Yes

Sort Of Books

Sort Of Books, as the name suggests, are open to a wide range of books - fiction, travel, biography, popular culture. The list was launched in 1999.

Editor(s): Natania Jansz, Mark Ellingham
Address: PO Box 18678, London NW3 2FL
Telephone: 0171 431 1925
Fax: 0171 431 1925
Email: nat@kenbury.demon.co.uk
Unsolicited Manuscripts: Letter first please

Southgate Publishers

Educational publisher. Books for primary teachers especially in the curriculum areas of environmental education, mathematics, personal and social education, music and dance, and assembly books. Publishes with the Campaign for Learning - books related to lifelong learning, including workforce training materials.

Address: 15 Barnfield Avenue, Exmouth, Devon EX8 2QE
Telephone: 01395 223801
Fax: 01395 223818
Email: djohnstone@southgatepublishers.freeserve.co.uk
Imprints: Mosaic Educational Publications
Parent Company: Southgate Publishers Ltd
Unsolicited Manuscripts: No - write first with synopsis, or telephone

Souvenir Press

Independent publishers, now in their 48th year with a wide-ranging largely non-fiction list including Human Horizons on disability (Condor trade paperbacks). Recently published the standard Solutions For Writers by Sol Stein. Best-selling authors include Arthur Hailey, Erich Von Daniken, Charles Berlitz, Herman Wouk, Knut Hamsun, Carl Rogers, Wilhelm Reich and Ronald Searle. 55 books a year including reprints.

Editor(s): Editor in Chief: Tessa Harrow
Address: 43 Great Russell Street, London WC1B 3PA
Telephone: 0171 580 9307
Fax: 0171 580 5064
Imprints: Souvenir Press, Condor, Condor Independent Voices, Human Horizons
Parent Company: Souvenir Press Ltd
Payment Details: Royalties twice-yearly
Unsolicited Manuscripts: Enquiry first summarising subject and author's CV

S

SPA Books Ltd

History - military and Scottish; art and crafts; biographies.

Editor(s): Steven Apps
Address: PO Box 47, Stevenage, Herts SG2 8UH
Imprints: Strong Oak Press
Unsolicited Manuscripts: No - synopsis please in first instance

Spellmount Limited

Publishers of high-quality history and military history books. All historical periods are covered but with particular emphasis on the Napoleonic period, World War 1 and World War 2. Autobiographies are not considered.

Editor(s): Jamie Wilson
Address: The Old Rectory, Staplehurst, Kent TN12 0AZ
Telephone: 01580 893730
Fax: 01580 893731
Email: enquiries@spellmount.demon.co.uk
Website: www.spellmount.demon.co.uk
Imprints: Spellmount
Payment Details: By negotiation
Unsolicited Manuscripts: Synopsis with return postage please

Square One Publications

Autobiographies - military memoirs a speciality, but others considered. All manuscripts read and comments given.

Editor(s): Mary Wilkinson
Address: The Tudor House, 16 Church Street, Upton-on-Severn Worcs WR8 0HT
Telephone: 01684 594522/593704
Fax: 01684 594640
Email: marywilk@tinyonline.co.uk
Imprints: Square One Publications
Payment Details: Arranged individually
Unsolicited Manuscripts: Yes

St Pauls Publishing

Theology, ethics, spirituality, biography, education, general books of Roman Catholic and Christian interest. No children's or poetry. Founded 1948.

Editor(s): Sebastian Karamvelil
Address: Morpeth Terrace, London SW1P 1EP
Telephone: 0171 828 5582
Fax: 0171 828 3329
Email: editions@stpauls.org.uk
Unsolicited Manuscripts: Yes

ST Publishing

Independent publisher specialising in youth culture, music and football. ST Publishing focuses on youth cults and music, Low Life is dedicated to pulp fiction related to youth cults, and Terrace Banter is a football imprint dedicated to the fans.

Editor(s): George Marshall
Address: PO Box 12, Lockerbie DG11 3BW
Email: stpbooks@aol.com
Imprints: ST Publishing, Low Life, Terrace Banter
Parent Company: ST Publishing
Payment Details: Advance plus royalties twice-yearly
Unsolicited Manuscripts: Synopsis and sample chapter preferred

S

Stacey International

Illustrated non-fiction, encyclopaedic books on regions and countries, Islamic and Arab subjects, world affairs, business guides, travel, art, dictionaries, archaeology, geology, botany, flora and fauna.

Editor(s): May Scott
Address: 128 Kensington Church Street, London W8 4BH
Telephone: 0171 221 7166
Fax: 0171 792 9288
Email: stacy-international@compuserve.com
Imprints: Stacey International, Stacey London, Royal Genealogies
Parent Company: Stacey Arts Ltd

Stagecoach

Educational resources for 3-6 years olds. Stagecoach - The First Educational Course For The Under-Fives. Structured worksheets promote reading, writing and mathematical skills. Total of 24 progressively advanced workbooks with removable sheets. Project packs also available for topic classwork. Details sent on request.

Editor(s): R L Day
Address: Carriers Crossing, Woodford Road, Stratford-sub-Castle, Salisbury SP4 6AE
Telephone: 01722 782369
Imprints: Stagecoach, Stage 1, Stage 2, Stage 3, Stage 4 (6 packs per stage)
Parent Company: Stagecoach

The Steel Construction Institute

Develops and promotes the effective use of steel in construction. It is an independent, membership-based organisation. SCI's research and development activities cover many aspects of steel construction including multi-storey construction, industrial buildings, light gauge steel framing systems, development of design guidance on the use of stainless steel, fire engineering, bridge and civil engineering, offshore engineering, environmental studies, and development of structural analysis systems and information technology.

Address: Silwood Park, Ascot, Berks SL5 7QN
Telephone: 01344 623345
Fax: 01344 622944
Email: library@steel-sci.com
Website: www.steel-sci.org

Rudolf Steiner Press

The works of Rudolf Steiner translated into English, and other authors whose work is related to Steiner's ideas. Also, books which contain new research and ideas of a spiritual and scientific nature. No fiction, poetry or children's books.

Editor(s): S Gulbekian
Address: 51 Queen Caroline Street, London W6 9QL
Telephone: 0181 563 2759
Website: www.rudolfsteiner.co.uk
Imprints: Sophia Books
Unsolicited Manuscripts: No

S

Stenlake Publishing

Photographic local history books; transport history books; maritime history books and industrial history books.

Editor(s): Oliver Van Helden
Address: Ochiltree Sawmill, The Lade, Ochiltree, Ayrshire KA18 2NX
Telephone: 01290 423114
Fax: Same as phone
Website: www.postcard.co.uk/stenlake
Payment Details: By negotiation
Unsolicited Manuscripts: No

Henry Stewart Publications

International publisher of business journals. Range includes journals of the following: brand management; database marketing; communication management; targeting measurement and analysis for marketing; non-profit and voluntary sector marketing; corporate reputation review; financial services marketing; corporate real estate; financial crime; financial regulation and compliance; money laundering control; small business and enterprise development; interactive marketing and vacation marketing.

Editor(s): International editorial boards
Address: Russell House, 28-30 Little Russell Street, London WC1A 2HN
Telephone: 0171 404 3040
Fax: 0171 404 2081
Email: ed@hspublications.co.uk
Website: www.henrystewart.co.uk

Stobart Davies Ltd

Wood and wood related crafts.

Editor(s): Brian Davies
Address: Priory House, 2 Priory Street, Hertford SG14 1RN
Unsolicited Manuscripts: Yes

Arthur H Stockwell Ltd

Book publishers - all types of work considered.

Editor(s): B Nott
Address: Elms Court, Torrs Park, Ilfracombe EX34 8BA
Telephone: 01271 882557
Fax: 01271 862988
Email: stockpub@aol.com

Stokesby House

Textbooks for secondary schools and colleges - biology, human biology and environmental studies.

Address: Stokesby, Norfolk NR29 3ET
Telephone: 01493 750645
Fax: 01493 750146
Email: stokesbyhouse@btinternet.com
Unsolicited Manuscripts: No

S

STRI - Sports Turf Research Institute

We write and publish a range of specialist titles relating to the maintenance, management and construction of natural turf playing surfaces including golf courses, sports pitches, bowling greens, lawn tennis courts, racecourses etc. We also publish a quarterly 36-page full colour magazine International Turfgrass Bulletin; an annual Journal Of Turfgrass Science and an annual trade directory, STRI-Green Pages. We also sell our titles, plus a growing list of other publishers' related titles, via mail order.

Editor(s): Dr Michael Canaway
Address: St Ives Estate, Bingley, West Yorkshire BD16 1AU
Telephone: 01274 565131
Fax: 01274 561891
Email: info@stri.co.uk
Website: www.stri.co.uk
Parent Company: STRI
Payment Details: On request
Unsolicited Manuscripts: By prior arrangement we do publish other author's titles

Stride

We expect poetry to show an engagement with the knowledge of contemporary poetics: we are not interested in rhyming doggerel, light verse or the merely confessional. We are interested in linguistically innovative work, and work in more traditional (whether formal or free) genres that reinvent the way we see the world. We are also interested in books of interviews for our Stride Conversation Pieces series; and documents (theses; essays; unedited interviews) for our Research Documents series. These should be in the field of arts, music (particularly jazz and 'out-rock') or literature.

Editor(s): Rupert Loydell
Address: 11 Sylvan Road, Exeter, Devon EX4 6EW
Email: rml@madbear.demon.co.uk
Website: www.madbear.demon.co.uk/stride/
Imprints: Stride Research Documents, Stride Conversation Pieces, Stride
Parent Company: Stride Publication
Payment Details: Free copies
Unsolicited Manuscripts: Yes with SAE

Summersdale Publishers Ltd

Non-fiction publishing house, specialising in travel, humour, gift, self-help and guide books. 40 titles in 1998.

Editor(s): Liz Kershaw
Address: 46 West Street, Chichester, West Sussex PO19 1RP
Telephone: 01243 771107
Fax: 01243 786300
Email: summersdale@summersdale.com
Website: www.summersdale.com
Payment Details: No advances, annual royalties
Unsolicited Manuscripts: No, send letter and synopsis in first instance

Supportive Learning Publications

Educational publishers specialising in the following: work books for children; photocopiable worksheet packs for schools; English as a second language for children and adults. Subjects covered include English, maths, science, history, geography, technology, art, craft, music, early learning etc. We also publish material specifically written for reluctant readers, produced as short plays or sketches with, usually, a comedy/adventure theme. The reading age of these plays is approximately 9 years but with an interest level of 7 to 14 years.

Editor(s): Phil Roberts
Address: 23 West View, Chirk, Wrexham LL14 5HL
Telephone: 01691 774778
Fax: 01691 774849
Email: slpuk.demon.co.uk
Website: www.slpuk.demon.co.uk
Payment Details: Negotiable
Unsolicited Manuscripts: Yes

S

Sussex Publications

Audio-visual materials only. No interest in books unless they are texts to accompany audiotapes, videotapes, slide sets, tape slide sets, computer programs, CD-ROMs and microfilms. All subjects covered.

Address: 4 Foscote Mews, London W9 2HH
Telephone: 0171 266 2202
Fax: 0171 266 2314
Email: microworld@ndirect.co.uk
Website: www.microworld.ndirect.co.uk
Imprints: Sussex Tapes, Sussex Video. Associates: Audio-Forum - The Language Source, World Microfilms, Pidgeon Audio-Visual
Unsolicited Manuscripts: N/A

Ta Ha Publishers Ltd

Books on Islam and Muslim world, and children's books.

Editor(s): A Clarke, A Thomson, A Siddiqui
Address: 1 Wynne Road, London SW9 0BB
Telephone: 0171 737 7266
Fax: 0171 737 7267
Email: sale@taha.co.uk
Website: http://www.taha.co.uk
Unsolicited Manuscripts: Yes synopses only with SAE

Taigh Na Teud Music Publishers

Publish Scottish traditional music and song with a specialisation in Highland and Gaelic material. Also some Gaelic non-music items.

Editor(s): Christine Martin (music), Alasdair Martin (Gaelic)
Address: 13 Breacais, Ard, Isle of Skye IV42 8PY
Telephone: 01470 822 528
Fax: 01471 822 811
Email: taighnateud@martin.abel.co.uk
Website: www.abel.net.uk/~martin
Imprints: Taigh Na Teud
Payment Details: Royalties paid 6-monthly in arrears - 10% retail
Unsolicited Manuscripts: Contemporary tunes in the Highland idiom

Take That Ltd

Financial markets, personal finance, computing, Internet, gambling.

Editor(s): C Brown
Address: PO Box 200, Harrogate HG1 2YR
Fax: 01423 526035
Email: sales@takethat.co.uk
Website: www.takethat.co.uk
Imprints: Take That Books, Net.Works, Cardoza, TTL
Parent Company: Take That Ltd
Payment Details: 10%, no advances
Unsolicited Manuscripts: Yes

T

Tamarind Ltd

Children's full colour picture books which give a high positive profile to black children. Multicultural Picture Books 2 - 12 (ages).

Editor(s): Ms S Sideri, Ms V Wilkins
Address: PO Box 52, Northwood, Middlesex HA6 1UN
Telephone: 0181 866 8808
Fax: 0181 866 5627
Email: TamrindLTD@aol.com
Unsolicited Manuscripts: Yes

Tarquin Publications

Mathematics, paper engineering, patterns, things involving paper cutting, folding or models. Fundamental science treated in a three-dimensional way.

Editor(s): Gerald Jenkins
Address: Stradbroke, Diss, Norfolk IP21 5JP
Website: www.tarquin-books.demon.co.uk
Imprints: Tarquin
Payment Details: Royalties and advance paid
Unsolicited Manuscripts: No - send a brief description in a letter

Tate Gallery Publishing Ltd

Publishers for the Tate Gallery in London, Liverpool and St Ives. As well as producing art books and exhibition catalogues we have a wide range of posters, postcards and stationery products.

Editor(s): Liz Alsop, Sarah Perry, Judith Severne
Address: Tate Gallery Publishing Ltd, Millbank, London SW1P 4RG
Telephone: 0171 887 8869
Fax: 0171 887 8878
Email: tgpl@tate.org.uk
Website: www.tate.org.uk
Imprints: Tate Gallery Publishing
Unsolicited Manuscripts: No

Taylor Graham Publishing

Publishers of academic books and journals, in areas of information technology, information management, librarianship, and education themes in general.

Address: 500 Chesham House, 150 Regent Street, London W1R 5FA

The Templar Company Plc

Children's picture books and novelties. Children's trade non-fiction; particularly natural history and early learning first concepts.

Editor(s): Dugald Steer, Sue Harris
Address: Pippbrook Mill, London Road, Dorking, Surrey RH4 1JE
Imprints: Templar Publishing
Payment Details: Advances and royalties for author and artist ideas taken up
Unsolicited Manuscripts: Yes

Tempus Publishing Ltd

History publishers with special interests in local and regional history. Large series of regional books containing old photographs (the Archive Photographs series), including books on town history, transport, sport and other regional history including oral history. Also some early history and archaeology books and general world history.

Editor(s): David Buxton (topographical, regional and oral history), Campbell McCutcheon (transport and industrial history), Peter Kemmis-Betty (early history and archaeology), Jonathan Reeve (general history)
Address: The Mill, Brimscombe Port, Brimscombe, Stroud GL5 2QG
Telephone: 01453 883300
Fax: 01453 883233
Email: tempusuk@tempus-publishing
Parent Company: Tempus Publishing Group
Payment Details: Royalty in most cases
Unsolicited Manuscripts: To the relevant listed editor

T
Tern Press

Artists, printmakers, printers, type designers, Nicholas and Mary Parry have continued their work with a love of literature since Art College. In 1972, they acquired their own presses and have now produced 150 editions of books, in which technique and materials reflect their chosen subjects. Natural history, early british, biblical, war, poetry. All illustrated.

Editor(s): Nicholas Parry, Bill Griffiths, John Porter, Meirion Pennar, Norman Jeffares, Professor Eric Robinson
Address: The Tern Press, St Mary's Cottage, 20 Great Hales SP, Market Drayton, Shropshire TF9 1JN
Telephone: 01630 652153
Unsolicited Manuscripts: Will be looked at and considered

Textile & Art Publications Ltd

Textile & Art Publications brings together a specialist group of individuals with many years' experience in the art world and in the production, publishing, distribution and marketing of international art books, often linked to exhibitions. We have unique access to many major private collections and a reputation for producing generously-illustrated books to the highest academic, design and production standards, concentrating on a limited number of major titles each year. The company is building a varied list of books, covering Oriental, Islamic, Pre-Colombian and Medieval art; and has also produced international language co-editions of its titles for other publishers.

Editor(s): Michael Franses
Address: 12 Queen Street, Mayfair, London W1X 7PL
Telephone: 0171 499 7979
Fax: 0171 409 2596
Email: post@textile-art.com
Website: www.textile-art.com
Imprints: Textile & Art Publications

Thames & Hudson Ltd

Thames & Hudson, which celebrated its 50th anniversary in 1999, is one of the world's best-known publishers of illustrated books. Concentrating on books of high textual and visual quality for an international audience, its programme of more than 150 titles per year focuses on the arts of all kinds, archaeology, architecture and design, graphics, history, mythology, photography, popular culture and travel and topography.

Editor(s): Editorial Head: Jamie Camplin
Address: 181a High Holborn, London WC1V 7QX
Telephone: 0171 845 5000
Fax: 0171 845 5050
Email: editorial@thbooks.demon.co.uk
Website: www.thameshudson.co.uk
Imprints: Thames & Hudson
Payment Details: Royalties paid twice-yearly
Unsolicited Manuscripts: Send preliminary letter and outline before manuscripts

Thames Publishing

Thames: books about English classical music and musicians, particularly of earlier part of 20th century. Autolycus: backlist only of poetry (no new publications).

Editor(s): John Bishop
Address: 14 Barlby Road, London W10 6AR
Telephone: 0181 969 3579
Fax: Same as phone
Imprints: Thames, Autolycus
Unsolicited Manuscripts: No

T

Third Age Press

An independent publishing company which recognises that the period of life after full-time employment and family responsibility can be a time of fulfillment and continuing development. The books encourage older people to make the best of the rest of their lives, but are also relevant to those working with older people or teaching students of gerontology or geriatrics. To date topics covered have included the following: writing and recording life stories, memory, health, alternative therapies, changes and challenges in later life, walking through Europe and the history of the old-age pension. Through its Perspectives series, Third Age Press also produces self-published memoirs.

Editor(s): Dianne Norton
Address: 6 Parkside Gardens, London SW19 5EY
Telephone: 0181 947 0401
Fax: 0181 944 9316
Email: dnort@thirdagepress.co.uk
Website: www.thirdagepress.co.uk
Imprints: Third Age Press
Unsolicited Manuscripts: Yes if within areas detailed

Thistle Press

Scottish regional travel guides; local history; archaeology and geology with Scottish content; general Scottish interest; academic books on the environmental sciences. Member of Scottish Publishers Association.

Editor(s): Keith Nicholson, Angela Nicholson
Address: West Bank, Western Road, Insch, Aberdeenshire AB52 6JR
Telephone: 01464 821 053
Fax: Same as phone
Email: info@thistlepress.co.uk
Website: www.thistlepress.co.uk
Payment Details: Annual royalties as per contract
Unsolicited Manuscripts: Yes

Thoemmes Press

Thoemmes Press publishes primary sources and reference works in the History of Ideas for the global academic community. We have an exciting core programme of Biographical Dictionaries in philosophy and more traditional product lines which make available long out-of-print and rare materials. Subjects covered include: ancient philosophy, 17th and 18th century philosophy, idealism, Scottish enlightenment, aesthtics, theology and Christian thought, social and political thought, history of economics, business and management history, philosophy and history of science, development of psychology and printing and the book trade. We are also sole distributors for Ganesha Publishing, which is devoted to printing western historical sources on Asia. Thoemmes Press offers a focussed service publishing single and multivolume hardbound products to libraries and individual academics around the world.

Address: Thoemmes Press, 11 Great George Street, Bristol BS1 5RR
Telephone: 0117 9291377
Fax: 0117 9221918
Email: info@thoemmes.com or sales@thoemmes.com
Website: www.Thoemmes.com
Imprints: Overstone - Historical Sources in Economic Thought, Ganesha Publishing - Western Historical Sources on Asia, Nico Editions - Classsic Works on the History of the Book

T
Thomas Cook Publishing

Produce a wide range of travel-related books, maps and timetables. Publications in the Thomas Cook Publishing portfolio include: European and Overseas Timetables - updated monthly; International Air Travel Handbook; Travellers Guides (54-book series); Touring Handbooks (13-book series); European and South Asian phrasebooks; World Atlas Of Travel; Golden Age Of Travel; Greek Island Hopping 1999; Your Passport To Safer Travel; Rail Maps of Great Britain and Ireland and Europe; Where To Ski And Snowboard; Hot Spots Guides (25-book series); Signpost Guides; Independent Traveller's Guides; Classic Short Breaks.

Editor(s): Stephen York
Address: PO Box 227 Thorpe Wood, Peterborough PE3 6PU
Telephone: 01733 503571/2
Fax: 01733 503596
Website: www.thomascook.co.uk
Parent Company: Thomas Cook Group
Unsolicited Manuscripts: Yes

Thorntons Of Oxford

Oxford's oldest bookshop on 4 floors with over 70,000 volumes. Academic and non-specialist books; book search facilities and numerous catalogues. Rare books and first editions, ancient and modern languages, literature and criticism are all included.

Address: Thorntons Of Oxford, 11 Broad Street, Oxford OX1 3AR
Telephone: 01865 242939
Fax: 01865 204021
Email: Thorntons@Booknews.demon.co.uk
Website: http://www.demon.co.uk/thorntons

Thoth Publications

Publishers of metaphysical, western mystery tradition, and esoteric works, with each manuscript given care and attention by those with the knowledge within the particular field.

Editor(s): Tom Clarke
Address: 64 Leopold Street, Loughborough LE11 5DN
Telephone: 01509 210626
Fax: 01592 238034
Email: ThothPub@aol.com

Timber Press

Timber Press is a leading publisher of books on gardening, horticulture and botany. Specialises in authoritative treatments of particular plant groups written by internationally renowned authors. Whether you are a keen gardener or a professional grower, Timber Press can help to inform you about the different genera, propagation and cultivation of many plants, trees and shrubs.

Editor(s): Neal Maillet
Address: 2 Station Road, Swavesey, Cambridge CB4 5QJ
Telephone: 01954 232959
Fax: 01954 206040
Email: timberpressuk@btinternet.com
Website: www.timberpress.com
Imprints: Amadeus Press
Parent Company: Timber Press, Portland, Oregon USA

Topaz Publications

Publishers of legal texts in relation to Irish law only.

Editor(s): Davida Murdoch
Address: 10 Haddington Lawn, Glenageary, Co Dublin, Ireland
Telephone: 00353 1 2800460
Fax: Same as phone
Unsolicited Manuscripts: No

$\mathcal{T}$

TQMI Media And Publications

TQMI provide books and CD-ROMs that enable organisations to: communicate the practices and principles of continuous improvement, clearly and effectively, to staff at all levels; educate and train staff in how to implement improvements; reinforce senior management's commitment to continuous improvement; motivate and encourage staff to become involved in improvement. We also help organisations customise these publications with their own logo etc, or write bespoke titles to meet customers' specific needs.

Address: Brook House, Grigg Lane, Brookenhurst, Hampshire SO42 7RE
Telephone: 01590 624646
Fax: 01590 624647
Email: publications@tqmi.co.uk
Website: www.tqmi.co.uk
Imprints: TQM International Ltd

Training Publications Ltd

Main areas: basic engineering manufacture, including NVQ-related material, science and technology. Subsidiary areas: small but expanding archaeological and ancient history list, also biology and natural history.

Address: 3 Finway Court, Whippendell Road, Watford WD1 7EN
Telephone: 01923 243730
Fax: 01923 213144
Email: trainingpubs@btinternet.com
Imprints: Entra, EMTA, EIT, EITB
Parent Company: Engineering And Marine Training Authority
Payment Details: Negotiable
Unsolicited Manuscripts: Yes

T

Transedition Limited

Transedition has three operations - packaging, rights acquisition and translation. Packages illustrated reference books for the international marketplace. Acquires English-language rights from European publishers and European rights from American publishers, which are translated, repackaged and sold as co-editions. Offers its translation services to other publishers through its subsidiary Translate-A-Book. Transedition buys or packages and translates and sells illustrated reference and coffee table books and series. Subject areas of interest are art and antiques, children's non-fiction, cinema, gardening, history, religion, sport, transport.

Address: 43 Henley Avenue, Oxford OX4 4DJ
Telephone: 01865 770549
Fax: 01865 712500
Email: all@transed.co.uk
Unsolicited Manuscripts: No

Trematon Press

Publish equestrian books, specialising in side-saddle riding.

Address: Trematon Hall, Saltash, Cornwall PL12 4RU
Telephone: 01752 842351
Fax: 01752 848920

T

Trentham Book Ltd

Books for professional use by teachers and lecturers and other practitioners in education, social work and law. Not books for classroom use; not children's books, reminiscence, biography, fiction or poetry. No packs or other non-book material.

Editor(s): Gillian Klein
Address: Westview House, 734 London Road, Oakhill, Stoke on Trent ST4 5NP
Telephone: 01782 745567/844699
Fax: 01782 745553
Email: th@trentham-books.co.uk
Website: www.trentham-books.co.uk
Imprints: Trentham
Payment Details: Annual royalty calculated 31st August and payable within six weeks thereafter
Unsolicited Manuscripts: Yes

Triangle Books

Publishers of Christian books, particularly in the areas of prayer, spirituality and personal growth. We also publish books on mission and the church in the modern world, as well as stories of faith in action. Triangle books are aimed at a popular Christian readership.

Editor(s): Alison Barr
Address: Holy Trinity Church, Marylebone Road, London NW1 4DU
Telephone: 0171 387 5282
Fax: 0171 388 2352
Email: abarr@spck.org.uk
Website: www.spck.org.uk
Parent Company: SPCK
Payment Details: By negotiation
Unsolicited Manuscripts: Send synopsis and sample chapter

Trinitarian Bible Society

Publishers of accurate and reliable protestant versions of the Bible, or part thereof, in several languages. Translations are drawn from the Hebrew Masoretic text and from the Greek Textus Receptus.

Editor(s): G W Anderson
Address: Tyndale House, Dorset Road, London SW19 3NN
Telephone: 0181 543 7857
Fax: 0181 543 6370

Triumph House

Triumph House publishes Christian poetry books on various themes. It also produces a quarterly magazine, Triumph Herald, featuring items such as personal testimonies, Bible stories, prayers and general Christian arts news. Includes a section for young Christians to share their poetry along with a few crossword puzzles and word searches. A year's subscription to the magazine (four issues) is £15 in the UK and £21 for overseas. The Spotlight Poets imprint also publishes books of poetry containing twelve authors with each one having ten pages of the book dedicated to them and their work. The poems can be on a variety of subjects and themes. Please write or telephone for an information pack on any of the above. You can also contact us by email, but please be sure to include your postal address.

Editor(s): Managing Editor: Steve Twelvetree; Editor: Kelly Deacon
Address: Remus House, Coltsfoot Drive, Woodston, Peterborough PE2 9JX
Telephone: 01733 898102
Fax: 01733 313524
Email: suzy@forwardpress.co.uk
Imprints: Spotlight Poets
Parent Company: Forward Press Ltd
Unsolicited Manuscripts: Send covering letter with sample poems only

T

Trog Associates Ltd

Producing management system document sets for Engineering, Environment, software development and IT Management: ISO9001 Product Design, ISO9001 Design/ Manufacturing, ISO9002 Service, ISO14001 Environmental, ISA2000 Health and Safety, ISO9000 Corporate Communications.

Editor(s): Author/Publisher/Trainer: Eric Sutherland
Address: Trog Associates Ltd, PO Box 243, South Croydon, Croydon, Surrey CR2 6NZ
Telephone: 0208 7863637
Fax: 0208 6863580
Email: trog@dial.pipex.com
Website: http:/www.nvo.com/management-systems-author

TSR

Publisher of the world-renowned adventure game Dungeons & Dragons which celebrates its 25th anniversary this year. The game further generated a wide variety of best-selling fantasy novels including the book series Dragonlance. The aquisition of TSR by Wizards of the Coast enabled the company to reach further into the fantasy market with major additions to its novel lines including the exciting new science fiction series Alternity. With established book lines including Forgotten Realms, Greyhawk and Planescape, plus award-winning authors Margaret Weis, Tracey Hickman, R A Salvatore and Diane Duane (of Star Trek fame), TSR is a well-respected name in fantasy fiction. Its silver anniversary is celebrated all year long with special products, classic best-sellers updated for the current market, and a few surprises designed to make 1999 a year to remember.

Address: Nicholsons House, Nicholsons Walk, Maidenhead, Berks SL6 6LD
Telephone: 01628 780801
Fax: 01628 780602
Email: lee_crocker@uk.wizards.be
Website: www.wizards-europe.com
Parent Company: Wizards of the Coast

Twelveheads Press

Has been publishing books about industrial, transport and maritime history since 1978. Specialises in the geographical area of the west of England, Cornwall in particular, but extends to other areas if appropriate to interests. Only publish books on subjects that the editors know well or are interested in, thus ensuring the highest standards.

Editor(s): Michael Messenger, Alan Kittridge, John Stengelhofen
Address: Chy Mengleth, Twelveheads, Truro, Cornwall TR4 8SN
Telephone: 01209 820978
Email: admin@twelveheads.demon.co.uk
Website: www.twelveheads.demon.co.uk
Imprints: Twelveheads Press
Payment Details: Royalties half-yearly
Unsolicited Manuscripts: No - send synopsis and details

Two-Can Publishing Ltd

Two-Can creates products that absorb and entertain, inform and explain, for children, teachers and parents around the world.

Editor(s): Jane Wilsher (Editorial Director)
Address: 346 Old Street, London EC1V 9RB
Telephone: 0171 684 4000
Email: info@two-can.co.uk

UCL Press

Social sciences, politics and international relations, media and culture studies, geography, archaeology, history and criminology.

Editor(s): Caroline Wintersgill, Luciana O'Flaherty, Kate Brewin
Address: 1 Gunpowder Square, London EC4A 3DE
Parent Company: Taylor & Francis Group
Unsolicited Manuscripts: No

𝓤

UKCHR - United Kingdom Council For Human Rights

Monitor human rights in the United Kingdom, where there has been a radical restructuring of society. This process continues under New Labour. Publish leaflets and booklets on human rights issues, and a reference book on race, poverty and health: Of Germs, Genes and Genocide.

Address: Flat No 7, Sunley House, 10 Gunthorpe Street, London E1 7RW
Telephone: 0171 377 2932
Fax: 0870 055 3979
Email: ukchr@ukcouncilhumanrights.co.uk
Website: www.ukcouncilhumanrights.co.uk

University Of Exeter Press

An established scholarly publisher. Around 25 titles a year in the arts and humanities, including European studies, medieval studies, history, classical studies, film history, theatre studies, linguistics, landscape studies.

Editor(s): Simon Baker
Address: Reed Hall, Streatham Drive, Exeter EX4 4QR
Telephone: 01392 263066
Fax: 01392 263064
Email: uep@ex.ac.uk
Website: www.ex.ac.uk/uep/
Unsolicited Manuscripts: No

University Of Hertfordshire Press

Best known as a publisher of books on Gypsies and Travellers (history, sociology, literature etc) including the English language editions of the international publishing programme known as the Interface Collection. Also publishes serious academic books on parapsychology including the highly respected Guidelines series (volumes to date include psychic testing and ESP), regional and local history, astronomy (in the series Building Blocks Of Modern Astronomy) and document management (on behalf of Cimtech Ltd) including the Document Management Directory, now in its tenth edition. The Press has recently appointed distributors in the UK and North America, is expanding its publishing programme, and welcomes approaches from potential authors in the areas within which it specialises.

Editor(s): W A Forster
Address: Learning and Information Services, University of Hertfordshire, College Lane, Hatfield AL10 9AD
Telephone: 01707 284681
Fax: 01707 284666
Email: uhpress@herts.ac.uk
Website: www.herts.ac.uk/uhpress
Imprints: University of Hertfordshire Press, Cimtech
Parent Company: University of Hertfordshire
Unsolicited Manuscripts: To the Editor

University Of Wales Press

History, religion and philosophy; European studies including literature and politics and Celtic studies including Welsh studies.

Editor(s): Susan Jenkins
Address: 6 Gwennyth Street, Cathays, Cardiff CF2 4YD
Telephone: 029 2023 1919
Fax: 029 2023 0908
Email: press@press.wales.ac.uk
Website: www.wales.ac.uk/press
Imprints: GPC Books, Gwasg Prifysgol Cymru
Parent Company: University of Wales
Payment Details: Royalty rates by negotiation
Unsolicited Manuscripts: No

𝒰
Usborne Publishing

Children's books. Usborne books are accessible, fun, visually exciting and inviting and start at a point which naturally engages a child's interest. As a result, Usborne books have been chosen by teachers, parents and carers for over twenty years to help children develop a love of reading and thirst for knowledge.

Editor(s): Peter Usborne, Jenny Tyler
Address: 83-85 Saffron Hill, London EC1N 8RT
Telephone: 0171 430 2800
Fax: 0171 430 1562
Email: mail@usborne.co.uk
Website: www.usborne.com
Unsolicited Manuscripts: No, all titles created in-house

Vacher Dod Publishing Ltd

Dod's Parliamentary Companion and Vacher's Parliamentary Companion were both founded in 1832, in the year of the Great Reform Act, serving Parliament for 162 years before finally merging in 1994 to create Vacher Dod Publishing Ltd - a publishing company focused on UK and European politics. Today, at another important turning point in the history of British and European politics, they publish Parliament's leading reference books and political databases covering the Westminster and Scottish Parliaments, the Northern Ireland Assembly, the Welsh assembly, Whitehall and the European Union. The Company has a huge amount of current and historical data available for reference and data processing.

Editor(s): Michael Bedford (House of Lords); Lesley Gunn (House of Commons); Rohan Dale (Europe)
Address: PO Box 3700, Westminster, London SW1E 5NP
Telephone: 0171 828 7256
Fax: 0171 828 7269
Email: politics@vacherdod.co.uk
Imprints: Dod's Parliamentary Companion, Vacher's Parliamentary Companion, Vacher's European Companion
Payment Details: By negotiation
Unsolicited Manuscripts: No

The Vegetarian Society

Articles to do with vegetarian lifestyle, health, nutrition, environment, travel products and vegetarian celebrities etc; all content must be directly related to vegetarianism.

Editor(s): John Schofield
Address: Parkdale, Dunham Road, Altrincham, Cheshire WA14 4QG
Telephone: 0161 925 2000
Fax: 0161 926 9182
Email: johns@vegsoc.demon.co.uk
Website: www.vegsoc.org
Imprints: The Vegetarian
Payment Details: I haggle
Unsolicited Manuscripts: Yes

Veloce Publishing Plc

Automotive (car and motorcycle) histories, full-colour automotive books, practical and technical automotive manuals and books.

Editor(s): Rod Grainger
Address: 33 Trinity Street, Dorchester, Dorset DT1 1TT
Telephone: 01305 260068
Fax: 01305 268864
Email: veloce@veloce.co.uk
Website: www.veloce.co.uk
Imprints: Veloce
Payment Details: Royalty basis
Unsolicited Manuscripts: Yes

V

Vennel Press

Small press specialising in contemporary Scottish poetry, and, in its Au Quai imprint, poetry in translation.

Editor(s): Richard Price, Leona Medlin
Address: 8 Richmond Road, Staines, Middlesex TW18 2AB
Imprints: Au Quai
Parent Company: Vennel Press
Payment Details: Negotiable
Unsolicited Manuscripts: No

Venton Educational Ltd

Poetry, Careers, West Country, Maritime, Motoring and Travelogues.

Editor(s): Mr C Venton
Address: 57 Seend Cleeve, Seend Melksham, Wiltshire SN12 6PX
Telephone: 01380 828654
Fax: Same as phone
Imprints: White Horse Library and Uffington Books
Parent Company: Colin Venton Ltd
Payment Details: By arrangement
Unsolicited Manuscripts: Yes

Veritas Foundation Publication Centre

Poland, Eastern Europe, religion, Catholicism and Christianity, prayer books, memoirs and history.

Editor(s): Thomas Wachowiak
Address: 63 Jeddo Road, London W12 9EE
Telephone: 0181 7494957
Fax: 0181 7494965
Email: thomas@veritas.knsc.co.uk
Payment Details: Author to cover all costs
Unsolicited Manuscripts: No

Verso Ltd

$\mathcal{V}$

Verso is a radical publisher, publishing about 40 titles a year. Titles are predominantly in the areas of politics, history, cultural studies and philosophy. Verso publish a number of trade titles but the bulk of the list is academically orientated.

Editor(s): Robin Blackburn, Sebastian Budgen
Address: 6 Meard Street, London W1V 3HR
Telephone: 0171 437 3546
Fax: 0171 734 0059
Email: enquiry@verso.co.uk
Website: www.versobooks.com
Payment Details: Advances given, standard royalties
Unsolicited Manuscripts: Yes

VERTIC (Verification Research, Training And Information Centre)

Publishes briefing notes, research reports and a verification yearbook on issues relating to the verification and monitoring of international agreements, especially in the areas of arms control and disarmament, the environment and peace accords.

Editor(s): Trevor Findlay
Address: Baird House, 15/17 St Cross Street, London EC1N 8UW
Telephone: 020 7440 6960
Fax: 020 7242 3266
Email: info@vertic.org
Website: www.fhit.org/vertic

$\mathcal{V}$

Verulam Publishing Ltd

Publishers and distributors. Subjects covering include: business, careers, computers, cookery, english, finance, gift books, health, history, language learning (textbooks, audio, video), new age and mysticism, parenting, quilting, self-help, sport and fitness, study guides, theatre and performing arts and travel.

Editor(s): David Collins
Address: 152a Park Street Lane, Park Street, St Albans AL2 2AU
Telephone: 01727 872770
Fax: 01727 873866
Email: sales@verulampub.demon.co.uk
Imprints: NTC, Contemporary Books, Take That Books, Impact Books, Websters International, Rutledge Hill Press, Stoddart Publishing and Key Porter Books
Unsolicited Manuscripts: No

VHA Publications

VHA Publications publish a broad range of titles on the decorative arts. The objective is to produce books which have an international appeal, and are of high quality design. Subjects include fashion, glass, ceramics, paintings, photography. We also publish accompanying books for VHA major exhibitions.

Editor(s): Miranda Harrison
Address: VHA Publications, 160 Brompton Road, London SW3 1HW
Telephone: 0171 983 9663
Fax: 0171 938 9973
Email: n.evans@vam.ac.uk
Website: www.vam.ac.uk
Imprints: VHA

Virgin Publishing Ltd

Publish a wide range of books for the general consumer market, but do not publish any poetry, children's books or general fiction. Specialise in non-fiction books about popular culture, especially music, TV, sport, and in certain genres of fiction published strictly within imprint guidelines.

Virgin Publishing Non-fiction (All published under Virgin imprint)
Non-fiction books for the general reader, specialising in popular culture, especially music, travel, TV, film and sport. Unsolicited manuscripts are not accepted. Unsolicited submissions of a synopsis and some sample text are accepted, but only within the subject areas indicated. Authors are advised to request and read the company's house style sheet before submitting proposals.
Editorial Director: Humphrey Price (general non-fiction); Senior Editor: Rod Green (film, TV and radio tie-ins, celeb humour, pop culture); Editors: Lorna Russell (film, TV and radio tie-ins, biography, true crime, paranormal); David Gould (popular reference); Jonathan Taylor (sport); Anna Cherrett (biography, occult history). Editorial Director: Carolyn Thorne (lifestyle, health, music, media, pop culture (illustrated only); Editors: Ian Gittens, Stuart Slater (music - reference, bios, criticism, illustrated). Senior Editor: Kerri Sharp; Editors: James Marriot, Kathleen Bryson (sexuality, true crime).

Virgin Publishing Fiction (Virgin imprint unless otherwise stated)
Unsolicited manuscripts not accepted. Unsolicited submissions of a synopsis and some sample text are accepted, but only for the imprints and series listed. Virgin do not publish one-off stand-alone novels. Authors' guidelines available for each imprint; submissions accepted only from authors who have read and followed the relevant guidelines. There are sometimes new series in development - authors should watch the press for announcements.
Editorial Director: Humphrey Price; Senior Editor: Kerri Sharp (erotic fiction by women - Black Lace); Editors: James Marriot (erotic fiction - Nexus); Kathleen Bryson (gay and lesbian erotica - Idol and Sapphire imprints)

Address: Thames Wharf Studios, Rainville Road, London W6 9HT
Telephone: 0171 386 3300
Fax: 0171 386 3360
Email: <name>@virgin-pub.co.uk
Imprints: Virgin
Payment Details: Usually by royalties on sales, but we'll consider other arrangements
Unsolicited Manuscripts: No

V

Volcano Press Ltd

Islam in Britain, Europe and the USA. Women's studies, preferably Muslim women and human rights issues.

Editor(s): A Hussain
Address: PO Box 139, Leicester LE2 2YH
Telephone: 0116 2706714
Fax: Same as phone
Email: asaf@volcano.u-net.com
Payment Details: Yearly 5-10% royalties
Unsolicited Manuscripts: No

Walden Publishing Ltd/World Of Information

Publisher of country business and economic information. Five annual reviews: Middle East, Africa, Asia and Pacific, Americas, Europe. Regional development series: The OAU Report (35 years in the service of Africa); The ASEAN Report (Embracing the challenge); The ADB Report (Sustaining Africa's growth); The OAS Report (50 years of the OAS).

Editor(s): Matt Brooks
Address: 2 Market Street, Saffron Waldon, Essex CB10 1HZ
Telephone: 01799 521150
Fax: 01799 524805
Email: waldenpub@easynet.co.uk
Website: www//worldinformation.com
Unsolicited Manuscripts: No

W

Wales Tourist Board

The Wales Tourist Board produces annually its A View of Wales magazine which features articles written by well known personalities and travel correspondents on their holiday experiences in Wales. The publication is primarily aimed at changing prospective visitors' perceptions of Wales, and encouraging new high-profile visitors to Wales. This is being done under the premise of 'Wales - two hours and a million miles away'.

Editor(s): D Rhys Jones
Address: Production Services Department, Brunel House, 2 Fitzalan Road, Cardiff CF24 0UY
Telephone: 01222 475214
Imprints: A View of Wales Magazine
Payment Details: By negotiation
Unsolicited Manuscripts: No, but prospective contributors welcome to contact the Editor

Walkways/Quercus

Walkways publishes books of walks, especially long-distance footpaths, with the emphasis on the western Midlands. Quercus publishes general interest books about the western Midlands region, including history, mysteries, landscape and geography, biographies and natural history.

Editor(s): John Roberts
Address: 67 Cliffe Way, Warwick CV34 5JG
Telephone: 01926 776363
Fax: Same as phone
Imprints: Walkways, Quercus
Payment Details: 10% royalty on retail price
Unsolicited Manuscripts: No, approach first

W
Wallflower Press

Recently established independent publisher specialising in film studies, media, cultural studies, and related subjects. A dozen books a year produced, both academic and of general interest.

Editor(s): Maria Esposito and Yoram Allon
Address: Cloisters Court, 77 Cromwell Avenue, London N6 5XG
Telephone: 0181 374 3992
Fax: 0181 374 7679
Email: wallflowerpress@btinternet.com
Website: www.wallflower.com
Parent Company: Wallflower Publishing Ltd
Payment Details: Royalties paid twice-yearly
Unsolicited Manuscripts: Synopses or sample chapters welcome

Warner/Chappell Plays Ltd

Publishers of plays, pantomimes and musicals.

Editor(s): Michael Callahan
Address: Griffin House, 161 Hammersmith Road, London W6 8BS
Telephone: 0181 563 5888
Fax: 0181 563 5801
Email: ukplays@warnerchappell.com
Imprints: Warner/Chappell Plays, Warner/Chappell Classics
Parent Company: Time Warner Inc
Unsolicited Manuscripts: No

Waterside Press

Law publisher with leading edge in criminal justice, youth justice, prisons, policing, family matters, mediation, conflict resolution, restorative justice, relationships, women's legal rights, domestic violence, victims, community programmes, justice and the arts. Independently owned and managed.

Editor(s): Bryan Gibson
Address: Domum Road, Winchester SO23 9NN
Telephone: 01256 882250
Fax: 01962 855567 or 01256 882250
Email: watersidepress@compuserve.com
Website: http://www.penlex.org.uk
Imprints: Waterside Press
Payment Details: Royalty basis; occasionally advances, but not usually
Unsolicited Manuscripts: Please approach us first before submitting ms

Paul Watkins

Small, enthusiastic press run by Shaun Tyas from a book-ridden Victorian terrace house in the centre of Stamford. Specialities include local and medieval history, maritime and literary criticism. No creative writing.

Editor(s): Shaun Tyas
Address: 18 Adelaide Street, Stamford, Lincs PE9 2EN
Telephone: 01780 756793
Email: apwatkins@msn.com
Imprints: Paul Watkins, Shaun Tyas
Unsolicited Manuscripts: Prefer synopsis

W

Wayland Publishers Incorporating Macdonald Young Books

Wayland - Childrens' non-fiction publishers. Specialises in books for the schools and public libraries sector. All curriculum subjects are covered, especially history, geography, PSE, RE, health and science. Age range 4 - 16. Macdonald Young Books - Childrens' fiction and non-fiction publishers. Specialise in books for the trade, schools and public libraries sector. Fiction publishing includes storybooks, picture books, gift books and poetry. Non-fiction covers all curriculum subject areas. Age range 3 - 16.

Editor(s): Steve White-Thomson (Publishing Director)
Address: 61 Western Roaaad, Hove, East Sussex BN3 1JD
Telephone: 01273 722561
Fax: 01273 723526
Website: www.wayland.co.uk
Imprints: Macdonald Young Books, Wayland
Parent Company: Wolters Kluwer
Unsolicited Manuscripts: Not accepted

Owen Wells Publisher

Books on law and practice for the probation service and related professions in the criminal justice system. Probably the smallest serious academic/professional publisher anywhere.

Editor(s): Owen Wells
Address: 23 Eaton Road, Ilkley, West Yorkshire LS29 9PU
Telephone: 01943 602270
Fax: 01943 816732
Email: ow@owpub.demon.co.uk
Imprints: Owen Wells Publisher

Trust For Wessex Archaelogy Ltd

Publishes specialist and academic monographs on archaeological sites and surveys in the Wessex region.

Editor(s): Julie Gardiner
Address: Portway House, Old Sarum Park, Salisbury SP4 6EB
Telephone: 01722 326867
Fax: 01722 337562
Email: wessexarch@dial.pipex.com
Unsolicited Manuscripts: No

White Cockade Publishing

Social and cultural history, oral history, architectural and design history, decorative arts; mainly nineteenth and twentieth century, and particular Scottish interest. Books to satisfy both the specialist and general reader.

Editor(s): Perilla Kinchin
Address: White Cockade Publishing, 71 Lonsdale Road, Oxford OX2 7ES
Telephone: 01865 510411
Fax: 01865 514034
Email: pk@whitecockade.co.uk
Website: whitecockade.co.uk
Unsolicited Manuscripts: Letter first

White Eagle Publishing Trust

All books are produced within the organisation. No manuscripts accepted from external sources or commissioned.

Address: New Lands, Brewells Lane, Liss, Hants GU33 7HY
Parent Company: The White Eagle Lodge
Payment Details: None
Unsolicited Manuscripts: No

W
White Row Press

Publisher of Irish interest non-fiction, and (sometimes) prose. Good, well thought out ideas welcome.

Editor(s): Peter Carr
Address: 135 Cumberland Road, Dundonald, Belfast BT16 2BB
Telephone: 02890 482586
Unsolicited Manuscripts: Yes if Irish interest non-fiction

Whiting And Birch Ltd

Publishers of professional and academic books and journals in the human science.

Editor(s): Diana Birch
Address: PO Box 872, London SE23 3HL
Telephone: 0181 244 2421
Fax: 0181 244 2448
Email: savpub@dircon.co.uk
Imprints: Whiting And Birch Ltd
Payment Details: By arrangement
Unsolicited Manuscripts: Prefer proposals

Whittet Books

Whittet Books publishes reference books on natural history; including domesticated animals such as poultry and also horses and horse breeds

Editor(s): A Whittet
Address: Hill Farm, Stonham Road, Cotton Stowmarket, Suffolk IP14 4RQ
Telephone: 01449 781877
Fax: 01449 781898
Email: Annabel@Whittet.dircon.co.uk
Parent Company: A Whittet & Co
Unsolicited Manuscripts: Yes

Whittles Publishing

Our expanding publishing programme covers two main areas: engineering and science (mainly civil engineering and construction, surveying and photogrammetry, imaging and applied photography, chemical engineering and materials); nautical/maritime and Scottish (lighthouse, lightships and things maritime, Scottish interest and Scottish reference).

Editor(s): Keith Whittles
Address: Roseleigh House, Harbour Road, Latheronwheel, Caithness KW5 6DW
Telephone: 01593 741240
Fax: 01593 741360
Email: whittl@globalnet.co.uk
Website: www.users.globalnet.co.uk/~whittl
Payment Details: Royalty payment will vary according to the project
Unsolicited Manuscripts: Yes

WI Books Ltd

WI Books is the publishing division of the National Federation of Women's Institutes. It publishes books for WI members on a range of subjects including cookery, crafts and gardening, often written by WI members who are already experts in their field.

Editor(s): Simon Goodenough, Marketing Manager: Claire Bagnall
Address: 104 New King's Road, London SW6 4LY
Telephone: 0171 371 9300
Fax: 0171 736 3652
Email: wienterprises@nfwi.org.uk
Website: http://www.nfwi.org.uk
Parent Company: WI Enterprises, National Federation of Women's Institutes
Unsolicited Manuscripts: Yes

W
Wild Goose Publications

Religious books, tapes and songbooks. We also publish books on social, justice, peace and political issues.

Editor(s): Managing Editor: Sandra Kramer
Address: Unit 16, 6 Harmony Row, Glasgow G51 3BA
Telephone: 0141 440 0985
Fax: 0141 440 2338
Email: admin@wgp.iona.org.uk
Website: www.iona.org.uk
Parent Company: The Iona Community
Payment Details: Royalties every 6 months
Unsolicited Manuscripts: Synopsis and sample chapter only

Neil Wilson Publishing Ltd

Food and drink, hillwalking and climbing, whisky, humour, biography, travel, leisure, true crime, Scottish and Irish interest are the main subject areas. Whisky and whisky-related topics are especially strong, and the authors include four former Glenfiddich Award Winners, with sales in excess of 250,00 copies.

Editor(s): Neil Wilson
Address: 303a The Pentagon Centre, 36 Washington Street, Glasgow G3 8AZ
Telephone: 0141 221 1117
Fax: 0141 221 5363
Email: nwp@cqm.co.uk
Website: www.nwp.co.uk
Payment Details: Royalties twice-annually
Unsolicited Manuscripts: Yes

Windhorse Publications

Books on Buddhism, meditation and related subjects.

Editor(s): Sara Hagel (Commissioning Editor)
Address: 11 Park Road, Moseley, Birmingham B13 8AB
Telephone: 0121 449 9696
Fax: 0121 449 9191
Email: sara-windhorse@compuserve.com
Website: www.fwbo.org/windhorse
Unsolicited Manuscripts: To Commissioning Editor

The Windrush Press

Independent publisher, established 1987. Military history, general history, 'ancient mysteries', Traveller's History series, humour, non-fiction. Not fiction, travel writing or poetry.

Editor(s): Victoria Huxley
Address: Little Window, High Street, Moreton in Marsh, Gloucestershire GL56 0LL
Telephone: 01608 652012/652025
Fax: 01608 652125
Email: windrush@windrushpress.com
Website: www.windrushpress.com
Unsolicited Manuscripts: Yes, letter synopsis/sample only, SAE essential for return

W

Winslow Press Ltd

Winslow is a specialist publisher and producer of practical resources for professionals working with the special educational and therapeutic needs of people of all ages. We produce practical and accessible resources for speech and language, education, health, rehabilitation, eldery care, occupational therapy and all aspects of social care.

Editor(s): Commissioning Editor: Stephanie Martin; Editorial and Production Controller: Sarah Miles
Address: Telford Road, Bicester, Oxon OX6 0TS
Telephone: 01869 244644
Fax: 01869 320040
Email: info@winslow-press.co.uk
Website: www.winslow-press.co.uk
Payment Details: Determined by contract
Unsolicited Manuscripts: Yes

WIT Press/Computational Mechanics Publications Ltd

A major publisher of engineering research. Produces books by leading researchers and scientists at the cutting edge of their specialities, thus enabling readers to remain at the forefront of scientific developments. List presently includes monographs, edited volumes, books on disk and software in areas such as acoustics, advanced computing, architecture and structures, biomedicine, boundary elements, earthquake engineering, environmental engineering, fluid mechanics, fracture mechanics, heat transfer, marine and offshore engineering, transport engineering.

Editor(s): Director of Publishing: Lance Sucharov
Address: Ashurst Lodge, Ashurst, Southampton SO40 7AA
Telephone: 0238 029 3223
Fax: 0238 029 2853
Email: witpress@witpress.com
Website: www.witpress.com
Parent Company: C M Inc
Payment Details: By contract
Unsolicited Manuscripts: Yes

Witan Books And Publishing Services

Founded in 1980 and guided by ecological and humanitarian principles. Publishes books on general subjects, especially biography, education, the environment, geography, history, politics, popular music and sport. Witan Publishing Services was developed as an offshoot to help writers get their work into print; it offers a comprehensive service including proofreading, editing, design and guidance to publication. Sample titles: Principles Of Open Learning; The Last Poet: The Story Of Eric Burdon; The Valiants' Years: The Story Of Port Vale; The Man Who Sank The Titanic?: The Life And Times Of Captain Edward J. Smith; The Mercia Manifesto: A Blueprint For The Future Inspired By The Past; The Potteries Derbies.

Editor(s): Jeff Kent
Address: Cherry Tree House, 8 Nelson Crescent, Cotes Heath, via Stafford ST21 6ST
Telephone: 01782 791673
Imprints: Witan Books
Parent Company: Witan Creations
Payment Details: Advances and royalties paid to authors
Unsolicited Manuscripts: Yes with SAE

Witherby And Co Ltd

Insurance publications: marine insurance, reinsurance, motor, liability, construction, offshore oil and gas, life assurance, captives, environmental, business interruption, aviation, insurance dictionaries, risk management. Shipping publications: surveying, safety, oil pollution, salvage, mooring, offshore engineering, the shipping of oil, gas and chemicals, marine survival and rescue, tanker structures, dictionaries.

Editor(s): Alan Witherby
Address: 32-36 Aylesbury Street, London EC1R 0ET
Telephone: 0171 251 5341
Fax: 0171 251 1296
Email: books@witherbys.co.uk
Website: www.witherbys.com

W

The Women's Press

Literary fiction; crime fiction; health; women's studies; handbooks; literary criticism; psychology; therapy and self-help; the arts; politics; media; writing by black women and women of colour; disability issues and lesbian issues. All books must be women-centered and have a feminist message or theme.

Editor(s): Elsbeth Lindner, Kirsty Dunseath, Charlotte Cole
Address: 34 Great Sutton Street, London EC1V 0LQ
Telephone: 0171 251 3007
Fax: 0171 608 1938
Imprints: Livewire Books for young women (12-16yrs)
Payment Details: Advance and royalties
Unsolicited Manuscripts: Yes

Women's Sports Foundation

Only UK organisation solely committed to promoting women and girls' sport. Produces a range of publications highlighting issues relating to women and girls' sport.

Address: 305-315 Hither Green Lane, Lewisham, London SE13 6TJ
Telephone: 0181 697 5370
Fax: Same as phone
Email: info@wsf.u-net.com
Website: www.wsf.org.uk

The Woodfield Press

Publishers of Irish local history, womens' studies and biography. Established in 1995; seven books published to date.

Editor(s): Freelance, Publisher: Terri McDonnell
Address: 17 Jamestown Square, Inchicore, Dublin 8, Ireland
Telephone: 01454 7991
Fax: 01492 0676
Email: terri.mcdonnell@itps.co.uk
Imprints: The Woodfield Press
Payment Details: Royalty - 10-12% of net invoice value

Woodstock Books

Facsimile reprints of literary texts in series: Revolution And Romanticism 1789-1834, edited by Jonathan Wordsworth; Hibernia, edited by John Kelly; Decadents, Symbolists, Anti-Decadents, edited by Ian Small and R K R Thornton.

Editor(s): James Price
Address: The School House, South Newington, Banbury OX15 4JJ
Telephone: 01295 720598
Fax: 01295 720717
Imprints: Woodstock Books
Unsolicited Manuscripts: No

Wordsworth Editions Ltd

Leading publisher of low-cost paperbacks. Series include Wordsworth Classics, Wordsworth Children's Library, Wordsworth Reference, Wordsworth Poetry Library, Wordsworth Classics Of World Literature, Wordsworth Military Library, Wordsworth Royal Paperbacks. Wordsworth are primarily reprint publishers, but occasionally commission books, especially in the reference area.

Editor(s): Editorial Director: Marcus Clapham
Address: 6 London Street, London W2 1HL
Telephone: 0171 706 8822
Fax: 0171 706 8833
Email: 100434.276@compuserve.com
Imprints: As described
Unsolicited Manuscripts: No

W
Wordwright Publishing

We are a packager gradually moving into publishing. We offer a full range of out-of-house services from concept to your warehouse: proofing, editing, writing to your specification, design, print-brokering, publicity and marketing. Subject matters include military, social and women's history. Also illustrated books on subjects like cookery, gardening, art, natural history; and juveniles.

Editor(s): Charles Perkins, Veronica Davis
Address: 25 Oakford Road, London NW5 1AJ
Telephone: 0171 284 0056
Fax: 0171 284 0041
Email: wordwright@clara.co.uk
Payment Details: Royalty or fee
Unsolicited Manuscripts: No best to submit an outline or query first

World Of Discovery/Oliver Books

Oliver Books, with 20 years' experience, publishes over 400 titles a year - calendars and ephemera in the rock, pop and film personality field. World Of Discovery, launched two years ago, markets a range of higher quality generic titles and fully licensed product. For the year 2000 there are more than 100 titles including 30+ licensed calendars. Endorsers include the BBC, Sky Television, The Tate Gallery, Harpers & Queen, and seven tourist authorities.

Address: Unit 9, Wimbledon Stadium Business Centre, Riverside Road, London SW17 0BA
Telephone: 0181 944 0944
Fax: 0181 944 1598
Email: matthew@oliverbooks.co.uk
Website: www.oliverbooks.co.uk
Imprints: World Of Discovery, Petprints
Parent Company: Oliver Books Ltd

World Scientific Publishing (UK) Ltd

International publisher of high-level books, textbooks, international proceedings and journals in physics, chemistry, mathematics, engineering, computer science, life science, medicine, economics and management science. World Scientific also publish the Nobel Lectures series written by Nobel laureates. Also of note is our sister company, Imperial College Press which was initiated in May 1995.

Editor(s): Sunil Nair
Address: 57 Shelton Street, London WC2H 9HE
Telephone: 0171 836 0888
Fax: 0171 836 2020
Email: sales@wspc2.demon.co.uk
Website: www.worldscientific.com
Imprints: Imperial College Press
Parent Company: World Scientific Publishing (PTE) Ltd, Singapore

Wrightson Biomedical Publishing Ltd

Publisher of books and journals in clinical medicine and biomedical science. Topics of particular interest: psychiatry, neuroscience, gastroenterology, dermatology, gerontology, cardiology. We are known for the high quality and speed of publication of our books.

Editor(s): Judy Wrightson
Address: Ash Barn House, Winchester Road, Stroud, Petersfield, Hants GU32 3PN
Telephone: 01730 265647
Fax: 01730 260368
Imprints: Wrightson Biomedical
Unsolicited Manuscripts: Yes

$\mathcal{W}$
Writers And Readers Ltd

Philosophy, science, politics, religion, history, literature, music, psychiatry, women's studies, black studies, social science, biographies, autobiographies, novels, arts, media, theatre and US studies.

Address: 6 Cynthia Street, London N1 9JF
Telephone: 0171 226 3377
Fax: 0171 359 1406
Email: begin@writersandreaders.com
Website: www.writersandreaders.com
Imprints: For Beginners, Black Butterfly Children's Books, Harlem River Press, Writers and Readers Inc (USA)
Payment Details: Negotiable
Unsolicited Manuscripts: Yes

Writers' Bookshop

Publishers of writers' aids. Annual directories such as the Small Press Guide and self-help titles such as Successful Writing by Teresa McCuaig, Poetry: How To Get Published, How To Get Paid by Kenneth C Steven and How To Write Non-Fiction Books by Gordon Wells. Manuscript submissions and ideas in all areas of interest to writers are invited.

Editor(s): Kerrie Pateman
Address: Remus House, Coltsfoot Drive, Woodston, Peterborough PE2 9JX
Telephone: 01733 898103
Fax: 01733 313524
Email: kerriepateman@lineone.net
Parent Company: Forward Press Ltd
Payment Details: 15% royalties
Unsolicited Manuscripts: Yes, please include postage for return

The X Press

Black interest popular novels, particularly reflecting contemporary ethnic experience: 20/20 - cult classic fiction; Nia - black literary fiction and non-fiction; Black Classics - reprints of American/African/British black classic novels.

Editor(s): Steve Pope, Doton Adebayo
Address: 6 Hoxton Square, London N1 6NU
Telephone: 0171 729 1199
Fax: 0171 729 1771
Email: vibes@xpress.co.uk
Website: www.xpress.co.uk
Imprints: 20/20, Nia, Black Classics
Parent Company: The X Press
Unsolicited Manuscripts: Yes

Yale University Press

Art, architecture, history and the humanities.

Editor(s): John Nicoll, Robert Baldock, Gillian Malpass
Address: 23 Pond Street, London NW3 2PN
Telephone: 0171 431 4422
Fax: 0171 431 3755
Email: sales@yaleup.co.uk
Imprints: Yale Universtiy Press, Pelican History of Art, Yale English Monarchs
Parent Company: Yale University Press, New Haven USA
Unsolicited Manuscripts: Yes

y
Roy Yates Books

Books for children in dual-language (bilingual) editions. Co-editions of established books translated into other languages. No original publishing undertaken.

Editor(s): Roy Yates
Address: Smallfields Cottage, Cox Green, Rudgwick, Horsham RH12 3DE
Imprints: Roy Yates Books, Ingham Yates
Unsolicited Manuscripts: No

Yes! Publications

Community publishing house based in Derry/Londonderry Northern Ireland. Established 1986. Main publication is Fingerpost Community Magazine, the longest-surviving community magazine in Ireland. Promotes local writers and issues by celebrating and giving credence to local stories and histories. Also promotes mutual understanding and tolerance by exploring issues of cultural identity in articles, essays, stories and poems.

Editor(s): Various
Address: 10-12 Bishop Street, Londonderry, Co Derry BT48 6PW
Telephone: 01504 261941
Fax: 01504 263700
Email: yes.pubs@business.ntl.com

Yore Publications

Specialist football book publisher, generally of an historical nature, from small paperbacks to substantial cased books. Currently the leading publisher of Football League club histories (over 20 to date) substantially written, illustrative and statistical. Also club (players) Who's Who books. Yore Publications is led by Dave Twydell, a member of the Football Writers' Association.

Editor(s): Dave Twydell
Address: 12 The Furrows, Harefield, Middlesex UB9 6AT
Telephone: 01895 823404
Fax: Same as phone
Email: yore.demon.co.uk
Website: www.yore.demon.co.uk/index.html
Imprints: Yore Publications
Payment Details: Varies
Unsolicited Manuscripts: Yes

Yorkshire Art Circus

Yorkshire Art Circus - leading community publishers, specialises in self-styled community books, using many voices around a given theme. Recent publications: Static - Life On The Site; The Story Of A House (Raymond Williams Prize winner 1998); Ranger, The Eyes And Ears Of The Peak National Park. Also publish autobiography. Springboard Fiction - publishes novels and short story anthologies by new writers. Recent titles: Annie Potts Is Dead by M Y Allam, Dark Places by Margery Ramsden.

Editor(s): Ian Daley, Adrian Wilson, Mark Illis
Address: School Lane, Glasshoughton, Castleford, West Yorks WK10 4QN
Telephone: 01977 550401
Fax: 01977 512819
Email: books@artcircus.org.uk
Website: www.artcircus.org..uk
Imprints: Yorkshire Art Circus, Springboard Fiction
Payment Details: Fiction - 7.5% royalty and small advance
Unsolicited Manuscripts: Yes

Z

Zed Books Ltd

Radical independent publisher of scholarly books in development and environment, gender and women's studies, cultural studies, sociology, politics, economics, current affairs and international affairs. Zed's authors come from all over the world and we seek to make our books widely accessible throughout North and South.

Editor(s): Robert Molteno, Louise Murray
Address: Zed Books Ltd, 7 Cynthia Street, London N1 9JF
Telephone: 0171 837 8466
Fax: 0171 833 3960
Email: zed@zedbooks.demon.co.uk
Website: www.zedbooks.demon.co.uk
Imprints: Zed Books
Parent Company: Zed Books Ltd
Payment Details: By agreement
Unsolicited Manuscripts: No - please send outline proposal